WEED BIOLOGY
AND CONTROL

Weeds are nourished by the same food that would nourish useful plants; and therefore, when allowed to grow along with them, must rob them of part of their food.

ADAM DICKSON, *A Treatise on Agriculture, 1785.*

All weeds, as such, are pernicious . . .

JETHRO TULL, *The Horse Hoeing Husbandry, 1731.*

WEED BIOLOGY
AND CONTROL

Thomas J. Muzik
PROFESSOR OF AGRONOMY, WASHINGTON STATE UNIVERSITY

McGRAW-HILL BOOK COMPANY
New York San Francisco St. Louis Toronto London Sydney Mexico Panama

WEED BIOLOGY AND CONTROL

Printed in the United States of America.

Library of Congress catalog card number: 74-78957

1234567890   MAMM   7876543210

44165

PREFACE

Man's welfare depends on his ability to control plant growth. This book was written for those who would like to gain a better understanding of the different systems presently employed for this purpose. I have not tried to give an exhaustive coverage of any particular technique or to give recipes for any particular locality. Rather I have tried to give a better perspective on the world problem of controlling weeds than is now provided by existing texts. Therefore, details applying to specific regions have been omitted, and illustrations have been drawn from all over the world.

Chemicals are tools. Used wisely they give man a greater dimension of power than is provided by older methods of vegetation control, e.g., machinery, fire, flooding, and mulching. Improperly used, they can cause great damage. Herbicides may be used not only to increase food production and improve visibility along roadsides but also to improve the quality of life more directly by making surroundings more attractive, improving recreational opportunities, and providing better cover for wildlife.

The sheer fun of working with plants is not to be underestimated. The farmer and the city gardener alike gain a good deal of pleasure from growing plants. Much of the joy, however, is tempered by the growth of weeds. Herbicides are a weapon that can relieve the grower of much of the drudgery and back-breaking labor involved in cultivating, hoeing, or weed pulling.

I have attempted to present as simply as possible the principles of the successful use of physical and chemical methods of controlling plant growth. Emphasis is placed on principles, since practices vary in different areas and at different times. Such changes in methods are occurring very rapidly. The principles, however, endure. An understanding of the factors that affect plant responses to chemicals will help the grower to use new chemicals wisely and efficiently.

v

As any field of science develops, a certain amount of chaos ensues as a result of the vast accumulation of unassorted information. I have attempted to put into perspective as much of the available information as possible. Therefore, principles and broad categories of chemicals and weeds are emphasized. In Chapter 9, for example, I have attempted to relate taxonomy, ontogeny, and chemical response in the plant kingdom. This attempt, even if only partially successful, should be especially useful for the beginning student. This is a very broad canvas indeed, and the picture I have painted will undoubtedly be refined in the future. I firmly believe, however, that emphasizing taxonomic relationships and life cycles is a sound approach to an understanding of the action of chemicals on plants.

Agriculture has been defined as a "controversy with weeds." Weeds cause more crop losses than diseases and insects combined. The efficient practice of weed control using the most modern techniques and tools available could advance world food production more than any other single practice. Freeing people of underdeveloped countries from spending most of their time growing enough food for a bare living would make it possible for each to develop a new spirit, to advance culturally and scientifically, and to take their places in improving the quality of civilization. Hunger, or the threat of hunger, stifles all the higher aspirations of mankind.

Few people, except perhaps the professional plant scientist, have any real understanding of the vital role that plants play in our lives. This is partly a result of increased specialization and urbanization in highly technological societies. The city dweller, surrounded by concrete, misses a lot of pleasure as well as spiritual fulfillment through his ignorance of and separation from plants. More ominous is the lack of this understanding by the people and governments of the developing nations which have little agricultural technology. Therefore we see the enormous waste of wealth devoted to "prestige projects" such as huge buildings, factories, and super-highways, with little consideration given to improving or strengthening the basic foundation for national progress—a sturdy and efficient agriculture. With 90 percent or more of the population devoting nearly full time to pulling or hoeing weeds, it is unlikely that the remaining 10 percent will build much of a country.

As a citizen who is deeply concerned about the desperate condition of many of the world's peoples, it is my hope that this volume will lessen in some small measure their deplorable situation, much of which is unnecessary and can be relieved by an application of readily available knowledge. Environmental changes, such as increased or more timely rainfall, may temporarily boost food production, but world food supplies will be increased on a long-term basis only through wise use of modern pesticides and machinery.

I wish to acknowledge the assistance of the many friends and colleagues who critically read all or portions of the manuscript. Special thanks go to R. B. Tukey, G. W. Fischer, and B. R. Bertramson for their encouragement and invaluable help in the initial stages of the preparation of the manuscript. I am especially grateful to G. W. Burt, C. L. Foy, A. S. Crafts, and O. A. Leonard for a critical review of the entire manuscript. For help with various chapters I wish to thank C. S. Agbakoba, W. C. Anliker, V. F. Bruns, N. C. Gomness, H. R. Guenthner, R. G. Harvey, A. G. Law, D. G. Peabody, B. F. Roché, W. C. Robocker, T. J. Sheets, and J. W. Whitworth, as well as the many students who suffered through the evolution of this material. The quotations on weeds were supplied by L. W. Rasmussen. In a field as complex as weed biology and control, no one man can hope to be an expert on all its phases, and therefore much of the value of this book is due to the willing assistance I received.

To my wife, Peggy, whose forbearance, understanding, and forgiveness made it possible, I dedicate this volume.

Thomas J. Muzik

WEED BIOLOGY
AND CONTROL

CONTENTS

Preface   v

CHAPTER ONE   WEEDS IN RELATION TO MAN   1

What is a weed? Origin of weeds. Why we have weeds. How weeds cause their effects. History of agriculture and the development of weed control. Stages in weed control. Story of chemical weed control.

CHAPTER TWO   PRINCIPLES OF HERBICIDE USAGE   15

Concepts of herbicide usage. Herbicides compared with other pesticides. Herbicides as tools. Herbicide rotation. Importance of growth activity. Mode of action of herbicides on plants. Sources of information about herbicides.

CHAPTER THREE   WEED DISPERSAL   28

Life cycles of weeds. Propagation. Dormancy. Weed dissemination.

CHAPTER FOUR   WEED ESTABLISHMENT   47

Growth and development. Germination. Root growth. Shoot growth. Leaf growth. Translocation patterns. Establishment. Competition. Factors affecting competitive ability. Association of weeds with certain crops.

ix

CHAPTER FIVE   PHYSICAL METHODS OF CONTROLLING WEEDS   68

Cultivation. Mowing. Flooding. Fire. Mulching. Competition. Nurse crops. Timing of operations.

CHAPTER SIX   SELECTIVITY   78

Rules for herbicidal action. Importance of previous history. Genetic differences. Foliar-applied chemicals. Soil-applied chemicals. Biochemical selectivity. Hormones and their relation to herbicidal action. Metabolism. Photosynthesis.

CHAPTER SEVEN   METHODS OF APPLYING CHEMICALS   96

Kinds of application. Formulations. Surfactants. Granules. Mixtures of herbicides. Mixtures of herbicides with fertilizers or other pesticides. Equipment for applying chemicals to plants. Hazards. Calculations. Procedure in the field.

CHAPTER EIGHT   CHEMICALS USED FOR WEED CONTROL   123

Classification of herbicides. The inorganic herbicides. The organic herbicides. Chlorophenoxys. Carbamates. Chloroacetamides. Triazines. Chlorinated aliphatic acids. Phenols. Substituted ureas. Miscellaneous chemicals. Fumigants.

CHAPTER NINE   CROP-WEED-HERBICIDE RELATIONSHIPS   149

Similarities in response to chemicals within plant groups. Monocotyledons. Annual monocotyledons. Perennial monocotyledons. Dicotyledons. Annual herbaceous dicotyledons. Perennial herbaceous dicotyledons. Perennial woody dicotyledons.

CHAPTER TEN   SPECIAL PROBLEMS IN CONTROL   169

Aquatic weeds. Irrigated crops. General vegetation control. Woody species. Perennial herbaceous weeds. Parasitic seeds. Home gardens.

CHAPTER ELEVEN   ABSCISSION, STIMULATION, INHIBITION, AND RELATED ASPECTS   190

Abscission. Desiccation. Decortication. Dwarfing. Growth stimulation. Prolonging storage. Hastening maturity. Color changes. Control of flowering. Increasing yield of latex.

CHAPTER TWELVE   TOXICOLOGY   198

Hazards from chemicals. Determining toxicity of a new chemical. Selection of test animals. Interpretation of results. Classes of pesticides. Tolerance levels. International trade in foodstuffs. General considerations.

CHAPTER THIRTEEN   BIOLOGICAL CONTROL   207

General principles. Weed control by insects. Other organisms. Interaction of chemicals and biological control. Comparison of biological and chemical weed control.

Glossary   217
Conversion Factors   227
Appendix   230
Decontamination Procedure   257
Author Index   259
Subject Index   261

CHAPTER ONE
WEEDS IN
RELATION TO MAN

This chapter introduces the history and development of weed control, prefaced by a definition of what a weed is, how weeds cause their deleterious effects, and how these effects are related to man.

WHAT IS A WEED?

Definitions

Without man there would be no weeds. All definitions of weeds are predicated on the relationship of the plant to the activities or desires of mankind. Thus, the common definitions are *a plant out of place*, or *an undesirable plant*, or *a plant with a negative value*, or *plants which compete with man for the soil*. Weeds are plants that thrive best in an environment disturbed by man. Man is the greatest disturber of environments that the world has ever known. The only characteristic common to all weeds is their excellent adaptation to the disturbed environment in which they are growing. Not shared by all, however, are the other so-called weed characteristics, such as abundant seed production, dormancy, ability to survive unfavorable growing conditions, competitive ability, shattering, and ability to spread vegetatively. Sometimes crop plants may be considered weedy if they are growing where they are not wanted, as, for example, asparagus in grape vineyards and orchards where it is considered one of the worst weeds.

As Harlan and DeWet (1965) point out, the concept of a weed

1

might be extended to animals as well, for there are also animals that are well adapted to human disturbance. The English sparrow, starling, Norway rat, house mouse, and rabbits in Australia are examples. A weed, therefore, in the broadest sense, may be considered as an organism that diverts energy from a direction desired by man. Further discussion in this volume will be restricted to plants. Man, too, thrives best in a disturbed habitat. The success of particular cultures or civilizations is measured by their ability to modify the natural environment in the direction necessary to ensure their own well-being. On the other hand, the population explosion may lead to man being considered undesirable. Some individuals such as thieves and other criminals, or even the modern-day "hippie," may be considered weedy.

Origin of weeds

Man is probably as responsible for the evolution of weeds as for the evolution of crops. To repeat, weeds are plants adapted to disturbed habitats. In prehistoric times, glaciers were the prime disturbers of established vegetation. Pleistocene glaciation provided pioneer habitats by alternately covering and exposing great areas of Europe and North America. Thus in the temperate zone, the major weeds are species that developed in or near the areas of disturbance caused by glaciation.

Agriculture has caused a far vaster and more rapid disturbance than glaciation. Most of the modern weeds did not exist before agriculture. Weeds probably evolved along with the crops or in some instances may actually have been the ancestors of the cultivated varieties. It has been suggested that crop plants may have arisen from weeds by a mutation to gigantism. Thus, cultivated carrots are larger than wild carrots, tame watermelon larger than the weedy species. This increase in size was not accompanied by an increase in competitive ability, and as a result man must give these plants special care so they will survive.

Weeds, then, come from (1) wild species long adapted to sites of natural disturbance, (2) new species or varieties that have evolved since agriculture was developed.

Obligate weeds

Many weeds have never been found in the wild stage, and grow only in association with man. These so-called *obligate weeds* (Zohary, 1962) include bindweed (*Convolvulus arvensis*), wild radish (*Raphanus raphanistrum*), canarygrass (*Phalaris paradoxa*), ryegrass (*Lolium temulentum*), and many others. The original habitat of these plants is not known but they resemble some of the cultivated crops which have not been found anywhere in the wild state.

Facultative weeds

Facultative weeds are those that grow both wild (in primary habitats) and with man (in cultivated habitats). The prickly pear (*Opuntia* spp.) and various species of wild onion (*Allium*), vetch (*Vicia*), etc., are examples of facultative weeds.

Weedy forms of crop plants

Many of our crops have weed forms; for example, weed potatoes, sunflowers, carrots, watermelons, wheats, barleys, rice, oats, and many others. Races of weeds frequently develop which mimic the crop sufficiently well that the seed is harvested along with the crop and sown with it at harvest time. For example, shattercane, a new weed in the Great Plains area, is considered an escaped forage sorghum. It is well adapted to row crops such as corn and sorghum, but shows more dormancy and shattering than the forage sorghums (Claasen, 1965).

Harlan (1929) describes a barley nursery in which the wild oat population closely mimicked the barley. When growing with winter barley, the wild oat formed a low winter rosette; in adjacent rows of tall spring barley, the wild oats grew tall and headed out. When the early barley matured, the oats matured along with it. All stages could be seen on the same day. This adaptive ability of weeds is very important to their survival.

Why we have weeds

The plant community is a complex association. Under a particular set of environmental conditions—climate, extremes of temperature, total rainfall and rainfall pattern, soil characteristics, fertility, etc.—there is a natural progression to a "climax" vegetation. When man attempts to change this natural progression in order to grow his crops, fruits, trees, and ornamentals, he is fighting an uphill battle against the natural succession of plant growth. For example, certain climates favor trees or brush over grasses. In these areas, it is very difficult to grow grasses along the roadsides, since the natural ecology leads to a woody plant as the climax. In other, drier areas, grasses are favored and the householder who wants trees find that they are difficult to establish.

Man has been forced to adapt his agriculture to the climatic conditions of certain regions. Thus we have regions or "belts" which produce certain crops, such as corn, wheat, rice, fruits, lumber, etc. The crops are seldom as well adapted as the species native to the area. It is doubtful that any major crop species would long survive without man's help, for they are not as well adapted to the environment as certain other plants which invade, compete, and would eventually "take over" the

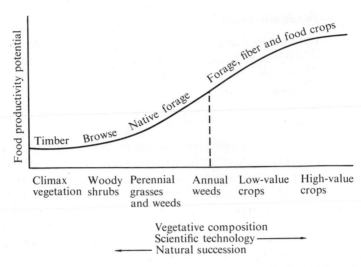

Figure 1-1   *Depending on the climatic variations involved, the "climax" vegetation may be grass, brush, timber, or a combination of all three. In drier regions, for example, grasses may dominate the lower areas, shrubby vegetation is frequently found on north-facing slopes, and trees appear at higher elevations. Nature moves in the direction of a climax vegetation, while man struggles against this natural progression and expends energy (muscular, mechanical, and chemical) to raise high-value crops. (Modified from Shaw and Danielson, 1961.)*

fields. These are the weeds. The invasion of crops by weeds is a replacement of less-adapted organisms—a kind of plant succession (Figure 1-1).

Left to her own devices, i.e., without the activities of man, nature would probably eliminate many of the weeds as major components of the vegetation.

Various aspects of modern agriculture favor invasion by weeds: (1) Crops are usually sown in rows leaving gaps that are available for colonization by other species. (2) Crops are usually grown in pure stands. A single species generally fails to fully exploit the habitat; for example, it may not use the available sunshine because its leaf area develops slowly, or it may have too short a growth cycle to use all the available water or nutrients because of the distribution of its root system. Weeds may then successfully use these wasted resources.

HOW WEEDS CAUSE THEIR EFFECTS

Competition

Weeds cause their effects primarily by competing with crops

for light, nutrients, water, and space. More water and nutrients are required to raise a ton of weeds than to raise a ton of most crops.

Weeds, like crops, vary in their competitive ability, but characteristically they exhibit, when young, a rapidly spreading and deeply penetrating root system which gives them an early advantage in obtaining water and nutrients.

Competition for light and space with the concomitant reduction in photosynthesis leads to crop losses.

Inhibitors

Many weeds such as quackgrass, false flax, and blue-flowering lettuce exude inhibitors from their living or dead roots which further reduce crop growth (Grummer and Beyer, 1959; Welbank, 1959; Kulp, 1961).

Interference with agriculture

Weeds cause greater losses than either insects or plant diseases (Table 1-1). They are the major barrier to food production and economic development in many regions of the world. Particularly in underdeveloped countries lacking in machinery and chemicals, weeds must be pulled by hand or cultivated with very simple tools. Most of the agriculturist's time is spent fighting weeds. Insects and plant diseases may be very serious from time to time but they do not present the eternal problems that weeds do. To name a few:

1. In dairying areas a serious problem is caused by weeds which give an off-flavor to milk. Wild onion and wild garlic, bitterweed *(Actinea odorata)*, and frenchweed *(Thlaspi arvense)* are examples of this kind of weed.

Table 1-1 Losses from weeds, insects, and diseases compared with pesticide sales and research efforts

SOURCE OF LOSS	ANNUAL LOSSES AND COST OF CONTROL, $ Million	1965 PESTICIDE SALES, $ Million	RESEARCH SUPPORT USDA AND STATE, $ Thousand	RESEARCH PERSONNEL*
Weeds	5,064	210,753	8,707	205
Insects	4,298	237,317	34,368	510
Plant diseases	3,779	48,603	44,164	656

*The number of research personnel in the field of weed control is far less than in either entomology of plant pathology. Further research in all aspects of vegetation control is of prime importance to mankind.

(Modified from W. R. Furtick, 1967. National and International Weeds for Weed Science. A Challenge for WSA. *Weeds*, **15**:291–295.)

2.   Serious illness or even death may be caused in cattle, horses, and sheep by excessive amounts of poisonous constituents or spines, including horsetail (*Equisetum arvense*), *halogeton*, or horse nettle (*Solanum carolinense*). St. Johnswort (*Hypericum perfoliatum*) may injure the soft tissues of the mouth. Difficulties in processing also are caused by burs or spines of various weeds getting caught in the wool or hair.

3.   Spiny weeds such as Canada or creeping thistle (*Cirsium arvense*) interfere with harvesting, especially in hand-harvested crops such as orchard and bush fruits or vegetables. In the tropics, workers refuse to enter sugarcane fields infested with pica-pica (*Mucuma pruriens*). The irritating hairs on this legume fall off on the slightest contact and cause severe inflammation and itching (Velez and Van Overbeek, 1950).

4.   Unripe seeds or stems of seeds may be harvested along with the cereal or legume crops. The decay of these moisture-containing plant parts causes undesirable high temperatures in the stored crops and may lead to spoilage. Many annuals and perennials, such as Canada thistle and bindweed, are often found growing vigorously in ripe grain or legumes.

5.   The contamination of seed stocks by weed seeds is discussed in some detail in Chapter 3. Suffice it to say here that weeds are spread more through contaminated seed stocks than by any other method. This was especially true in the days before the importance of clean seed was recognized. Many weeds were undoubtedly spread in this fashion. The movement of armies with feed grain for horses caused much weed spread in the days before mechanization.

6.   Hay containing mature thick hard stems is less attractive to livestock. Foliage of certain weeds, such as bracken fern and various sedges, makes the hay less palatable.

7.   Damage to machinery or clogging of harvest equipment may occur when substantial stands of old perennial weeds or brush are cut, thus necessitating a delay for cleaning or repairing the equipment.

Alternate hosts for insects and diseases

Many weeds serve as alternate hosts for insects and fungi. The leaf hopper, which lives on shepherd's purse (*Capsella bursa-pastoris*), carries a virus which causes curly top in sugar beets, beans, and tomatoes. The insect survives on the weed between crop periods. The common barberry is an alternate host for wheat rust, and black currant for white pine blister rust. A number of cruciferous weeds and numerous grasses (*Agropyron* sp.) act as hosts for foot rot (*Ophiobolus* and *Helminthosporium*).

Water losses

Weeds of waterways cause enormous losses of water. In irrigated areas they reduce the stream flow, cause silt deposition, and furnish protection to rodents which burrow in the bank. It is estimated that enough water to irrigate 330,000 to 780,000 acres is lost annually in the irrigated areas of the 17 western states of the United States (Timmons, 1960; see also Chapter 8). Boat transport is severely limited by aquatic weeds in many regions. Fishing, swimming, and recreation may be almost eliminated by weed infestations.

Human and animal health

Human health is affected by poisonous plants, especially those which cause allergies. Indeed, more than half the world population is affected by plant allergies. Most of these are caused by pollen, but contact with the leaves of poison ivy, poison oak, or poison sumac can cause considerable distress. In the tropics, the manchineel tree (*Hippomane mancinella*) causes severe burns to cattle or humans who rest under it during rains, and it is said to kill anyone who sleeps under it. Accidental ingestion of poisonous fruits such as nightshade or use of stems of poisonous plants such as hemlock as blowguns occasionally cause illness, particularly among children. A number of weeds such as corn cockle (*Agrostemma githago*), darnel (*Lolium temulentum*), and certain species of *Senecio* produce seeds which are poisonous when present in flour and bread. Many people in South Africa have been killed by such poisoning (King). Nightshade berries (*Solanum* spp.) are difficult to remove from fresh or canned peas. Seeds or fruit with characteristics similar to the crop are difficult to separate and often necessitate the installation of expensive machinery.

HISTORY OF AGRICULTURE AND THE DEVELOPMENT OF WEED CONTROL

Man—a hungry creature in search of food

The history of mankind is basically the story of a hungry creature in search of food (Van Loon, 1945). Until he began to use tools and later to domesticate plants, he was weak and few in number. A million years ago approximately 125,000 people inhabited the earth. It is about this period of time that the records have been found of the first use of simple stone tools.

As he spread out over more of the earth's surface, man slowly increased in population until 10,000 years ago he numbered about 3 million. Nomadic and hunting peoples need an estimated 10 square miles of land to support one person, and there are about 30 million square miles of usable land on the earth's surface (exclusive of oceans, deserts, mountains, and other uninhabitable areas). Thus the total population of nomadic peoples which the earth could support is about 3 million or 0.1 percent of the present population.

Man first domesticated plants and animals about 10,000 years ago—the most significant single occurrence in human history (Macneish, 1964). This was the beginning of farming, and farmers began replacing hunters about that time, a process which continues today. The 1000-fold increase in numbers of mankind from 3 million to more than 3 billion is due mainly to his success at domesticating plants. His future welfare depends on this ability to control plant growth to his advantage since all animal life, both wild and domestic, is dependent on plants.

Of more than 300,000 known species of plants in the world less than 3,000 have any history of use as food and only about 300 are widely grown for food. Remarkably, of these 300 species a mere dozen or so provide about 95 percent of our annual world food supply. These are wheat, corn, rice, potatoes, sweet potatoes, sugarcane, cassava, beans, peas, coconut, and bananas. Between man and a continuing food supply stand four natural hazards: weather, weeds, insects, and plant diseases. Sometimes these hazards work independently; many times they work hand in hand. As for the weeds, there are several hundred species that are serious competitors with crops for water, mineral nutrients, light, space, and other growth requirements.

Primitive agriculture

Perhaps the first action that distinguished primeval man from animals was the pulling up of a weed to aid the growth of some of the wild fruits and nuts upon which he subsisted. The first "weeds" may have been shrubs that were cut down or broken off so that man could reach the desirable fruits. In so doing, man reduced the competition for "good plants" by destroying or hampering the growth of the "bad" or competing weeds. Basically, all through history man has striven, by means of chemicals for weed, disease, and insect control, to give his crop plants the maximum freedom from pests so they could develop and produce food. The extent to which he has succeeded has been the measure of the success of his family, his tribe, his nation, and his civilization.

Development of energy sources

Man's development of energy sources may be traced through periods in which he used only his own muscles, then crude tools (1 million years ago), animals (10,000 years ago), and machines (300 years ago), and more recently, atomic energy and chemicals. Each stage represents an increased dominance over his environment. Mechanical energy opened the way for more efficient use of man power and the widescale agriculture of the modern era. The use of chemical energy is a more recent development. Yet, none of the older methods have been discarded completely (Figure 1-2).

(a)   (b)

(c)

Figure 1-2 *None of the ancient methods of weed control have been abandoned. Hoeing is still a common practice. (a) Female worker photographed in England in 1964; (b) peasant in Afghanistan using wooden hoe in 1962 (photo courtesy of Azam Gul); (c) men hoeing weeds in mint fields in the United States in 1966 (photo courtesy of D. Swan).*

When we pull a weed from our lawn or garden, we perform an action that has been repeated throughout countless millenia from the time of our first "human" ancestor.

Much of the world's agriculture is still conducted by primitive means, and many existing cultures have not progressed beyond the hand-pulling or forked-stick stage of agricultural development. Quite obvious is the potential usefulness of chemical herbicides in releasing the farmer in less-well-developed technologies from the tyranny of endless rounds of hand weeding in order to produce enough food to maintain his family on a bare subsistence level.

The proper use of modern weed control methods would do more to promote world food production than any other single factor.

STAGES IN WEED CONTROL

The various stages in weed control may be summarized as: (1) bare hands, (2) pointed sticks, (3) metal hoes or machetes, (4) metal hoe tied to horse or oxen, (5) planting of crops in rows to facilitate "horse-hoeing" and the resulting development of plows, cultivators, rotary weeders, etc., (6) chemical weed control (Figure 1-3). The planting of crops in rows began only about 200 years ago. The internal combustion engine, which led to the tractor and rapid cultivation was invented in 1901.

The development of machinery and chemicals has not increased potential crop yields per unit area; rather, these modern tools have increased efficiency and yield per man-hour invested.

STORY OF CHEMICAL WEED CONTROL

Plant hormones

The history of chemical weed control began with the work of Charles Darwin. In 1881, he reported that light produced growth-regulating effects. He exposed the coleoptiles of oats (*Avena* sp.) and canarygrass (*Phalaris* sp.) to light from one side and found that the stem tip produced a chemical which caused curvature in a lower portion of the coleoptile. Other physiologists (Sachs, 1865–1887) reported that "chemical messengers" were related to the flowering behavior of begonias and squash. Various investigators attempted to discover the nature of these growth effects. The chemical messenger or plant hormone was identified as indoleacetic acid in 1933. Later work has shown that other plant hormones (the gibberellins and kinins) also produce strong effects on plant growth and development.

Herbicide development

Synthesis of indoleacetic acid and the discovery that its application externally could cause dramatic effects on plant growth led to the manufacture of related compounds. The most important of these from a weed-killing standpoint is 2,4-dichlorophenoxyacetic acid, which was first reported as a new chemical in 1941 and first applied in field trials in 1944.

Prior to the development of the growth-regulator herbicides, various other types of chemicals (oils, dinitro, acids, etc.), were being developed. For example, in 1897, copper salts, sulfuric acid, and iron sulfate were being tested in grain crops; calcium cyanamide was used as a

(a)

(b)

(c)

(d)

(e)

(f)

Figure 1-3 *The practice of vegetation control from primitive man's first attempts at improving conditions for desirable plants to the techniques developed in today's advanced civilization. Each picture represents a different stage in the use of energy, from (a) pulling weeds to (b) using a forked stick, (c) machete or cutlass, (d) hoe, (e) plow attached to a man, (f) plow attached to a tractor, and finally, (g) a "chemical hoe."*

(g)

weed killer in 1900, and arsenicals about 1908. In 1919, sodium chlorate was first widely used for perennial weed control. New herbicides are being produced every year in large numbers. The use of these chemicals for the practice of selective control of weeds has transformed many aspects of plant husbandry. Indeed, crop rotation in many areas is giving way to chemical rotation. This has promoted a vast chemical industry devoted to the discovery and development of new herbicides. The characteristics of some of these chemicals will be discussed in Chapter 8. Most of these chemicals have been discovered through empirical methods, by taking bottles off the shelf and testing the contents for activity. Many companies maintain staffs of chemists whose main task is to synthesize new compounds or analogs of existing compounds. These compounds are screened on numerous species under greenhouse conditions, then the more active chemicals are tested in the field; if they pass the rigid tests of toxicity and fill a need at less cost than existing methods, they enter into the arsenal of weapons of the modern agriculturist.

Most of the herbicidal chemicals used in agriculture today have been developed within the last 15 years. The oldest of the systemic herbicides, 2,4-D, was developed only about a quarter of a century ago. This is a young science and bears great promise for the future. Even now, as a result of the widespread use of 2,4-D (about 100 million acres annually), shifts in weed populations are evident. Weeds that are resistant to 2,4-D, such as the grasses and certain species of broadleaves, are becoming more prevalent. At the same time, the development and spread of ecotypes and races of "resistant" weed species is being encouraged. For example, it is now possible to grow several ecotypes of bindweed and to selectively control all but one ecotype by spraying with 2,4-D. Similar responses have been found with many other weeds. This process of selection is comparable to that which occurs in insects but it takes longer in plants for two reasons: (1) Insects may reproduce several times within a year but plants form seed only once a year, and (2) the susceptible plant population is constantly being renewed by seeds buried in the soil which germinate over long periods of time.

Plant breeders must increasingly consider the reaction of new varieties to widely used herbicides else they may find the value of a new plant introduction to be severely limited. Some varieties of corn, for example, are quite sensitive to 2,4-D, while others are very resistant.

The number of cultivations (see also Chapter 5) can be reduced or almost totally eliminated by the appropriate use of herbicides. Since cultivation has the undesirable effect of bringing weed seeds to the surface where they can germinate, a reduction in the number of cultivations will correspondingly reduce the number of weeds. It is possible to design cultivation procedures to improve tilth and water-retention properties of particular soils if the weed population is controlled by other means.

QUESTIONS

1. Would it be more difficult to eradicate a facultative weed or an obligate weed?
2. How did weeds originate?
3. Why do we have weeds in crops?
4. What was Darwin's contribution to plant growth regulation?
5. Define the term *weed*.
6. What characteristics enable plants to function as weeds?
7. What is the one common characteristic of all weeds?
8. What is a *climax vegetation*?
9. How do scientific technology and nature conflict?
10. In what ways is man like a weed?
11. How can a crop be a weed?

REFERENCES

Claasen, M. M. 1965. Shattercane. *Crops and Soils*, **18**:15–16.

Darwin, C. 1881. "The Power of Movement in Plants." D. Appleton & Company, Inc., New York.

Grummer, G., and H. Beyer. 1959. The Influence Exerted by Species of *Camelina* on Flax by Means of Toxic Substances, in "The Biology of Weeds," J. L. Harper (ed.), pp. 153–157, Blackwell Scientific Publications, Ltd., Oxford.

Harlan, H. V. 1929. The Weedishness of Wild Oats. *J. Heredity,* **20**:515–518.

Harlan, J. R., and J. M. J. DeWet. 1965. Some Thoughts About Weeds. *Econ. Botany,* **19**:16–24.

King, L. V. 1966. "Weeds of the World." Interscience Publishers, New York.

Kulp, E. L. 1961. Factors Affecting the Response of Blue Flowering Lettuce (*Lactuca pulchella*) to Herbicides. M.S. thesis, Washington State University.

Macneish, R. S. 1964. The Origin of New World Civilization. *Sci. Amer.,* **211**:29–37.

Shaw, W. C., and L. L. Danielson. 1961. The Control of Weeds in Seed Crops. *Yearbook of Agriculture*, 280–287.

Timmons, F. L. 1960. Weed Control in Western Irrigation and Drainage Systems. *Joint Report, Agricultural Research Service and Bureau of Reclamation, ARS* 34–14.

Van Loon, H. 1945. "The Story of Mankind." Garden City Publishing Company, New York.

Velez, I., and J. Van Overbeek. 1950. Plantas Indesables en los Cultivos Tropicales. Editorial Universitaria, Rio Piedras, Puerto Rico.

Welbank, P. J. 1959. Toxin Production from *Agropyron repens*, in "The Biology of Weeds," J. L. Harper (ed.), pp. 138–164, Blackwell Scientific Publications, Ltd., Oxford.

Zohary, M. 1962. "Plant Life of Palestine." The Ronald Press Company, New York.

CHAPTER TWO
PRINCIPLES OF
HERBICIDE USAGE

Herbicides are tools which enable man to grow desirable plants easily and cheaply, but they have important characteristics which distinguish them from other types of tools as well as from other pesticide chemicals. These differences are presented in this chapter, together with some of the factors underlying plant response to herbicides and some of the principles underlying herbicide practices. Several major problems, such as misapplication and drift, are discussed. Additional sources of information about herbicides and growth regulators are given for the interested reader since the material presented is intended only to highlight certain key features.

CONCEPTS OF HERBICIDE USAGE

Aim of weed control

It should be kept in mind that the aim of weed control is not to kill weeds but to tip the balance of nature in favor of the desirable species. This principle applies to noncropland such as roadsides and fence rows as well as to gardens, grain pastures, or cotton fields. Complete and permanent kill of all vegetation is seldom possible or desirable. Erosion along steep banks and road edges can be very serious if there are no plants to hold the soil (Figure 2-1). Herbicides may be used not only to control weeds in agronomic crops, orchards, gardens, etc., but also to make landscapes more attractive, provide better cover and feed for wildlife, and improve visibility along roadsides.

Figure 2-1 *Erosion on steep slope caused by application of soil sterilant. Sodium chlorate applied beside the wooden trestle may create a fire hazard and increase erosion.*

Every person who deals with weeds is, therefore, attempting to raise a "crop," i.e., to get rid of the undesired species so that the desired plant will grow. This is true whether one is dealing with annual or perennial weeds in field crops, or brush control in pastures, or even the removal of trees and shrubs along African rivers to reduce tsetse fly infestation. The crop along roadsides, for example, may be grass, low-growing brush, evergreens, or an indigenous species of herbaceous annuals or perennials. In any event, some species will grow on the land sooner or later. The herbicide, therefore, should be selected for its harmlessness to the desired vegetation as well as for its toxicity to the weed.

There is little to be gained by indiscriminate application of chemicals simply because a weed is there. Weeds, like mountains, seem to offer a challenge to many individuals. Roadside weeds like wild carrot (*Daucus carota*) or tansy (*Tanacetum vulgare*) usually offer no particular hazard or threat to cropland. Cattails (*Typha latifolia*) in certain areas may be quite innocuous and offer a pleasing variation in foliage as well as good bird cover. In other areas, they may seriously impede drainage and must, of course, be removed. In many regions, however, they cause little or no problem since they do not ordinarily withstand cultivation. If relatively harmless species like these are removed, very likely a more serious weed such as ragweed (*Ambrosia* spp.), thistle (*Cirsium* spp.), or some other noxious species will invade and then cause serious problems to the public and to the farmer.

Climatic and ecological limitations

There is a tendency for state highway departments to favor grass along the roadsides and shoulders. If the climate favors a shrub vegetation over grass, it might be wiser and cheaper and more in the public interest to plant a low-growing shrub adapted to the area or to encourage a native species, rather than attempt to eliminate the shrubs and encourage the grass. If planting is not economically feasible, herbicides should be selected that are relatively harmless to the desirable species. If a selective chemical is not available, careful placement of the chemical instead of a broadcast spray may permit selective control. As shown in Figure 1-1, under any set of environmental conditions there is an inexorable trend in nature to a "climax" vegetation. Man will be more successful if he cooperates with nature than if he blindly struggles against her.

Some examples of improper herbicide application may serve to emphasize this point. One often sees "brown tunnels" along roadsides where 2,4-D is applied to brush or perennial weeds after the weeds are several feet high. This practice not only causes unnecessary ugliness, but it is also ineffective as a control measure because the plants are too large to be readily killed. For effective control, they should have been sprayed when they were small and relatively succulent. A more pertinent question is, "Why spray at all?" If the climate favors shrubs and trees, it is probably hopeless to try to establish grass in these areas. Planting a low-growing shrub adapted to the area, or spot treatment to eliminate the taller species, would be a more sensible course of action.

A current problem in many areas is the sandbur (*Cenchrus pauciflorus*). In the drier areas of the Pacific Northwest, for example, the weed has become dominant along many miles of roadsides due to the mistaken, albeit well-meaning, activities of man. The vegetation met in these regions by the early settlers was blue bunch wheatgrass (*Agropyron* spicatum), needlegrass (*Stipa* sp.), and Indian ricegrass (*Oryzopsis* sp.). When roads were cut through, downy brome (*Bromus tectorum*) invaded and became dominant along the highway edges and shoulders. Many miles of roadsides were sprayed with simazine to control this weed. Sandbur, which appears to be tolerant of simazine, thereupon spread rapidly and is now dominant. The simazine, which in these dry areas will persist for a long time, effectively prevents the development of other annuals or perennials from seed. Thus, we have had a progression from desirable vegetation (the bunchgrass) to a moderately undesirable species (downy brome) to a very undesirable species (sandbur). The sandbur invades adjacent pastures and causes injury to cattle and other stock. Eventually, after the simazine decomposes, it should be possible to plant the area with a desirable perennial grass, but it will be difficult to establish the grass with the competition from the sandbur. The farmers would much prefer the downy brome that was killed to the sandbur that replaced it.

Planting new roads with species appropriate to the region is often the cheapest, most effective way of developing a ground cover. With little competition from existing vegetation, the desirable plants will be relatively easy to establish. Where, however, a large population of weeds exists, as along many of our roads, great care should be exercised before setting out to kill a weed merely because it is there. Unless the end result is clearly envisaged, the program may be costly and time-consuming, and may lead to a more serious weed problem. Unless the weeds are actively harmful, i.e., cause accidents by interfering with visibility, invade cropland, cause allergies, or serve as alternate hosts for insects or diseases, we might well be better off leaving them alone.

HERBICIDES COMPARED WITH OTHER PESTICIDES

A pesticide is a chemical which kills or inhibits the growth of an organism which man finds undesirable. The suffix *cide* means killer. Thus, we have herbicides, "plant killers," insecticides, "insect killers," and fungicides, "fungus killers." Other pesticides include nematocides, rodenticides, bactericides, etc.

Selectivity relationships

The control of weeds offers different and in some ways more difficult problems than the control of other pests, such as insects, bacteria, or fungi. Weeds are associated with the crop but do not grow inside it [except for a few parasites such as dodder (*Cuscuta* sp.)]. Also, weeds are often closely related to the crop plants, whereas bacteria and man or fungi and higher plants are very different. Finding distinct differences in response to chemicals is not surprising between widely separated organisms such as bacteria, a single-celled animal near one end of the evolutionary scale, and man, a warm-blooded, multicellular, complex animal at the other end. Fungi and higher plants too are very different. Weeds, on the other hand, may be of the same genus as the crop plant and closely resemble it morphologically and physiologically. Controlling the weed chemically without damaging the crop then becomes a very subtle matter. Closely related species tend to have similar growth requirements, leaf shapes, root distribution, growth cycles, and times of germination. The more closely one species resembles another, the more difficult it becomes to find a difference which can be exploited; i.e., it is much more difficult to control perennial grasses selectively in turf than it is to control perennial grasses in legumes.

Insects are, of course, animals and therefore very different from plants and thus relatively easy to control without damage to the desirable plant. In general, however, insecticides are more toxic to man and animals than either fungicides or herbicides.

Safety factors

Herbicides are among the least dangerous to man of the agricultural chemicals. A few herbicides are dangerous if ingested (see Chapter 12 and Appendix), but present very little danger under ordinary methods of application. Some solvents and carriers are more toxic than the chemical itself.

The Federal government exercises control over the safety of herbicides and other pesticides in two departments: the U.S. Department of Agriculture (USDA) and the Food and Drug Administration (FDA) of the U.S. Department of Health, Education and Welfare. Approval of both agencies must be obtained before a pesticide can be offered for sale.

The USDA requires registration of all labels and detailed information on efficacy of the chemical for a particular purpose, the need for such a chemical, safety for the user and other people or animals, and possibility of damage to other crops. Data are also required on its persistence in soil with possible adverse effects to plants, animals, or aquatic species.

The FDA requires information on (1) the amount of chemical or metabolites that may remain on harvested food crops, (2) a practical analytical method for detecting the substances, and (3) any harmful effects from feeding trials on test animals. Tolerances are then established for residues of the pesticide at harvest, each having at least a 100-fold safety factor. The company producing the new chemical must bear the cost of obtaining this data.

Rules for safe application

FDA and many state inspectors constantly sample harvested crops and food products which are then tested for possible excessive pesticide residues. If excesses are found, the product is seized. Much effort is being made to put new information on safe pesticide usage into the hands of the farmer and home gardener as promptly as possible. The U.S. Department of Interior suggests a number of useful rules:

1. Be sure there is a real need for the pesticide use.
2. Treat the minimum necessary area.
3. Select the chemical that will be least dangerous to fish and wildlife. Judge the chemical by both its acute toxicity and its disappearance. Avoid chemicals that accumulate in soil.

4.   Use no more than the necessary amount of chemical. Be sure no areas receive a double dose.

5.   Consider the carrier in which the pesticide is mixed, for some carriers are toxic to animals.

6.   Plan the time and location of treatment to avoid hazards. Try to avoid the main nesting and migration periods of birds. Do not apply near dug wells or areas from which the pesticide may be carried by runoff into other areas.

7.   Read the pesticide label completely before use.

Great power for good or ill lies in the use of pesticides. Proper use will lead to better and more economical food, higher nutrition, and a better civilization. Improper use may lead to human and animal illness, crop damage, unnecessary expense, ill will between neighbors, and possible unwise legislation.

HERBICIDES AS TOOLS

Lack of "automatic breakdown"

Herbicides are powerful tools to enable man to grow the vegetation most suitable to his needs, but there is nothing magical about them. They will not substitute for good husbandry, careful management, or planning. Herbicides differ from other tools in that a piece of machinery will break down if improperly handled, or an axe or knife will fail to cut if not kept sharp; but herbicides may be used incorrectly for long periods without the applicator necessarily being the wiser. In other words, there is no automatic breakdown factor, and error may be perpetuated for months or even years. For example, improper calibration of equipment leads either to lower application than necessary to obtain control or to the application of excessive amounts. These misapplications may or may not damage the crop but will in any event waste the chemical and run the danger of residues in the harvested crop. Also, applications of excessive dosages may leave dangerous amounts in the soil which will damage the succeeding crop or lead to illegal residues of chemical in it. The applicator may never see any visible sign of damage if the margin of safety with the particular herbicide is high. A good example is the use of 2,4-D on cereals, where excessive amounts may be sprayed without visual crop damage and less than the correct amount will give partial control of the weeds. Newer chemicals are too expensive to afford misapplication and in many instances do not have a sufficient margin of safety to permit overlapping. Many of the new herbicides are wettable powders which are more difficult to apply evenly over a field, i.e., they must be agitated in the tank to maintain dispersion and thus require special equipment.

Misapplication

Careless application causes unnecessary crop losses, poor weed control, and friction between neighbors or between rural and urban areas. It pays the operator to know exactly how much chemical is going on the land, how to avoid overlapping but maintain contiguity between successive swaths, how to avoid drift, and how to maintain a uniform application rate. One of the worst examples of poor application techniques still current in many regions is applying dry sodium chlorate to perennial weeds "until the ground is white." This is entirely too subjective a criterion and may lead to undesirable results such as poor weed control, soil erosion, or residues of chemical in the soil which prevent plant growth and thus remove land from production for years (Chapter 8).

Friction between neighbors or between rural and urban areas is often caused by drift, that is, the aerial movement of either particles or vapor. The greater the distance from the ground that application is made and the greater the wind, the greater the danger of drift, other things being equal. Small particles drift farther than large, and as large particles drift downward they become smaller due to evaporation. Damage to sensitive plants has been reported as much as 30 miles from the point of application. Anyone who sprays chemicals is as responsible for keeping the chemical in bounds as a rancher is responsible for keeping his animals fenced in. The applicator should spray close to the ground in enough volume to provide large droplets and avoid spraying in winds over 10 miles per hour (Chapter 7).

HERBICIDE ROTATION

Residues in plants and soils

Residues in the soil may damage subsequent plantings or the crops may absorb enough chemical that they will contain amounts above the permissible residues for that crop. Certain weeds, too, will be resistant to any selective herbicide and these will multiply if only one herbicide is used. Herbicide rotation, therefore, becomes as critical as crop rotation.

For example, when triazines are used on maize (corn) in most areas, the farmer is advised to plant maize again in the same field because of the possible injury to sensitive crops which might be next in the rotation. Thus a farmer who is regularly rotating corn for 2 years with beans for 1 year, for example, could use simazine only in the first year of corn and then, in the second year, switch to Eptam or some other herbicide which is not toxic to beans or which will disappear quickly from the soil. Certain perennial weeds such as bindweed (*Convolvulus arvensis*) tend to flourish in areas where simazine is used because of lack of competition from the annual weeds.

Development of resistant plants

Crop rotation, of course, has the advantage that different planting times and cultivation periods tend to keep the weed population reduced. Changing herbicides has a similar effect since the spectrum of activity of each herbicide is different. For example, growing a winter grass crop (wheat) in rotation with a spring legume crop is quite effective in reducing weed populations for two reasons: (1) because of different periods of the year that the ground is covered with vegetation and the different periods of cultivation (fall vs. spring), and (2) because certain weeds tend to dominate in certain crops. When 2,4-D is used in an area for many years, it is usually found that species resistant to it, like the grasses and certain broad-leaved weeds, multiply. In these areas it is necessary to cultivate or to use an herbicide like diuron or simazine which will control those weeds. Grass crops in general tolerate 2,4-D and other phenoxy herbicides very well, whereas they are sensitive to the aliphatic acids and certain carbamates which can be used safely on many broad-leaved crops. It is easier to selectively control grass weeds in broad-leaved crops than in grass crops and vice versa (Chapter 9).

IMPORTANCE OF GROWTH ACTIVITY

Any system of weed control (physical or chemical) will be more successful if it is adapted to the growth activity of the plant. Thus, flaming is most effective on young succulent weeds; flooding kills by denying oxygen to roots and is more effective in sandy soils than in clay soils; cultivation kills by starvation; etc. Cultivation, especially for perennial weeds, should be designed to take maximum advantage of the growth activity of the plants, i.e., to encourage depletion of the food reserves as much and as rapidly as possible.

Rapid growth, as a rule, also makes the plant more susceptible to herbicides. A young vigorous plant has few dormant buds and is actively absorbing, translocating, and metabolizing. For this reason the herbicide is readily translocated throughout the plant. Poorly growing or dormant plants are less likely to be controlled by herbicides (Leonard, 1967).

New chemicals continue to appear and new machinery to be developed, but the basic reasons for cultivation (to prevent seed formation and starve the plant) or for chemical application (to kill or inhibit the weed so that the desirable plant can grow) remain the same.

Environmental conditions markedly affect the growth activity.

Figure 2-2 *Importance of time of spraying on weed and crop response. Plots in winter wheat field were sprayed in autumn (bare ground at left) or in spring (at right). Both the wheat and weeds were killed by the fall application of atrazine, but application in the spring at the same rate gave good control of the weeds without injury to the wheat.*

Cold or dry weather reduces growth activity and may affect the response of the crop and weed to herbicides (Muzik and Mauldin, 1964; Figure 2-2). Herbicides are not absorbed or translocated well in inactive plants or tissues. One of the major difficulties in controlling perennial weeds with large underground root and rhizome systems is that many of the underground organs are inactive and consequently no herbicide is translocated to them. These dormant underground buds and roots may resume growth later and reinfest the area. Any condition which reduces growth activity, such as low temperature, drought, or low fertility, will reduce the plant's susceptibility to most herbicides.

MODE OF ACTION OF HERBICIDES ON PLANTS

Multiple effects

A plant is a delicately balanced organism and any single change will have multiple effects. Thus, an herbicide may affect several facets of growth, any one or all of which may contribute to the death of the plant. It is clear, however, that all herbicides interfere with basic life processes in such a way that the plant cannot survive. Many herbicide molecules probably resemble molecules used by the plant. Since the herbicide molecules are not exact replicas, they enter only part way into the life processes. By so doing, however, they effectively block the normal metabolic pathways and consequently cause severe injury. In this way the action of certain herbicides is perhaps like a faulty key in a lock. The herbicide molecule or key is similar enough to the plant molecule that it enters into the processes, i.e., into the lock, but the lock cannot turn because the key does not quite fit. As long as the key is in the lock, the lock cannot be opened. Eventually the plant growth will be inhibited because of this interference.

Importance of dosage

As previously pointed out, selective action may be affected in part by growth activity which affects the action of the chemical by determining the amount of chemical which will enter, how far, and to what sites it will translocate. It appears that a sufficient amount of most chemicals will be lethal, a lesser amount harmful, a still lesser amount stimulatory, and an even smaller amount of negligible effect. The chemical or its metabolic products must persist in the plant in a toxic form for as long a time as necessary for the killing action to take place. The herbicide must be mobile so that it moves readily throughout the plant. A mature perennial plant obviously takes a more stable and more mobile chemical than a seedling. For example, a broadleaf seedling can be readily killed with a volatile oil which translocates very little and persists only a short time; whereas in order to overcome the great regenerative power of a perennial like wild morning glory (*Convolvulus arvensis*), a persistent and mobile chemical (such as Picloram, TBA, dicamba) is needed.

The most widely used herbicides today are 2,4-D, simazine, and diuron (Van Overbeek, 1964), with 2,4-D by far the leader. About three-fourths of all chemical weed control is conducted with these chemicals; the remaining quarter of the world usage is shared by DNBP (dinoseb), NPA (naptalam), dalapon, CDAA, CIPC (chloropropham), and amitrole.

The evidence now available, according to Van Overbeek, indicates that 2,4-D kills by causing abnormal plant growth which kills like cancer; simazine and diuron inhibit photosynthesis; DNBP prevents formation of high-energy phosphate (ATP); CIPC and CDAA inhibit cell division in the root tip; dalapon causes protein breakdown; and amitrole interferes with glycine metabolism.

This view of herbicide action is undoubtedly oversimplified. All herbicides have multiple effects and our state of knowledge is such that we cannot definitely state that any particular chemical produces its effects always in the same way. For example, besides causing cellular and tissue proliferation and disorganization, 2,4-D also causes stunting of stems and roots, increased respiration, decreased photosynthesis, increased susceptibility to insects and diseases, abnormal potassium metabolism, and movement of proteins and amino acids from root to stem. It is quite likely that any of these effects might be toxic under certain conditions or to certain plants. For example, stunting of roots might be critical under drought conditions but less important under moist condition; i.e., dry weather during the 2 weeks immediately following 2,4-D application to young wheat results in more damage than if adequate moisture is available.

SOURCES OF INFORMATION ABOUT HERBICIDES

Conferences

There are many regional, national, and international conferences on weed control. These are held at frequent intervals and the results of their proceedings are published. The United States is one of the most active regions, and several organizations in this country promote better weed control. The Western Weed Control Conference (now called Western Weed Science Conference) was the first to be organized (1938), followed by the North Central (1944), Northeastern (1947), and Southern (1948) Weed Conferences. The first National Weed Control Conference was held in 1953 and a national society, the Weed Society of America (now called the Weed Science Society of America), was organized in 1956. There are similar organizations in Canada, Europe, and Great Britain. Increased interest is being shown in all parts of the world, although research is still rather limited outside North America and Europe.

Journals

The Weed Science Society of America publishes a quarterly journal called *Weed Science* (formerly *Weeds*), and the British and European conference proceedings are published in a quarterly journal called *Weed Research*. Other botanical journals carry articles on weeds from time to time, but the two cited are the only ones devoted wholly to weeds. Various publications are issued by states, provinces, and countries describing the method best adopted for weed control problems in each area. *Weed Abstracts*, an abstracting journal devoted entirely to reporting work on weeds, is published quarterly. This publication prints summaries of papers published anywhere in the world and is an excellent source of reference. Other journals, such as the *Botanical Gazette*, *American Journal of Botany*, *Plant Physiology*, *Physiologia Plantarum*, *Annals of Botany*, *Science*, and *Economic Botany*, occasionally publish papers on weed investigations. The state of the art is reviewed about every 4 years in *Reviews of Plant Physiology*.

Local authorities

Anyone desiring to use herbicides is well advised to contact local authorities before making any application. Local environmental conditions may make the herbicide ineffective or unsuitable for the particular crop variety, or the soil conditions may be such that the herbicide activity will be greatly modified.

The relative balance and importance of weed species in a particular area may be affected by changing crops or cropping methods (tillage, fertilizer practice, seed source), irrigation, invasion of new weed species, and by the application of modern weed control practices. New physiological races or ecotypes differing in response to control methods may occur in different areas so care must be exercised in relating weed control methods for the same species in two different regions. Even where different ecotypes do not exist, climate and local growing conditions may affect the plant's response to chemicals. Selective spraying in each crop varies with environmental conditions to a great extent. A suitable soil structure and moisture are critical for successful use of soil-applied herbicides. Rainfall variation may cause great differences in effectiveness, and a change from clay to sandy soil may seriously affect the effectiveness and safety of the herbicide.

In most publications on weeds, numerous herbicides are cited for each weed problem. The question is often asked, "Why not select the best herbicide and forget the rest?" The answer is that there is no one herbicide which is "best" for a weed under all possible crop, climate, and soil conditions. Each weed-crop-environmental complex requires a special technology. For example, Canada (creeping) thistle (*Cirsium arvense*) may grow in turf, pastures, orchards; in fields of legumes, cereals, vegetable crops; by roadsides, around buildings, etc. No one chemical or application technique can be equally effective under all conditions. Therefore it is strongly recommended that the person interested in weed control read the label on the container carefully and contact local authorities before making any herbicide applications.

QUESTIONS

1. How do herbicides differ from other tools, such as a hoe or a plow, in the control of weeds?
2. What undesirable results may occur from careless application of herbicides?
3. Why is the control of weeds in crops often more difficult than the control of bacteria in man?
4. What are the roles of the U.S. Department of Agriculture and the U.S. Food and Drug Administration in the control of herbicide usage?
5. Why isn't it possible to select the one best chemical for control of weeds in a particular crop?
6. Why is cooperation with nature necessary when developing a desirable vegetation?

7. Name three situations in which weeds may be useful or innocuous.
8. Why is herbicide rotation often necessary?
9. How does growth activity of the plant relate to its response to herbicides?

REFERENCES

Leonard, O. A. 1967. How Plant Physiology Affects Weed Control under Mediterranean Conditions. *Agrichem. West,* 10.

Muzik, T. J., and W. G. Mauldin. 1964. Influence of Environment on the Response of Plants to Herbicides. *Weeds,* **12**:142–145.

Van Overbeek, J. 1964. Survey of Mechanisms of Herbicide Action, in L. J. Audus (ed.), "Biochemistry and Mode of Action of Herbicides," pp. 387–400. Academic Press, Inc., New York.

CHAPTER THREE
WEED DISPERSAL

The reproduction of weeds and the factors affecting their distribution in time and space are discussed in this chapter. Weeds have a remarkable capacity for survival under a variety of conditions. Their efficiency in spreading both vegetatively and by seed is a vital factor in their ability to infest new areas. Dormancy or the suspension of growth for extended periods of time enables weed seeds to remain quiescent in the soil for decades, only to germinate when conditions for growth become favorable. Although plants have developed a variety of special adaptations to disseminate their seed, man is the major agent of weed dispersal.

LIFE CYCLES OF WEEDS

Annuals

Weeds may be classified as *annuals*, *biennials*, and *perennials*. An annual completes its life cycle in 1 year from germination to seed production and then dies. Winter annuals are those which germinate in the fall and live through winter, producing seed in the early summer. Summer annuals germinate in the spring and produce seed in the autumn of the same year. Winter annuals tend to be more serious in fall-planted crops like alfalfa and grass. Summer annuals such as pigweed, wild oats, and lambsquarters tend to be more serious in summer crops like spring wheat, corn, and many spring legumes. This relationship occurs for two reasons: (1) cultivation for spring-planted crops tends to destroy the fall germinating weeds, and (2) fall-planted crops have a competitive advantage over the spring-germinating weeds. The first plants occupying an area tend to exclude others.

Biennials

A biennial completes its life cycle in 2 years. The first year it produces a rosette and the second year it flowers, sets seed, and dies. Only a few weeds fall in this category: bull thistle (*Cirsium vulgare*), tansy ragwort (*Senecio jacobaea*), wild carrot (*Daucus carota*), and mullein (*Verbascum thapsus*). A cold period is needed for flower initiation and therefore biennials characteristically occur in temperate areas. The rosette period generally is the most sensitive to herbicides.

Perennials

A perennial plant is one that lives for more than 2 years and may live almost indefinitely. Simple perennials such as dandelion (*Taraxacum vulgare*), dock (*Rumex* sp.), and plantain (*Plantago* sp.) reproduce naturally only by seed but can reproduce from cut pieces. Creeping perennials may reproduce by tubers, creeping roots, stolons, or rhizomes.

Creeping perennials are probably the most difficult to control. After the top of the plant is destroyed, regrowth will occur from the underground parts. Even after the mature plants are killed, seeds in the soil may reinfest the area. The young seedlings (6 to 8 weeks old) of perennials can be killed as easily as annuals by cultivation or appropriate chemical, but one treatment is not likely to be sufficient for older plants. Vigilance will be necessary for many years to kill seedlings before they establish new patches of the perennial weeds. Many of these seeds may be dormant for years but still viable and capable of germination when conditions become favorable, as will be discussed more fully later in this chapter.

Tillage, mowing, and other mechanical methods may be used to prevent the weeds from going to seed. Since an individual plant may produce thousands or even millions of seeds, one escape may cause a severe infestation. Herbicides, of course, may also be used to kill weeds before they set seed. Vigilance in spotting the invaders before they can multiply is of prime importance.

PROPAGATION

Vegetative reproduction

Vegetative or asexual propagation is important in the spread of perennial weeds. Many weedy grasses and broadleaves have underground stems (rhizomes) and roots that elongate under the soil and periodically put up shoots that emerge several feet from the parent plant. Control measures, either mechanical or chemical, must take these underground portions of the plant into consideration. After the top of the plant is destroyed, regrowth will occur from the underground parts, necessitating frequent cultivation. Soil-applied chemicals should be applied several feet outside the visible infestation.

The principal types of underground stems are the rhizome, tuber, bulb, and corm. Some weeds have more than one type of underground stem. The rhizome resembles a root superficially, but it may be distinguished by its nodes and internodes and scale leaves, as well as its anatomical structure. It is slender and extends horizontally through the soil, serving frequently as a very effective means of vegetative extension as in quackgrass, Canada thistle, and bindweed.

In some plants, as in the potato, the rhizome may serve as a storage organ, extending outward in the soil for several inches with a thickened terminal portion that develops a fleshy storage organ, the tuber.

In the corm, the stem is short, vertical, and fleshy with a tuft of aerial leaves above and a mass of adventitious roots below. The stem is sheathed by the leaf bases as, for example, in nutgrass (*Cyperus rotundus*). Nutgrass has one corm near the surface of the soil and a chain of several tubers underground connected by rhizomes (Figure 3-1).

The bulb is an underground bud with fleshy scales and a short axis as in wild onion and wild garlic, which closely resemble tame onion and tame garlic, respectively, although the wild species are considerably smaller.

The stolon resembles a rhizome in habit but remains aboveground. It also arises from a lateral bud near the base of the stem axis. It develops adventitious roots and is a means of vegetative extension in certain stoloniferous grasses and the strawberry.

Roots, rhizomes, tubers, bulbs, and corms survive over winter, serving to perpetuate the plants in regions of cold winters. They may also serve as means of spread either through natural growth or through the inadvertent efforts of man and animals. For example, tillage equipment tends to drag them around the fields, and the use of certain tubers and bulbs as food by animals tends to help spread them.

Sexual reproduction

Genetic influences

Some plants are inherently abundant seed producers, while others are poor seeders. For example, the hedge mustard may produce half a million seeds on one plant, and green foxtail about 150,000 seeds per plant. It has been estimated that tumbling pigweed may produce 6 million (Quick, 1961) or 10 million (Boswell, 1961) seeds per plant. Wild oats, one of the most serious weeds in many cereals and legumes, produces about 250 seeds per plant.

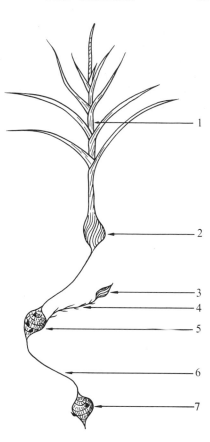

Figure 3-1 *Nutgrass* (Cyperus rotundus), *(1) shoot, (2) basal bulb, (3) young tuber, (4) young rhizome with scale leaves, (5) mature tuber, (6) mature rhizome (no scale leaves), and (7) bud on tuber. Rhizomes are produced from the axillary buds.*

There is no marked difference in the seed production of annuals, biennials, or perennials.

Environmental influences

Conditions under which the plants develop may drastically affect the number of seeds produced. Two plants of poppy (*Papaver rhoeas*) genetically similar but grown under different conditions of soil fertility may in one case produce a single capsule containing four seeds and in another 400 capsules (800,000 seeds per plant; Harper, 1959).

Effect of chemicals on seed production and germination

Application of herbicides or growth regulators to plants may decrease, increase, or have no effect on the seed yield, depending on the chemical applied, the amount applied, the species, and its stage of growth at time of application.

Growth-regulating chemicals appear to be translocated to the most active regions of the plant. When the plant is young and growing rapidly in most of its tissues and organs, chemicals translocate readily throughout the plant. As the plant matures, however, growth and elongation become localized at the extremities of the plant, in the stem and root apices. Chemicals applied to a mature plant tend to accumulate first in these apical regions. If the plant is initiating a floral bud, then the chemical will be translocated to this bud because it is in a stage of active growth and development. Carbohydrates, proteins, and other materials are being conducted actively to the developing flower. The herbicide is carried along with these nutrients in a passive fashion, more or less as a passenger. Movement to the floral meristems during early flowering or preflowering stages probably occurs along with the food transport and therefore these developing cells may be more severely injured at this time. Applications made a few days or weeks earlier or later do not cause injury to the flowers or fruits because the sites of active growth are elsewhere. Application during very early flowering appears to be most effective in reducing seed set. For example, spraying 2,4-D on wheat in the "boot" stage may cause a 30 to 50 percent loss in yield, although the leaves and stem appear unaffected.

Spraying with 2,4-D in late flower or early pod stage reduced germination by over 50 percent in field mustard. Less than 2 percent of the seedlings were able to survive compared to 98 percent in the seeds from untreated plants (Steinbauer, 1946).

Flower types

Flowers contain the ovaries in which the seeds are developed. A complete flower contains calyx, corolla, stamens, and pistils or pistil. Incomplete flowers are missing one or more of these parts. Most weeds have perfect or hermaphroditic flowers; that is, both sexes occur in the same flower.

Monoecious weeds are those in which the female and male flowers are separated in different parts of the same plant. This occurs in certain grasses, corn, saltbush, and nettle.

Dioecious weeds are those with two sexes each in a different plant. Canada thistle (*Cirsium arvense*) and sheep sorrel (*Rumex acetosella*) are examples. Sometimes colonies of these species are found which are exclusively male or female although generally one would expect an equal distribution of the sexes. Male colonies, of course, would flower but not set seed.

Seed formation occurs only in the higher plants, the angiosperms and gymnosperms. Reproduction of other plants is by spores as in the algae, mosses, bracken fern (*Pteridium* sp.) and horsetail rush (*Equisetum* sp.).

Seed structure

The typical seed contains an embryo and stored food material surrounded by a seed coat. The food may be stored in the embryo or in the endosperms. Seeds vary in size from minute dustlike particles to some weighing several pounds. Frequently accompanying the seed are certain tissues of the fruit, flower, specialized leaves, or other organs. The entire structure is known as the dispersal unit. An excellent discussion of germination is found in Koller (1959).

Storage conditions

The condition of storage modifies the life-span of seeds and underground organs enormously. A particular storage condition may lengthen the life-span of one species and shorten that of another. The viability of many seeds is destroyed by storage in manure or silage. The lactic and acetic acid content of the silage and heating and decomposition in the manure are the principal causes of death. Passage through the animals, especially poultry, reduces viability of most seeds.

It has been well established, however, that some seeds may live as long as several hundred years. Weed seeds in the soil are known to live for many years, particularly if deeply buried, giving rise to new infestations when conditions are favorable (Barton, 1961; Quick, 1961). Rhizomes, tubers, and corms of many perennials may become dormant under unfavorable growing conditions and live for several years. None have been reported, however, to live as long as seeds.

DORMANCY

Dormancy is a state of suspended development. A certain degree of dormancy is common to nearly all plants. Man has selected crop plants for their lack of dormancy, thus leading to even germination and uniform growth and fruiting. For the wild plant such germination is a hazard. Man's selection has operated in the other direction for weeds, unwittingly selecting those which germinate unevenly over a period of time. A weed whose seeds germinate uniformly, for example, could be killed with a single cultivation. In the wild, such a plant species might be completely eliminated by a single unfavorable season. Weeds whose seeds germinate over long periods of time are more likely to escape cultivation or chemical sprays.

The fact that seeds of many wild plants remain in the soil for long periods of time means that the soil is well supplied with seeds capable of germination when the soil is disturbed. This complicates the task of the farmer and gardener in fighting weeds. Once the soil is well stocked with seeds, it takes years of cultivation for complete germination and final destruction. There may be tons of weed seed per acre, waiting for a favorable season, or to be brought close enough to the surface to sprout and grow. These unseen generations of weeds are a serious threat in every field where crops have grown for a number of years.

Types of dormancy

Three types of dormancy are recognized: *innate*, *induced*, and *enforced* (Thurston, 1959). Innate dormancy is genetic, and induced and enforced dormancy depend on the interaction of the seed with its environment. Innate dormancy is the failure of fresh seed to germinate even under favorable conditions. Induced dormancy is that caused by unfavorable conditions.

Innate dormancy

Innate dormancy may be caused by: (1) an impermeable or mechanically resistant seed coat, (2) endogenous chemical inhibitors, or (3) rudimentary embryo.

1.   The seed coat is a complex structure and may be impermeable to water or gases until the coats are destroyed mechanically or by microorganisms as in bindweed or black locust. Seeds may fail to germinate— even though water and air can get in—because of the mechanical resistance of the seed coat which may withstand pressures of 1000 psi (pounds per square inch). Pigweed (*Amaranthus retroflexus*), mustard (*Brassica nigra*), and shepherd's purse (*Capsella bursa-pastoris*) have this type of dormancy.

2.   Inhibiting chemicals in the fruit or seed coats, or within the embryo or endosperm, may delay germination. For example, the fruits of the tomato and cucumber and the coats of lettuce and beets contain substances which prevent germination. This is also true of many tree fruits. In the soil, these inhibiting materials diffuse away from the seeds or are absorbed by the soil particles, until they reach a level at which they are ineffective. Their period of effectiveness depends on their stability or on the prevention of diffusion out of the seeds by semipermeable membranes in either the living protoplasm or nonliving seed coat.

The events that overcome dormancy sometimes suggest a highly specific adaptation to the environment. Sumac (*Rhus* spp.) and fireweed (*Epilobium angustifolium*) proliferate after a forest fire because the fire causes a waterproof layer of the dispersal unit to become permeable. Certain plant species are found in pastures because their hard seeds are made water-permeable by bacterial action as they pass through the digestive tract of ruminants. This process enhances their prospects for germination, and moreover deposits them in a moist, manured environment. The open range is thus kept well stocked with pasture plants. This arrangement sometimes backfires, however, allowing undesirable plants such as mesquite (*Prosopis* sp.), sagebrush (*Artemisia* spp.), or camelthorn (*Alhagi camelorum*) to overrun the range and oust more desirable plants. Indeed, camelthorn seedlings in an arid region have failed to survive unless embedded in manure (Kerr et al., 1965).

The amount of inhibitor in the dispersal unit of many species is apparently adjusted so that the amount of rainfall needed to leach it out sufficiently to permit germination will at the same time moisten the soil sufficiently to ensure the plant's subsequent growth. Wild milograss (*Oryzopsis miliacea*) varieties are "gauged" to the rainfall pattern of their habitat. Such rainfall-dependent germination control is important for the survival of plants in arid or semiarid zones, where rainfall is limited and erratic.

Another regulatory mechanism found in many dispersal units is the "temperature gauge." In its simplest form the temperature gauge restricts germination of a species to a specific temperature range that is often very narrow and precise. This, then, distinguishes plants that start their lives in cool climates and seasons from those that do so in warm ones. More highly developed regulatory temperature is found in plants that will germinate only when they are submitted to a specific change in temperature. Most common are the "cold-requiring" seeds. In order to germinate, these seeds require either one or two prolonged exposures (each of several weeks) to near-freezing temperatures, alternating with one or two exposures to higher temperatures. Weedy plants such as gromwell (*Lithospermum arvense*) and desirable plants such as apple, peach, and other plants that exhibit such mechanisms are invariably inhabitants of temperate climates; their ability to avoid germination before prolonged exposure to cold is of high survival value, since it minimizes the danger that seeds may germinate before the hazard has passed.

Dispersal units incorporate not only rainfall and temperature gauges, but also sensitive mechanisms that respond to light. In darkness, lettuce seed germinates tolerably well only within a narrow temperature range. Given light it germinates promptly and uniformly over a very wide range and under a variety of conditions that would absolutely inhibit germination in the dark. Dry lettuce seed is insensitive to light, but a few minutes after the seed is moistened it becomes light sensitive, so sensitive that exposure for a few seconds to light with an intensity of a few footcandles suffices to produce the full effect. The obvious analogy to photographic exposure extends further: If a soaked seed is exposed to light and then dried, it will retain the "message" it received, and when it is subsequently remoistened, it will germinate in darkness.

Like a photographic plate, seeds can be over- and under-exposed.

The brief flash of light that stimulates germination in lettuce and tobacco plants would be insufficient for the rush *Juncus maritimus;* on the other hand, although continuous illumination works as well as a flash in the case of lettuce, it would inhibit wild milograss or the saltbush (*Atriplex rosea*), plants fully stimulated by a brief exposure.

Sensitivity to the period of light and dark may determine the season of germination just as it determines flower initiation and the onset or end of dormancy in the buds of trees and shrubs. Inhibition by over-exposure to light may be of value in preventing germination from occurring on an exposed soil surface, where treacherous conditions such as rapid drying or high temperature are common. This may be why the germination of many desert plants is inhibited by overexposure. Conversely, inhibition by underexposure may be of value in preventing germination from taking place in poorly illuminated or overpopulated localities. This may explain why many aquatic and marsh plants require light for germination (Koller, 1959).

3. Some embryos are rudimentary, i.e., not fully developed when the seed falls. The seed will not germinate until growth is complete. Smartweed (*Polygonum* spp.) and rush show this characteristic.

Several mechanisms may be found in a single seed. A well-known example of independent mechanisms occurs in the ordinary garden cress, which germinates only in response to a combination of light and temperature stimuli. *Trigonella arabica*, on the other hand, is a desert annual that has a dispersal unit equipped with at least four independently operating controls: a water-soluble inhibitor, a "hard" seed coat, and sensitivity to both temperature and light.

The regulation of germination acts to preserve the species by conserving embryonic material and by helping to select a favorable environment for further development of the offspring. In evolutionary terms the origin and spread of these regulatory mechanisms may be easily imagined. Once created, whether by mutation or the reassortment of genes, the higher survival value that they imparted to their bearers provided the latter with distinct advantages over their kind that lacked these advantages. Selection and breeding by man have in many cases reversed this process, producing plants that germinate at man's will rather than in response to natural signals. These tame plants have minimal germination control. On the other hand, nature's own selection has been, and apparently still is, tending toward more efficient control and regulation of dormancy as a means for the preservation of plant species.

Induced dormancy

Seeds which ordinarily would germinate immediately if planted under favorable conditions may be thrown into dormancy by an unfavorable environment so that they will not germinate even when conditions become favorable. This is termed *secondary* or induced dormancy.

Seeds which have been exposed to excessive light, for example, may be changed so that they will not germinate later in darkness. Lack of moisture, high CO_2 pressure, low O_2 pressure may also change seeds so that they refuse to germinate when conditions are favorable. Thus seeds which have been lying on the soil surface where they are exposed to drying and sunshine may act quite differently than seeds planted immediately. Likewise, seeds buried deeply in soil may refuse to germinate for several months when brought near the surface where conditions for germination are excellent.

Enforced dormancy

Seeds may be prevented from germinating by various environmental factors such as lack of moisture, lack of oxygen, or low temperature. When the external limitation is removed, as in seeds brought to the surface by plowing, the seeds germinate.

Death of seeds

Seeds die in the soil as a result of (1) disappearance through respiration of the food supplies stored in the seed, (2) enzyme action and oxidation leading to denaturing of the stored foods, (3) coagulation of proteins, (4) accumulation of toxic products, (5) degeneration of the nuclei. Aged seeds produce more mutations than young seeds, which suggests that the nuclei are being affected, possibly through the decomposition of the nucleic acids, over long periods of time. Mutations occurring as a result of long storage may serve as an adaptive mechanism to evolution (Barton, 1961).

WEED DISSEMINATION—THE SILENT TRAVELERS

Agents

The major agents of seed dispersal are (1) man, (2) other animals, (3) wind, and (4) water. Of these, man is by far the most important.

Introduced species play an important role as weeds in all parts of the world. Most of these were introduced inadvertently during the sustained movements of large numbers of people. Regions where conflict has been the rule for centuries, e.g., the Balkans in Europe, have exceptional weed populations. The ebb and flow of armies with associated weeds in animal feed, soil, human food, etc., contributed much to making this area rich in weedy flora. The Crusaders introduced many European weeds into Asia, and early settlers from Europe introduced many weeds into North and South America.

In general, as man has moved into heavily wooded regions—such as the forests of North and South America, Africa, and Asia—and cut down the trees, he established open sunny areas well adapted to most weed species. For example, in eastern North America, which was heavily wooded at the time of European discovery, one of the first items on every settler's agenda was to cut down the trees and plant crops. In so doing he established conditions well adapted to European weed species, which thereupon flourished. In the original forested condition, these would not have survived.

Weed movement from east to west

Probably the best-documented story of weed invasion within historic times occurred in North America. According to Fogg (1966), of the approximately 700 weeds imported from Europe into eastern North America, about 420 species or 60 percent belong to the following seven plant families:

FAMILY	LATIN NAME	NO. OF SPECIES
Composite	Compositae	112
Grass	Gramineae	65
Mustard	Cruciferae	62
Mint	Labiatae	60
Pea	Leguminosae	54
Pink	Carophyllaceae	37
Figwort	Scrophulariaceae	30

Two facts stand out about these invaders: (1) Most are herbaceous rather than woody plants. (2) These families are considered to be of recent evolutionary origin in contrast to such ancient families as the Magnoliaceae, Lauraceae, etc., which are primarily woody and have made almost no contribution to most weed populations. If modernity implies aggressiveness, as some botanists believe, it is not surprising that the seven families listed should constitute such an impressive block of aggressive weed immigrants.

Some of the common weeds that were imported intentionally are categorized below:

1. Ornamentals: Bouncing bet (*Saponaria officinalis*), yellow toadflax or butter-and-eggs *(Linaria vulgaris),* mullein pink *(Lychnis coronaria),* scotch broom *(Cytisus scoparius),* gorse *(Ulex europaeus),* Japanese bamboo (*Polygonum* sp.), and many others were introduced as garden plants. All escaped from cultivation and have become widely

naturalized. Water hyacinth (*Eichhornia crassipes*) and water fern (*Salvinia auriculata*), both serious weeds of waterways, were introduced into many regions as ornamentals. Both of these pests cause serious interference with water usage in the warm climatic regions where they are adapted.

　　2.　Forage and grazing plants: Numerous species of grasses important to livestock and such plants as sweet clover (*Medicago* sp.) and vetch were imported by early settlers. Some of these have become naturalized as weeds.

　　3.　Vegetables: Many vegetable species, especially from the Mediterranean area, including radish, turnip, carrot, and parsnip, have become weeds along roadsides, open fields, and farmlands.

　　4.　Condiments or kitchen herbs: This group includes many important seasoning plants such as thyme, fennel, mustard (*Brassica* sp.), and purslane (*Portulaca oleracea*), one of the most widespread and pernicious weeds.

　　5.　Medicinal plants: The pioneers brought with them many home remedies including henbane (*Hyoscyamus niger*), horehound (*Marrubium vulgare*), and elecampane (*Inula helenium*).

Many of the weeds were introduced inadvertently as impurities in seeds, implements, or packing materials, or in the ship's ballast. A sailing vessel with light cargo filled its hold with soil which it dumped overboard at the first port of call. Hundreds of European species were introduced into North America in this way, including many weedy grasses (crabgrass and goosegrass), wild garlic, the docks, many chickweeds and knotweeds, a host of mustards (including wintercress, peppercress, and shepherd's purse), bindweed, hemp nettle, mullein, plantain, and many composites such as the burdock, thistles, chicory, dandelion, and sow thistle.

Weed movement from west to east

The west-to-east movement of weeds has not been nearly as great as the east-to-west movement. The thrust of the pioneers from Europe to North and South America and across the continents was, of course, mainly from east to west. Nevertheless, a few American species have been introduced into Europe where they behave as weeds. Among these are horseweed (*Erigeron canadense*), tumbling pigweed (*Amaranthus albus*), tickle grass (*Panicum capillare*), etc. Only a few weed species came to North America from Asia. Most of these are inhabitants of woodlands, rather than of open, sunny areas. Examples of aggressive Asian species are Japanese honeysuckle (*Lonicera japonica*), which has spread over thousands of square miles of woodlands, Japanese hop (*Humulus japonica*), oriental bittersweet (*Celastrus orbiculata*), the tree-of-heaven (*Ailanthus altissima*), and Japanese bamboo (*Polygonum cuspidatum* and *P. sachalinense*).

North-south and south-north movements

Relatively little invasion of weeds in northerly or southerly directions has occurred. The climatic differences, of course, are more extreme, going longitudinally rather than latitudinally on the earth's surface. A few tropical species have spread into the southern United States. The aquatic weeds, water hyacinth and water fern, are found in most subtropical and tropical regions of the world. Terrestrial species such as Mexican tea (*Chenopodium ambrosioides*), annual morning glory (*Ipomea* spp.), and carpetweed (*Mollugo verticillata*) have moved north from Central America and Mexico. Nutsedge (*Cyperus rotundus*) and Johnson grass (*Sorghum halapense*), which are generally found in warm climates, have spread into the Pacific Northwest. The smooth pigweed (*Amaranthus hybridus*), a native of tropical America, is a serious weed in cultivated crops in southern California.

Introduction across major barriers

Dispersal of seeds and organs of vegetative reproduction (tubers, bulbs, rhizomes) across major barriers such as mountains or oceans usually occurs through the agency of man. Birds may carry an occasional seed; and violent atmospheric upheavals such as hurricanes and typhoons may theoretically carry seeds enormous distances. Compared to man, however, other agents are insignificant.

The major methods of introduction of weeds from continent to continent have been by weed-infested (1) crop seed, (2) stock feed, (3) packing materials, and (4) nursery stock. As previously discussed, in his hurry to grow new plants, man failed to take proper sanitary precautions. Dumping of soil carried as ballast in early sailing days also helped introduce weeds across oceans. Canada thistle is supposed to have been imported in this way, both as seeds and as rhizomes in the soil. The Indian name for plantain was "white man's foot" because it sprang up wherever the white man walked.

From England, the Pilgrims brought wheat, peas, and other seeds and at the same time inadvertently brought some of the weeds of these crops. This introduction of plants from Europe and elsewhere has continued over a 475-year span, until at the present time approximately two-thirds of the current crop plants and weeds in the United States are introduced. The introduction of plants for cultivation around the world carried with it the introduction of a whole horde of weeds, some of which have been extremely destructive, costing many billions of dollars in crop losses. Many times plants which are only moderately serious in one area may become serious pests in another. This is usually due to their freedom from the predators that attack them in their native home (Chapter 13).

Dispersal within small areas

Dissemination of weeds within a country or region may be accomplished by (1) weed-infested seed and feed, (2) animals or birds carrying seed in digestive tracts or on hair or wool, (3) use of manure from infested areas, (4) transport and use of machinery, especially harvesting, threshing, and clearing equipment, (5) windblown seeds, and (6) water-carried seeds. In some of the areas of the world now being opened up for farming with irrigation, a rare opportunity exists. No weeds have grown in these areas because the land has lain undisturbed by the plow for centuries. If the importation of weed seed can be avoided, the major battle against weeds will be won.

1.   Contamination of crop seed with weed seed is by far the most serious means of weed spread. It has been estimated that 70 to 80 percent of the seed planted by farmers is from unreliable sources—from neighbors, peddlers, elevators, or even seed from his own fields. The farmer is well advised to purchase seed certified to be free from weeds. Several horror stories can be told of the dangers of planting weed-infested seed. In one instance, a farmer purchased feed oats at a local elevator and used them for seed. It was shown that there was an average of 30 mustard seeds per pound of oats. At a seeding rate of 3 bushels per acre, this farmer seeded 2880 mustard seeds per acre or one in each 4- by 4-foot area (Barnes and Barnes, 1960). These authors cite another case:

> One example will show what can happen by the purchase of so-called "bargain seed." The seed used for this illustration is designated as Sample No. 49, sweet clover, at the State Seed Laboratory, Springfield, Illinois. Eighty-eight percent of the original bushel was pure sweet clover seed which germinated 35 percent. This bushel of 60 pounds contained 18.5 pounds of live clover seeds and 34.3 pounds of dead seeds, also 4.22 pounds of weed seeds including 11 different species, 2.84 pounds of inert matter and 0.14 of one pound of other crop seeds. The weed seeds contained 7,800 Canada thistle, 5,760 curled dock and 114,240 wild mustard seeds. If this "bargain" sweet clover seed were sown at the rate of 12 pounds per acre there would have been seeded on each acre 1,560 Canada thistle, 1,152 curled dock and 22,848 wild mustard seeds. Each square rod would have received 9 Canada thistle, 7 curled dock and 142 wild mustard seeds which would have made a good stand without any clover. The farmer was actually paying $19.14 for 60 pounds of pure viable seeds when he purchased the "bargain seed" at $5.90 a bushel. At the same time that farmer could have purchased sweet clover which was 99.5 percent pure and 95 percent viable

from his local dealer at $8.40. The local seed which sold for almost $10.00 a bushel less contained almost three times as much good seed as did the "bargain seed."

2.   Weed seeds retain much of their viability even after passing through animals or poultry. Before moving animals to clean ranges, it is advisable to quarantine them for a week or so to rid them of the weed seeds. The use of screenings for feed is a dangerous practice because they often contain large amounts of weed seed. For example, in 1954, Henry Wolfe, then Weed Specialist for Washington State Extension Service, was attracted by the debris on the floor of a boxcar on a siding in Quincy, Washington. This car had been used to deliver Canadian screenings to the feedlots now operating in the town of Quincy. Mr. Wolfe gathered a small portion of the seed from the bottom of the car, and ran an analysis as to variety of weeds and viability of the seed in that portion. It was his opinion following his viability test that these seeds had not been sufficiently devitalized prior to their entrance into the feed trade. The sample contained about 40 percent weed seed and 60 percent cracked wheat. The number of weed seeds in the boxcar, which contained an estimated 120,000 pounds of screenings, is shown in Table 3-1 for 23 different species.

The dispersal units of some plants, such as cocklebur (*Xanthium* sp.) or beggarticks (*Bidens* sp.), carry hooks that catch and tangle in animal fur or human clothing. Others, such as the puncture vine (*Tribulus terrestris*), have sharp, strong barbs that pierce horny paws or automobile tires. Non-poisonous dispersal units with a tasty or nutritive fruit attract animals which propagate the seed in a variety of ways. Many small-seeded berries, such as grapes, are eaten whole; the seeds are carried off in the animal's stomach and excreted without a loss of viability. Other dispersal units are harvested as food by ants, mice, or squirrels. Some fruits (e.g., bitter brush) are collected for their pulp, and the inedible seeds are left to germinate in the nest. Some seed-eating animals collect more than they can consume; others cannot keep track of their numerous caches, thus leaving many seeds to germinate. The juicy, sticky fruit of the parasitic mistletoe is well adapted to dispersal by birds because it adheres to their beaks and is wiped off upon a new host branch. A remarkable dispersal unit is the fruit of the squirting cucumber, which consists of a sticky fluid under a great hydrostatic pressure. When it is disturbed by a passing animal, this fruit bursts, squirting its seeds in a powerful jet of fluid that glues them to the animal's skin or fur (Koller, 1959).

3.   Manure from infested areas should not be used without treatment to kill the weed seeds. This can be done by heating, fumigation, steamrolling, grinding, cooking, and fermentation.

4.   Frequently thousands of weed seeds are buried in chaff, dirt, and inert matter in combines, which is probably one of the reasons

Table 3-1 Estimated number of weed seeds in a
boxcar containing 120,000 pounds of screenings

KIND OF WEED	NUMBER OF SEED *millions*
Canada thistle	2,160
Quackgrass	2,160
Wild oats	73,440
Barnyard grass	2,160
Corn cockle	2,640
Pigweed	10,800
Green foxtail	2,160
Fanweed	2,160
Lambsquarters	45,360
Black mustard	2,160
Russian thistle	19,000
Buckwheat	3,646,080
Sunflower	4,320
White mustard	2,160
Hairy stickseed	51,320
False flax	4,320
Smartweed	6,419
Ball mustard	186,729
Knotweed	8,649
Haresear mustard	39,249
Wintercress	2,160
Popcorn flower	8,320
Salvia species	15,120
Total	4,139,046

that crops "run out" or become so badly mixed that new seed is required
every few years. Producers of certified seed should make it a common
practice to dismantle the combine and remove this residue before attempting
to harvest.

5.   Windblown seeds are nearly impossible to keep out of crops.
The best defense is to keep weeds with wind-borne seeds away from the
crop fields, clean up the fence rows and waste areas to prevent these weeds
from sending their offspring by air into the cultivated fields, and use vigilance
to kill any of the invading plants before they produce seed.

6.   Water-carried seeds are an especially serious problem in
irrigated crops. The use of weed screens is a desirable practice, but vigilance
will still be necessary to extirpate the escapees before they produce seed.
Seeds of many weed species, such as bindweed, can live at least 5 years
when immersed in water (Bruns and Rasmussen, 1957).

Special adaptations for seed dispersal

Weeds have a variety of adaptations to improve distribution. The fruit in some of the sedges contains air and floats in water. Some seeds, such as those of docks, are winged and will float in the air or in the water for some distance. Other adaptations are burrs which stick to animals; and hairs, bristles, or scales which help the seed to move when the wind blows. In some instances, as with the tumbling pigweed (*Amaranthus graecizans*) or Russian thistle (*Salsola kali*), the whole plant is blown by the wind (Figure 3-2). The seeds do not shatter readily and as the plant blows around the landscape, seeds drop off a few at a time.

In some species, such as vetch and geranium (*Geranium* sp.), the fruit consists of strips of tissue joined edge to edge. As the fruit dries, tension between the strips increases until they part explosively, dispersing the seed. Some trees, notably the rubber tree (*Hevea brasiliensis*), disperse their seeds in a similar fashion. In other species the dispersal unit is equipped with humidity-operated devices for self-burial. The wedge-shaped dispersal units of the wild oat (*Avena fatua*) and stork's-bill (*Erodium cicutarium*) have a long, humidity-sensitive tail that coils into a tight spring when it is dry and uncoils when it is moist. Barbs projecting from the wedge allow it to move only in the direction of its point. With daily variations in humidity the tail coils and uncoils repeatedly, driving the barbed wedges forward, until it reaches a depth where humidity is constant.

Figure 3-2 *Russian thistle* (Salsola kali vari. tenuifolia) *plants blown by the wind in such quantities that they block the highway. Seed dispersal is accomplished by this tumbleweed action. (Photo courtesy of D. Swan.)*

QUESTIONS

1. Define the weed classifications *annual*, *biennial*, and *perennial*.
2. What is a winter annual?
3. How may seed dormancy in soil serve to advance evolution?
4. Is induced dormancy more common in cultivated or wild plants? Why?
5. How is dormancy advantageous to a species?
6. Why do you suppose that cultivated oats are seldom a weed problem but wild oats are very serious?
7. How does seed dormancy (crops and weeds) inconvenience man?
8. What are the characteristics of families of weeds introduced from Europe to America? From Asia to America?
9. Why is east-to-west or west-to-east movement of plants more extensive than north-to-south or south-to-north?
10. Do herbicides always reduce seed yield?
11. What is a monoecious flower?
12. What percentage of the current crops and weeds is introduced to this country? Why are introduced weeds frequently more serious problems than native plants?
13. Why don't domesticated plants survive in the wild?
14. What is a dispersal unit?
15. How does aerial humidity help to distribute seeds?
16. How does passage of seeds through ruminants help stock the range?
17. How does the rain gauge work in seed dormancy?
18. What is the analogy of lettuce seed germination and photography?
19. Does light stimulate or inhibit germination?
20. Would you expect to find many biennial species in the Tropics?

REFERENCES

Barnes, J., and J. Barnes. 1960. "Weeds and Weed Seeds." Warrex Co., Chicago, Ill.

Barton, L. V. 1961. "Seed Preservation and Longevity." Plant Science Monographs, Interscience Publishers, New York.

———. 1962. The Germination of Weed Seeds. *Weeds*, **10**:174–181.

Boswell, L. V. 1961. What Seeds Are and Do, in "Seeds," *USDA Yearbook of Agriculture*, 1–10.

Bruns, V. F., and L. W. Rasmussen. 1957. The Effects of Fresh Water Storage on the Germination of Certain Weed Seeds. *Weeds*, **5**:20–24.

Fogg, J. M. 1966. The Silent Travelers, Handbook on Weed Control, *Brooklyn Botanic Gardens Record*, **22**:4–7.

Harper, J. L.   1959.   Factors Controlling Plant Number, in "The Biology of Weeds," J. L. Harper (ed.), pp. 119–132, Blackwell Scientific Publications, Ltd., Oxford.

Kerr, H. D., W. C. Robocker, and T. J. Muzik.   1965.   Characteristics and Control of Camelthorn. *Weeds*, **13**:156–163.

Koller, D.   1959.   Germination. *Sci. Amer.*, April issue.

Quick, C. R.   1961.   How Long Can a Seed Remain Alive? in "Seeds," *USDA Yearbook of Agriculture*, 95–98.

Steinbauer, G. P.   1946.   Viability of Seeds from Weeds Sprayed with Herbicides. *Proc. Assoc. Official Seed Analysts*, pp. 69–82.

Thurston, J. M.   1959.   Dormancy in Weed Seeds, in "The Biology of Weeds," J. L. Harper (ed.), pp. 69–92, Blackwell Scientific Publications, Ltd., Oxford.

CHAPTER FOUR
WEED ESTABLISHMENT

This chapter shows the relationship between the growth of the plant and the way it responds to various stimuli, including chemicals, competition from other plants, and cultivation.

GROWTH AND DEVELOPMENT

An understanding of the growth and development of the plant from seed to maturity is desirable in order to develop an understanding of the importance of stage of growth to herbicidal action. All plants are most susceptible to herbicides when they are young. In addition, cereals have two stages of susceptibility to 2,4-D: (1) before tillering, and (2) in early bud or boot stage. Mature perennial plants are, as a rule, most sensitive at the early stages of flowering. A dicotyledonous plant is shown in Figure 4-1*a*. Sections of a typical leaf, stem, and root are shown in Figure 4-1*b*, *c*, and *d*, respectively.

Germination

Germination is the period during which physiological processes are initiated in the seed leading to the elongation of cells and the formation of new cells, tissues, and organs, i.e., the period between hydration and the onset of meristematic activity. The young plant, or seedling, usually elongates very rapidly making new increments of growth. The age at which a seedling becomes a mature plant varies from species to species. The term *seedling* is much abused. Exact definition is important since seedlings are generally more sensitive to chemicals than are mature plants. The seedlings

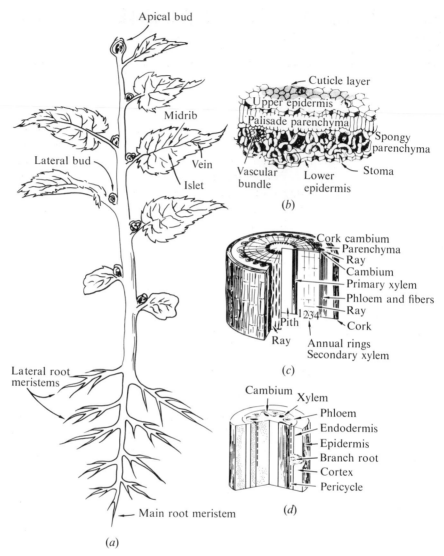

Figure 4-1 *(a) Whole plant and enlarged details of (b) leaf, (c) stem, and (d) root.*

of certain perennials resemble annuals in their response until they reach a certain age. For example, it has been reported that bindweed (*Convolvulus arvensis*) gains the ability to regenerate from roots at the age of about 10 weeks, whereas quackgrass may take 16 weeks to develop this same ability (Crafts and Robbins, 1962). Up to this point these plants can be killed easily by cultivation or contact herbicides.

The seedling stage is that period of growth on the primary root before adventitious or secondary roots are formed. The evidence at hand indicates that grasses change their response to herbicides after adventitious roots are formed, usually in the direction of added resistance or lack of response. For example, barnyard grass (*Echinochloa crusgalli*) is relatively sensitive to dalapon (2,2-dichloropropionic acid) prior to adventitious root development, but rapidly develops resistance as the adventitious roots grow (Roché and Muzik, 1964).

Size of stem and foliage alone is a poor criterion since in many species, particularly under unfavorable growing conditions, the plants may be several weeks old and only a few centimeters high, yet still flower and produce seed. As a result of unfavorable weather and intermittent germination, a population of plants of equal size and appearance may contain individuals quite different in age and physiology. Chemicals applied to such populations may give apparently contradictory and misleading effects.

Root growth

Primary root

Elongation of the primary root usually occurs in the embryo before growth is initiated in the apical bud (Figure 4-2). The primary root typically grows directly downward, penetrates the soil rapidly, and becomes the initial absorbing and anchoring organ. Most chemicals applied to the soil prior to crop-weed emergence will be absorbed first by the primary root, although the coleoptile and young stems may also absorb toxic amounts of certain herbicides. In the grasses, adventitious roots are present in the embryo and these grow rapidly. If the primary root continues to develop and forms a conspicuous structure from which numerous laterals diverge, it is referred to as a *taproot*, whether slender or fleshy. If the primary root and its laterals develop more or less equally, the root system is *fibrous*. Intergrades exist between the types.

The root consists of several regions: (1) root cap, (2) growing point or root meristem, (3) region of elongation, (4) zone of differentiation, and (5) region of maturation. The root cap consists of several layers of cells covering the root apex. The cap persists throughout the life of the roots. As growth proceeds, it is reduced outwardly by the abrasion and disintegration of the outer cells as the root penetrates the soil, and is renewed within by new cells from the meristem. The growing point of the root (root meristem) is directly back of the root cap. New cells are formed in this region. In the region of elongation back of the growing point, the newly formed cells increase in size, chiefly by elongation in the axial direction. This region is relatively short and merges into the zone of differentiation in which most of the cells begin to develop special characteristics. In the region of

(a)   (b)

(c)   (d)

Figure 4-2 *Stages of germination in rubber (Hevea brasiliensis). Note (a) emergence and (b) elongation of primary root followed by (c) emergence and (d) elongation of stem.*

maturation the cells attain the characteristics which they possess at maturity, i.e., thick or thin walls, pits, loss or retention of protoplasm, etc. The designation of these regions is a matter of convenience; no sharp boundaries delimit the zones. There may be continuing cell division in certain tissues of the developing axis while the adjacent cells are elongating. Some cells in the mature region retain meristematic properties.

Root hairs reach a maximum production in the region of matura-tion. They are formed by the extension of the outer walls of the epidermal cells to form elongated thin-walled tubes. They are usually short-lived and soon collapse. New ones are formed continuously so that a definite zone of root hairs is maintained behind the elongating portion of the root. These root hairs are the primary absorbing cells of the root and are the major source of entry of water and herbicides into the plant. As the root penetrates progressively deeper, this absorbing zone is found at greater and greater depths. Naturally, this will affect the plant's response to soil-applied chemicals. Those chemicals which do not leach readily will not reach the absorbing region of the roots and the plant may escape danger.

Lateral roots

Lateral roots arise within the root, generally in the pericycle. Cells in this region begin to enlarge and divide, forming a conical growing point. As a result of further growth, the lateral root primordium enlarges and elongates, forcing the endodermis and the overlaying cortical tissue outward, eventually displacing or rupturing them. The xylem and phloem of the lateral root are in direct contact during formation with the vascular elements of the main axis so that continuity of translocation is maintained. Although soil type, fertility, and moisture will affect the total growth of the root, the pattern of development remains essentially the same.

Damage to roots from herbicides

Damage to roots from herbicides affects the normal pattern of development in many ways. For example, growth regulators such as the chlorophenoxy herbicides may cause the formation of numerous abnormal short stubby roots. The pericycle tissue is caused to proliferate and give rise to a thick layer of cells followed by the formation of numerous closely appressed root primordia. The cells in the cortex increase in size but undergo relatively little division. Both wheat and bindweed exhibit this response to foliar applications. The response of the root systems of wheat and other monocotyledons to foliar application of 2,4-D is frequently greater than that of the stems (Johanson and Muzik, 1961) and is remarkably similar to that of bindweed considering the difference in the response of the stem (Figures 4-3 to 4-5).

When a drop containing 2,4-D was placed directly on the root tip of wheat, the root slowed in growth for 5 to 6 days to about 30 percent of the previous rate of elongation. This rate increased until about 7 days after treatment, then it became the same as in untreated roots. A cluster of very short lateral roots appeared at the site of treatment, which at this time was several centimeters back of the root tip. No lateral roots were produced on the treated root below the cluster of short thick roots for the duration of the experiment (Figure 4-3d). A similar sequence of damage probably occurs in a root which comes in contact with 2,4-D in the soil.

From these experiments it appears that the rate of elongation of a root encountering 2,4-D in the soil would be reduced or completely stopped if the 2,4-D encountered was sufficient in amount. The interference with its normal growth pattern would be reflected in a lesser ability to absorb and translocate water and minerals. Young plants sprayed with 2,4-D may

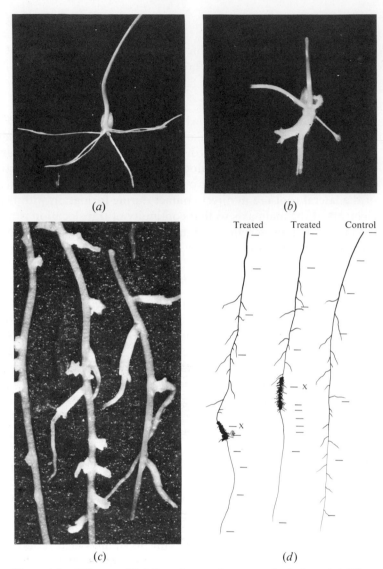

Figure 4-3 *Influence of 2,4-D on shoot and root growth of wheat. (a) Wheat seedling germinated on filter paper impregnated with distilled water. (b) Seedling germinated on filter paper impregnated with 2,4-D. Roots are club shaped, short, and thick with bulbous tips. (c) Roots from seedlings whose leaves had been dipped in 2,4-D solution. Lateral roots are stunted and thickened. (d) Growth of roots on untreated plants and those treated by placing a single drop of 2,4-D on the root tip. Marks show daily elongation before and after treatment at X. Rate of growth of treated roots decreased for several days. Clusters of lateral roots were formed at a point of application about 6 days after treatment. Note lack of lateral root formation after treatment. (From Johanson and Muzik, 1961.)*

have difficulty surviving a spell of dry weather or may be more severely affected by drought than unsprayed plants.

Effect of soil moisture

Root growth and distribution are greatly affected by soil moisture. Root distribution determines the zones in the soil from which the herbicide will be extracted. In areas with dry summers and fall rains, as in the Mediterranean, California, and parts of Northwestern United States, the winter annuals and perennial grasses will have many roots near the surface of the soil, whereas the summer annuals and perennial dicotyledons will generally have relatively few shallow roots, especially where they compete with the winter annuals and perennial grasses. Observations on the depth of roots of woody plants in California indicate that roots are sparse in the upper 15 centimeters (Leonard, 1967). The concentration of many herbicides is greatest at the soil surface, and plants which have a great proportion of

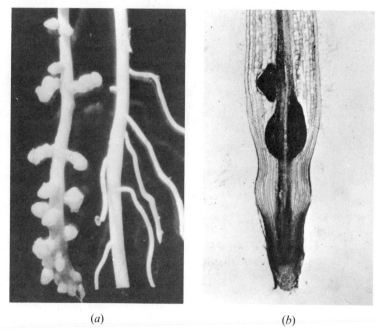

(a)   (b)

Figure 4-4 *Abnormal root development of bindweed* (Convolvulus arvensis) *caused by application of 2,4-D to the leaves. (a) Roots of treated plant at left, untreated at right. (b) Longitudinal section of root from treated plant showing early stage in abnormal development; thickening of cortex, proliferation of pericycle, and formation of numerous root primordia. (From doctoral dissertation, J. W. Whitworth, Washington State University, 1961.)*

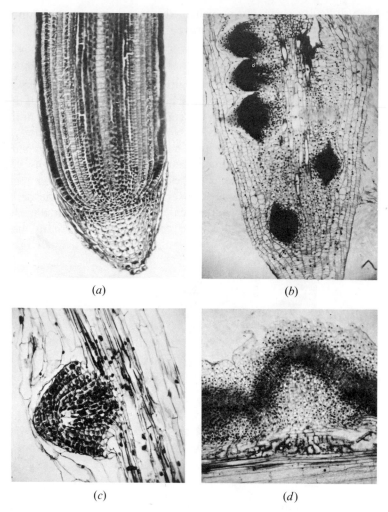

(a)   (b)

(c)   (d)

Figure 4-5 *Longitudinal sections of roots of Brevor wheat. (a) Root tip of untreated plant. (b) Root tip that has ceased elongation after penetrating an agar band impregnated with 2,4-D. Differentiation of closely spaced lateral primordia occurs near root tip, and cortical cells are enlarged. (c) Lateral root primordium from untreated plant. (d) Production of numerous root primordia in root of plant treated with 2,4-D on the foliage. (From Johanson and Muzik, 1961.)*

their roots in this region are affected more than plants with deeper root systems. Thus, since many woody plants and some herbaceous perennials such as bindweed have few roots in upper layers of soils, they escape injury from dosages of soil-applied herbicides that kill shallow-rooted weeds.

It is sometimes possible in establishing a spray program to take advantage of climatic conditions which force one plant into dormancy yet let another species grow vigorously. In regions with pronounced dry seasons it is obvious that deep-rooted plants continue to grow later in the season than associated plants having shallow roots. Perennial dicotyledons, especially woody plants, often continue to grow further into the summer than do perennial grasses, and perennial grasses continue to grow longer into the drought period than do annual grasses and most annual dicotyledons. Man may control soil moisture by irrigation or by reducing the plant population by cultivation, cutting, grazing, herbicide applications, or burning, thus enabling the surviving plants to grow for a longer period. This control is very important in the growth of annual crops where moisture is limited, or in establishing perennials such as trees; it also affects the optimum time of herbicide application for each species. Where the weeds are dormant or growing slowly due to dry weather or low fertility, it may be necessary to fertilize and irrigate before applying the herbicide in order to achieve a good kill.

Shoot growth

The stem, together with its appendages, foliage leaves, and inflorescence, constitutes the shoot (Figure 4-1a). It is usually aerial, but may be subterranean in part. The typical angiosperm stem is erect and unbranched, bearing leaves and flowers on a vertical axis, or much branched with branches of equal size so that a bushy crown is developed. Stems may be prostrate as in sweet potato, twining as in bean, or climbing by tendrils as in cucumber. In certain plants the stem fails to elongate, forming instead a short crown of leaves that results in a bulb, a head, or a simple rosette.

Areas of meristematic activity, elongation, and maturation occur in stems but differ markedly from those in roots. The stem meristem is at the tip but is not protected by cells similar to a root cap. It is exposed except for the leaves and bud scales that diverge from it. The meristematic growing point at the apex consists of actively dividing, thin-walled parenchyma cells.

Elongation occurs over a considerably longer distance in the stem than in the root. In rapidly growing stems, this region may extend over several inches. Curvatures and twisting of the stems (epinasty) induced by 2,4-D and similar chemicals occur in this region. Growth-regulator herbicides tend to concentrate in the actively growing regions.

Primary and secondary tissues

The primary tissues of the stem and the root are derived from their respective apical meristems. Primary tissues (Figure 4-1c) are epidermis, cortex, pericycle, endodermis, primary xylem (tracheids, vessels, fibers, parenchyma), and primary phloem (sieve tubes, companion cells, fibers, parenchyma).

Secondary tissues are derived from the cambium. Monocotyledonous plants have no cambium and therefore have no secondary tissues. The production of these tissues leads to lateral growth and increase in diameter. The increase in diameter of trees is due to the production of the xylem (wood) since the phloem is usually destroyed within a few years after formation. Secondary phloem tissue consists of parenchyma, fibers, sieve tubes, and companion cells; secondary xylem consists of parenchyma, fibers, tracheids, and vessels. Various specialized cells and tissues may occur in certain plants.

The living portion of the plant is called the *symplast*, and the nonliving cell wall is called the *apoplast*. Both are continuous phases of the plant body. Herbicides applied to leaves translocate mainly in the symplast; herbicides applied to roots translocate mainly in the apoplast. Water and mineral transport upward is conducted in the tracheids and vessels even after death of cells. Movement of elaborated food materials downward and upward from the leaves is primarily in the living sieve tube (Figure 4-1a and c).

Damage to stems from herbicides

Damage to the phloem from growth-regulator herbicides like 2,4-D is an important factor in stunting and killing the plant. This effect is caused by the abnormal proliferation of the parenchyma cells and cambium with consequent damage to the sieve tubes (Eames, 1950) and lack of xylem development (Loustalot and Muzik, 1953).

There is no cambium in the grasses and other monocotyledons which therefore have no secondary growth and little increase in diameter. The vascular tissues are scattered throughout the stem. A layer above each node called the *intercalary meristem* persists in a meristematic condition after the tissues above or below become mature. Sometimes grasses will exhibit swelling and root formation at some of the younger nodes following 2,4-D application. This is due to cellular proliferation in the intercalary meristems of these regions. Generally, however, grasses exhibit a relatively slight response to 2,4-D unless sprayed when very young or during early flowering.

Leaf growth

The leaf is an organ that is very sensitive to chemicals. Leaves are formed in the apical meristem. The point of divergence of a leaf is called a *node*. Usually one or several buds develop in the axil of the leaf. Typical patterns of growth of many species may be modified by appropriate chemicals.

A typical leaf consists of an expanded blade or *lamina* and a stalk or *petiole*. There is considerable variation in the length and sharpness of delimitation of the blade from the petiole. Some leaves are *sessile*, i.e., have no petiole. A special type occurs in the grass leaf in which a basal sheath surrounds the axis, and at its upper limit there may be a *ligule* or collarlike membrane which clasps the stem.

Leaf venation is either parallel or netted. In leaves with parallel venation (the monocotyledons) the primary veins extend through the lamina without conspicuous anastomoses, while in the netted type (generally the dicotyledons), the veins form a complicated reticulum. In the net-veined types the veins end ultimately in a small area of chlorophyll parenchyma called a *vein islet* (areole). Leaf responses to many soil-applied chemicals, such as monuron, are first visible as chlorotic areas in the vein islets.

Tissues

The leaf contains the same types of tissues as the stem (epidermis, parenchyma, mechanical, and vascular). These are continuous with similar tissues of the stem axis. Conduction of exogenous chemicals from the leaf through the petiole to the stem is usually through the phloem of the vascular tissue.

The leaf consists of three major regions: (1) the epidermis, which covers its entire surface, (2) the mesophyll, consisting of parenchymatous cells, and (3) the veins (Figure 4-1*b*).

The entire outer surface of the leaf is covered with a single layer of epidermal cells; this layer is continuous except where it is interrupted by stomatal openings. The stomatal opening is a narrow slit in the epidermal layer which permits movement of gases between the inner leaf cells and the atmosphere. It is bounded by a pair of guard cells with concave facing surfaces and continuous end walls. The guard cells determine the size and shape of the stomates. Liquids may also enter the stomates, especially if wetting agents are added to the solution.

Hairs

Epidermal hairs on leaves may be of various types, one-celled or multicellular, conical, pointed, unbranched, or variously branched. They may sometimes play a role in the selective action of a chemical by preventing ready contact with the leaf surface. Thus, water fern (*Salvinia auriculata*) or mullein (*Verbascum thapsus*) plants are hardly injured by aqueous solutions of 2,4-D because the droplets are held away from the leaf surface by the hairs. Adding a surfactant to reduce surface tension or applying the chemical in oil vastly increases the toxic action on these species as a result of better contact on the leaf surface. Some leaves have a mesh-work of soft weak hairs which retain the chemical better than a clear surface and thus enhance activity. Surfactants (Chapter 7) change wetting characteristics to a considerable extent.

Leaf absorption

In general, water-soluble herbicides are absorbed most readily by the leaves when the plants are not moisture stressed. This is partly due to structural changes in the leaf but also due to the moisture content of the leaf cells. As the plants become more and more moisture stressed, absorption decreases. This decrease can be partially offset by the use of oil-soluble herbicides, or by injuring the stems and foliage, or by applying herbicides to the soil where they may be absorbed through the roots.

Many chemicals produce very typical effects on leaves. By examining the resulting malformations, an expert can usually determine which class of chemical (although not always the specific compound) was applied to the plant.

Damage to leaves from herbicides

The first signs of plant damage from herbicides are usually visible in the leaves. Effects may vary from twisting, cupping, and abnormal vein and blade development, to loss of color in the youngest leaves (as with amitrole) or yellowing of the old leaves and withering (as with the triazines and substituted ureas). For example, the most visible external effects of 2,4-D are the lessened growth of the leaf areas between the veins. Thus, depending on the stage of growth at the time of treatment, the leaves may vary in appearance from nearly normal to some consisting mainly of veins. The sensitivity of leaves of certain species is very marked. One ounce of 2,4-D is sufficient to cause malformation in 35 acres of cotton. Compound leaves sometimes exhibit fusion of the leaflets. The leaves of monocotyledons are in general much less sensitive to 2,4-D and related compounds than the leaves of most dicotyledons.

Leaf distortion is sometimes accompanied by the development of "replacement tissue," or thick-walled parenchymatous cells that are not separated by intercellular spaces. This tissue replaces the normal chlorophyll-bearing mesophyll cells (Watson, 1948). Failure of normal lateral leaf expansion produces a narrow blade with many closely placed veins. In severely affected leaves the veins form a closely tangled fused mass, with normal interveinal tissue being absent (Eames, 1951). Depending on the stage of growth of the leaf when it was exposed to the 2,4-D, the severity of injury increases from the first leaf above the last normal leaf to a point of greatest severity, and from this point decreases in intensity toward the top of the stem where normal leaves are produced after the 2,4-D stimulus is removed. This period of recovery may vary from a few days to several weeks, depending on the amount of 2,4-D applied. The effects of other growth-regulating herbicides—silvex, dicamba, MCP, etc.—are probably similar but have not been worked out in detail.

Cuticle

The cuticle is a varnishlike layer covering the entire shoot and thus forming the most important single barrier to herbicide entry. It consists of fatty acids, esters, and soaps formed by an oxidative drying process on exposed cell wall surfaces. Its ability to take up water allows expansion as water becomes available and contraction otherwise. Cuticles tend to increase in thickness with leaf age and with higher light intensities, and they are thicker on upper leaf surfaces than on lower. Sometimes the cuticle is not continuous on a young rapidly growing leaf, which thereby permits more ready entry of applied chemicals.

Permeating the cuticle and parts of the cell wall are cuticular waxes which are composed principally of fatty alcohols and esters. These are extruded from the cytoplasm through the cell wall. The penetrability of aqueous sprays through the cuticle is determined principally by the waxes. The waxes may have various forms, including granules, rods, and nets (Schieferstein and Loomis, 1959).

Electron microscope studies indicate that tiny channels of protoplasm, the ectodesmata, may permeate the walls of epidermal cells and serve as convenient channels for entry of aqueous materials (see also Chapter 6).

Translocation patterns

The patterns of food translocation in plants change with season and stage of maturity. Herbicides applied to leaves tend to move with the photosynthates in the phloem, and those applied to soil move with the water in the xylem. Translocation is greatest to actively growing tissues, such as root and stem tips, flowers, and young fruits. In perennial plants, the first new shoot growth after a dormant period comes from food reserves transported in the phloem in an apical direction. Under these conditions, application of herbicides to the foliage may result in considerable transport to the shoot apices but little or none to the roots. Such applications are generally ineffective. Some basal transport from the lowermost mature leaves may develop within a few days, and the quantity of food materials and herbicide moving basally increases until such time as the plants become moisture stressed. Often, roots which have become moisture stressed, and therefore inactive, become active again after the soil moisture has been replenished. Basal transport of food materials to the roots increases with this renewed growth activity, and associated with this increase is enhanced toxicity of certain foliar-applied herbicides. Thus the optimum spraying period for the control of perennial weeds often represents a compromise between the period of maximum basipetal translocation and decreasing tissue sensitivity.

ESTABLISHMENT

A general principle in weed control is that the first plants which occupy an area tend to exclude all others. In nature, the species that is adapted best to the environment will finally become dominant. In cultivated crops, the weeds that are favored by the cultural practices do best, i.e., plants which do not have their life cycles interrupted will persist. The method of management, especially cultivation, is often more critical than the crop species involved so far as determining the weed problem.

Competition

Competition tends to be greater between plants of similar vegetative characteristics as well as similar soil, water, nutrient, and climatic requirements. Grass weeds, for example, compete more with cereals because they tend to have roots of similar spread and depth, and broadleaf weeds compete more with broadleaf crops (Chapter 9). Different crops have different competitive ability. Barley and spring rye are better competitors than spring wheat, peas, or lentils.

Competition of weeds with crops reduces yields severely. More loss occurs from weeds than from insects or fungi; this is because fungi and insects are not always present but crops always have weeds. General rules are:

1. Competition is most serious when the crops are young, i.e., within the first 6 to 8 weeks after germination.

2. Weeds of similar growth habit to the crop plant are often more serious competitors than weeds of dissimilar habit. Thus broad-leaved weeds usually decrease yields more in broad-leaved crops, and grass weeds are more serious in grass crops, although this is not meant to imply that broad-leaved weeds are not important in grass crops and vice versa. Root systems and growth habits are likely to be similar in related plants and thus cause greater competition than will occur between plants of distinctly different growth habit.

3. Weeds compete for water, nutrients, space, and light, but may also release toxins in the soil which inhibit crop growth.

4. A moderate infestation is sometimes as serious as a heavy infestation.

In sorghum, weed germination immediately after planting caused more severe competition (losses from 8 to 41 percent) than weeds germinating 1 to 2 months after sorghum planting (Wiese et al., 1964). In winter wheat, control of the winter annual weeds in the fall or early spring is very important. Beans are able to compete with weeds successfully if they are maintained weed free for 5 to 7 weeks (Dawson, 1964; see also Figure 4-6).

Yield reductions from pigweed (*Amaranthus hybridus*) averaged 39 percent for corn and 55 percent for soybeans. For corn, the increase in pigweed dry weight equaled dry weight decrease in the corn, i.e., the dry matter per acre remained constant. On the other hand, the combined dry weight of soybeans and pigweed was 133 percent of the soybeans alone. This may have been due in part to the fact that the pigweed was taller than the soybeans (Mootani et al., 1964).

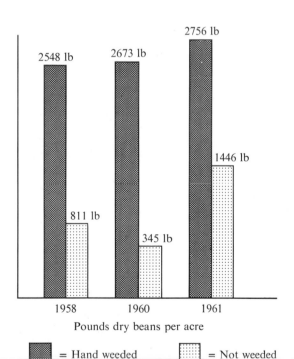

Figure 4-6 *Influence of weed competition on yield of beans. Hand weeding greatly increased yields. Comparable results were obtained from the use of herbicides. (Washington State University Ext. Circ. 328, J. H. Dawson, V. F. Bruns, and B. Roché, 1962.)*

Soybean yields (Staniforth and Weber, 1956) were reduced about 10 percent by annual weeds. Broad-leaved weeds reduced growth more than grass weeds. The weight of the foliage of the soybeans and weeds combined was nearly equal to the weight of the weed-free soybeans alone.

Various experiments have shown that sparse stands of weeds may be almost as effective as dense stands in reducing yields. Swan and Furtick (1962) reported that one plant of coast fiddleneck (*Amsinckia intermedia*) per square foot reduced yield 10 bushels per acre. An increase in weed population did not further reduce yields. Spraying 2,4-D on weed-infested plots increased the yield if the weeds were sprayed at an early stage of growth. Late-emerging fiddleneck did not cause as much competition to the wheat.

On the other hand, Swan (unpublished data) found that blue mustard (*Chorispora tenella*) reduced the yield of winter wheat proportionately as the weed population increased (Table 4-1)—up to 9 plants per square foot. Carter et al. (1946) reported that heavy stands of peppergrass reduced the yield of wheat by 45 percent.

Table 4-1 Competition of blue mustard with winter wheat (Gaines Variety)

TREATMENTS*	POPULATION, *Plants/sq. ft.*	YIELD, *Bushels/acre*
Weeds removed in December	0	61.8
Weeds removed in March	1	52.1
Weeds removed in March	3	47.9
Weeds removed in March	9	42.2
Weeds not removed	1	47.0
Weeds not removed	3	39.2
Weeds not removed	9	32.4

*Natural populations, all densities (0, 1, 3, 9 plants per square foot) established by hand.
(Courtesy, Dean Swan, unpublished data.)

Simazine applied to several species of conifers gave excellent control of the annual weeds, and growth of all species was excellent (Muzik and Dingle, unpublished data). Bindweed, however, was not affected by the chemical; by the end of the second summer it had grown over the treated plots completely, covering the trees from top to bottom, yet in the untreated plots and in the adjacent fields, only an isolated stunted bindweed plant could be found.

This particular problem was solved by applying 2,4-D to the bindweed shortly after it emerged, keeping the spray off the leaves of the conifers.

In other areas where there was no bindweed or other deep-rooted perennial weed, the treatment with simazine was very successful. In the untreated plots, the growth and survival of all the conifers was greatly reduced by the uncontrolled weeds.

Factors determining competitive ability

Factors which determine the vigor and competitive ability of crop plants and the density of the stands are (1) variety, (2) tillage practices, (3) soil-water relation, (4) soil fertility, (5) soil reaction, (6) date and rate of seeding, (7) crop rotation, and (8) timing of seeding in relation to moisture, temperature, and cultivation.

Variety

It is important to choose a variety of the crop plant which is well adapted to local conditions of soil, water, and climate. Poorly competing crop plants are generally much more easily infested with a variety of weeds. Plant breeders have developed varieties of the major crop plants which are well adapted to a number of specific regions, and it is important to the farmer to select the best and most vigorous variety. As pointed out in Chapter 1, man has selected crops because they produce larger fruits, tubers, bulbs, etc., than their wild relatives. This mutation to *gigantism* was not always associated with vigor and resistance to disease or ability to compete with weeds. Thus many of our crops are not good competitors.

Many of the varieties adapted to growth in areas of primitive agriculture are characterized by an early rapid growth which permits them to compete with the weeds. These varieties are usually low yielding and do not respond well to fertilizer application, except to grow taller and lodge more readily. The weedy environment has forced the farmer to grow a competitive crop even though its yields are small. Introduction of higher yielding but less competitive varieties is of little or no value unless the weeds can be controlled. Many of the new potentially high-yielding grain varieties (rice, wheat) are short varieties (dwarf, semidwarf) which do not compete well, especially with the taller weeds. Weed control is vital in these crops if the full yield potential is to be achieved.

Tillage practices

The frequency and time of cultivation, as well as whether it is shallow or deep, may influence the establishment of weeds. For example, quackgrass does not regenerate below 12 inches, although morning-glory will regenerate from a depth of 6 feet. Therefore, plowing below 12 inches will favor morning-glory over quackgrass. Weeds tend to germinate at certain seasons, generally either spring or autumn, and can be killed by cultivation before planting the crop. In areas where fall-germinating annual weeds are the problem, it may be advisable to switch to a spring-planted crop and cultivate in the fall to kill the weeds. Deep plowing brings deeply buried seeds to the surface where they may germinate, while at the same time it buries the newly produced seed, thereby delaying its germination.

Soil-water relations

Water relations, particularly the quantity of rainfall and its distribution, are critical to growth. Soil type, texture, and the height of the water table are also important.

Soil fertility

The fertility of the soil affects both the vigor of the crop plant and the vigor of the weeds. Many weeds can utilize fertilizers as well as or better than the crop plants. However, if most of the weeds can be stunted or destroyed by cultivation or sprays, the extra vigor that fertilizers impart to crop plants makes them better competitors. Placement of the fertilizer directly on the furrow appears to have advantages over broadcast fertilization because it makes the fertilizer directly available to the crop.

Soil reaction

Certain weeds tend to be associated with acid soils, such as *Rumex acetosella*, sheep sorrel. Weeds of this sort have been called *acid indicators*, but they are by no means entirely restricted to acid soils.

Date and rate of seeding

The date of seeding and the rate of seeding affect the vigor of crop plants. Generally speaking, the greater the density of planting, the greater the density of the original stand and the keener the competition the crop plants will give the weeds. Also, if seeds can be planted early and germinate before the weeds do, this will give the crops an advantage. Conversely, if the date of seeding can be delayed until most of the weeds have germinated, they can be killed before planting the crop.

Crop rotation

Crop rotation, alternating row crops and broadcast crops, is advantageous in reducing the weed stands because it varies the type of tillage and alternates the season of the year that the land is densely covered with plant growth. Fewer disease and insect problems are to be encountered also, thus leading to more vigorous crop plants. It is also frequently helpful to alternate spring- and fall-planted crops.

Timing of seeding in relation to weather and cultivation

By appropriate manipulation of herbicides and machinery, the farmer may take advantage of good weather conditions. For example, in a heavy soil under very moist conditions, as may happen when heavy rains occur prior to the planting season, the soil may become too wet for the heavy equipment used for cultivation yet be excellent for crop and weed growth. Under these circumstances, the weeds may be controlled by aerial spraying and the planting done with relatively light equipment. If the planting is delayed until the ground is dry enough for cultivation, the best period for crop growth may be lost.

A fairly recent method which shows promise is called the *stale seedbed*. In this method, a seedbed is prepared. No seeds are planted for several days, however, until most of the weeds have germinated. The weeds are then killed, using a nonselective chemical which is active through the leaves but not residual in the soil, such as one of the contact herbicides. Following application of the chemical, the crop is planted with as little disturbance of the soil as possible to avoid bringing fresh weed seed to the surface. As long as the weed seed is deeply buried it is less likely to germinate.

Association of weeds with certain crops

The association of a particular weed with a certain crop is most likely to be determined by the type of cultivation rather than by the specific crop. In many cases it is possible to vary the cultural practices in order to control early-germinating or late-germinating weeds. One factor contributing to the association of certain crops and weeds is the similarity in seed size, time of maturity, and time of germination. Wild oats in spring cereals, downy brome in winter wheat, and nightshade (*Solanum* spp.) in peas are good examples of this. Another factor, which is steadily becoming important with the widespread use of herbicides, is the tendency for weeds which resemble the crop morphologically and physiologically to dominate. Thus annual grasses, which are more difficult to kill selectively in annual grass crops, are becoming more prevalent in cereals, and broadleaf weeds more common in broadleaf crops, such as peas, beans, and tobacco. The greater the similarity between the crop and the weed species, the more difficult it is to discover a chemical that will control the weed without damaging the crop.

Cultural practices—kind of irrigation (sprinkler or rill), broadcast, drill, or row cultivation—will determine to a large extent the weed problem. Rill-irrigated farms may have different problems than sprinkler-irrigated farms even though they raise similar crops and are adjacent. On the other hand, all drill crops, all row crops, and all broadcast crops tend to have similar problems.

QUESTIONS

1. Which organ of the embryo develops first in germination of the seed?
2. Define *germination*.
3. Define *seedling*.
4. Where and what is the main absorbing zone of the root? Does it change position as the root grows?
5. How does the position of the absorbing region of the root affect the action of soil-applied herbicides?
6. Does the leaf have the same kinds of tissues as the stem and root?
7. Define *cuticle*. How is it formed?
8. Where do lateral roots originate?
9. What are the kinds of underground stems?
10. What is an "islet" in the leaf?
11. What are the parts of a typical leaf?
12. Define *node* and *internode*.
13. Define *apoplast* and *symplast*.
14. What are the major regions of the leaf?
15. Why do we tend to have winter annual weeds in winter annual crops?
16. How is crop vigor important in weed control?
17. Would you expect more weeds in spring barley or in lentils?
18. How does crop rotation help to reduce weed populations?
19. Why is it necessary to compromise between the time of maximum leaf tissue sensitivity and periods of maximum translocation?
20. How may root distribution affect the plant's susceptibility to herbicides at different seasons of the year?
21. How do translocation patterns change with age and stage of growth?

REFERENCES

Carter, A. S., J. H. Lefforge, and L. C. Shenberger. 1946. A Study of the Effect of Infestations on Field Peppergrass (*Lepidium campestre*) on the Yield of Wheat. *Proc. Assoc. Office Seed Analysts of N. Am.*, **36**:103–105.

Crafts, A. S., and W. W. Robbins. 1962. "Weed Control," McGraw-Hill Book Company, New York.

Dawson, J. H. 1964. Competition Between Irrigated Field Beans and Annual Weeds. *Weeds*, **12**:206–208.

Eames, A. J. 1950. Destruction of Phloem in Young Bean Plants after Treatment with 2,4-D. *Am. J. Bot.*, **37**:840–847.

———. 1951. Leaf Ontogeny and Treatments with 2,4-D. *Am. J. Bot.*, **28**:777–780.

Johanson, N. G., and T. J. Muzik. 1961. Some Effects of 2,4-D on Wheat Yield and Root Growth. *Bot. Gaz.*, **122**:188–194.

Leonard, O. A. 1967. How Plant Physiology Affects Weed Control under Mediterranean Conditions. *Agrichem. West*, **10**:14–16.

Loustalot, A. J., and T. J. Muzik. 1953. Effects of 2,4-D on Apparent Photosynthesis and Development Morphology of Velvet Bean. *Bot. Gaz.*, **115**:56–66.

Mootani, M. K., E. L. Knake, and F. W. Slife. 1964. Competition of Smooth Pigweed with Corn and Soybeans. *Weeds*, **12**:126–128.

Roché, B. F., and T. J. Muzik. 1964. Ecological and Physiological Study of *Echinochloa crusgalli* and the Response of Its Biotypes to Sodium Dichloropropionate. *Agron. J.*, **56**:155–160.

Schieferstein, R. H., and W. E. Loomis. 1959. Development of the Cuticular Layers in Angiosperm Leaves. *Am. J. Bot.*, **46**:625–635.

Staniforth, D. W., and C. P. Weber. 1956. Effects of Annual Weeds on the Growth and Yield of Soybeans. *Agron. J.*, **48**:467–471.

Swan, D. G., and W. R. Furtick. 1962. Competition of Fiddleneck with Wheat. *Weeds*, **10**:121–123.

Watson, D. P. 1948. An Anatomical Study of the Modification of Bean Leaves as a Result of Treatment with 2,4-D. *Am. J. Bot.*, **35**:543–555.

Wiese, A. F., J. W. Collier, L. E. Clark, and U. D. Havelka. 1964. Effects of Weeds and Cultural Practices on Sorghum Yields. *Weeds*, **12**:209–211.

CHAPTER FIVE
PHYSICAL METHODS OF
CONTROLLING WEEDS

The principles involved in control of annual and perennial weeds by non-chemical methods are demonstrated in this chapter.

Physical methods of weed control are those methods that do not utilize chemicals or insects or animals, although most of these methods can be efficiently combined with chemicals. Choice of the weed control method to be used is not only affected by the resistance of the crop and susceptibility of the weed to a particular herbicide but also by the vigor and competitive ability of the crop and by the environment. The nearness of susceptible crops may also be an important factor since this places limitations on the spray application of certain herbicides. For example, 2,4-D sprays are restricted near grape vineyards, cotton fields, and orchards. Where danger to a subsequent crop exists, the farmer may be forced to forego the use of an herbicide in a particular crop rotation. Some of the physical methods of weed control are: (1) cultivation, (2) mowing, (3) burning, (4) flooding, (5) mulching, and (6) competition.

CULTIVATION

General principles

The main reason for cultivation of crops is weed control. Tillage alone or in combination with good cropping methods and chemicals is often the best and most economical method of weed control (Robinson, 1964). Enough soil is moved by cultivation each year to build a dike 100 feet high and 1 mile wide from San Francisco to New York. At least half of this cultivation is done for weed control (Shaw and Loustalot, 1963).

Many types of plows, harrows, discs, cultivators, blades, etc., have a place in cultivation. Which of these tools is used depends upon a number of factors: (1) life cycle of crop and weed (annual, biennial, or perennial), (2) depth and spread of the root system, (3) age and size of the infestation, (4) the kind of crop grown in the area, (5) soil type and topography, and (6) weather conditions. Old weed infestations are more difficult to control than new infestations because, among other factors, they have greater food storage in the root systems. The kind of crop is important because of (1) its life span, time of seed germination, time of seed maturity, etc., in relation to the weed, and (2) its competitive ability. Soil type and topography determine whether lightweight shallow cultivation equipment or equipment for deep plowing can be used. Weather conditions may determine the success of an operation. If heavy rains come early, the ground may be too wet for cultivation machinery.

Annual and biennial weeds

In the majority of cases, tillage is the most practical method of controlling annual and biennial weeds. The cultivation should be shallow, since this helps to keep seeds near the surface where they will germinate, whereas deep plowing buries seeds and thereby delays germination. The main aim of cultivating annual and biennial weeds is to reduce competition as well as to prevent flowering and seeding. Therefore, it is usually begun as early in spring as possible and continues until a crop is planted. Row crops and even some drilled or broadcast crops, such as fall-sown wheat, are cultivated by light harrowing in the spring to control certain summer annual weeds such as wild mustard.

Perennial weeds

The chief aim of cultivating perennial weeds is to kill them by starvation. Thus cultivation is an attempt to (1) prevent food manufacture, and (2) speed up the use of plant foods already stored by encouraging new growth.

When we cut or break off the terminal bud of a plant, such as a rosebush or apple, several of the lower buds begin to grow, thus depleting the plant's store of food. "Pinching back" or removal of the terminal bud is often done to ornamentals to obtain bushier and stockier plants. The dominance of the terminal bud is due to its monopoly of the nutrients and production of a hormone, indoleacetic acid (IAA), which, diffusing downward, prevents sprouting of the lateral buds (see also Chapter 6). Removal of the terminal bud stops the production of the inhibiting hormone, thus permitting the lateral buds to grow. Many mechanical methods of controlling perennial plants are based on this simple principle.

Cultivation of weeds stimulates bud sprouting; but in the case of perennial weeds with underground parts, the sprouting is not visible for many days. Frequently the first effect of cultivation is an increase in the number of visible stems. This phenomenon is due to the removal of the terminal buds, thus permitting the lateral buds under the ground to sprout. This is desirable because, as previously mentioned, the aim of tillage is to starve the plant by forcing it to exhaust its stored food.

Cultivation for perennial-weed control must be properly timed for best results. The frequency of cultivation will vary slightly from one area to another. The depth of cultivation is relatively unimportant for perennial weeds except as it influences frequency and costs, but as a rule, the plowing should be deep enough to thoroughly disturb the underground root system. Generally, cultivations are more effective in the spring and summer than in the fall, probably because the regrowth of the plants tends to be more rapid during these seasons. The faster the weeds grow, the quicker they will use their stored food and thus die; unfavorable weather, therefore, usually lengthens the time necessary for control by cultivation.

The period of time required for eradication is determined by (1) the amount of stored food available at the beginning of the cultivation cycle, (2) the type of weather encountered during the cultivation, and (3) the thoroughness of the job. The amount of food stored depends on a number of factors such as (a) climatic conditions, especially temperature and day length, (b) available moisture, both total and seasonal availability, (c) soil type and fertility, and (d) the past practices on the area, i.e., whether this has been a crop or noncrop area. Some species of weeds, particularly the deeply rooted ones, such as wild morning-glory, Canada thistle, Russian knapweed (*Centaurea repens*), and perennial sow thistle (*Sonchus arvensis*), are more difficult to control by cultivation than the shallow-rooted perennials such as quackgrass (*Agropyron repens*). Cold or dry weather will reduce the growth activity of the weed and thus delay the starvation process so that more time will be needed to achieve good control. A regular schedule should be rigorously followed. If one or two cultivations are missed, the weed will have an opportunity to manufacture new food supplies and the whole job may have to be done over.

When new foliage is produced by any plant, it uses more food than it produces for several days. This may vary somewhat between species, but it usually runs from about a 2- to 3-week period. Thus cultivation several days after new growth has emerged from the soil is much more effective than a cultivation cycle which does not consider the growth of the plant. Farmers who cultivate by the calendar are not nearly as effective as those who time their operations according to the development of the plant. Experiments have shown that the number of cultivations may be considerably reduced if the cycle of cultivation is adjusted to fit into the cycle of growth. Remember that cutting off the top of the plant has the effect of inducing bud growth below by removing apical dominance. Because cultivation may appear to increase the amount of infestation, many farmers have hesitated to plow for fear they might spread the infestation. Actually, this phenomenon is of considerable use to the agriculturist because the more buds that are induced to sprout, the faster the roots may be starved. Any weed may be killed by cultivation if the proper precautions are observed; however, it may take several years in the case of deep, widespread, old infestations.

MOWING

Mowing is a reasonably effective way of controlling certain annual weeds if done often enough to prevent flowering and seeding; however, it is relatively ineffective on perennial weeds. Mowing is often used along roadsides and wasteplaces, and in lawns, pasture, and meadows because it removes unsightly growth as well as weakening the weeds. Trimming the lawn induces tiller formation and consequently a denser and more handsome stand of grass which competes well with the weeds. Height of mowing may be a critical factor. It should be low enough to cut off the flowers of the weeds, but not low enough to reduce the competitive ability of the crop. Height of mowing may be important with certain lawn weeds, such as crabgrass (*Digitaria* spp.). Mowing operations should be timed with stage of maturity in order to remove the flowers before they mature into seeds. This may be a very short period of time with some weeds. Mowing is a widely used practice in orchards in order to encourage a good cover crop.

FLOODING

Flooding as a means of weed control was derived from the culture of rice and has been used as a method of emergency weed control. This method consists of surrounding weed infestations with dikes and covering the land with 6 to 10 inches of water for 3 to 8 weeks in the summertime. The area must be completely submersed since even a few leaves projecting above the surface will prevent death of the plant. This method, which is more effective in sandy soils than in heavy soils, apparently works by denying oxygen to the roots and leaves. Some noxious perennial weeds that it has satisfactorily controlled (Robbins et al., 1956) are Russian knapweed (*Centaurea repens*), bindweed (*Convolvulus arvensis*), camel thorn (*Alhagi camelorum*), hoary cress (*Cardarea draba*), and horse nettle (*Solanum carolinense*). On the other hand, the seeds of weeds such as bindweed can withstand immersion in water for many years (Bruns and Rasmussen, 1957).

FIRE

Fire may be used selectively or nonselectively and apparently kills by coagulating the protoplasm. The thermodeath point of most living cells lies between 45° and 55°C for most plants; however, dry seeds are much more resistant to heat than are green growing plants. Along gravel routes and railroad tracks where cultivation is not practical, flamethrowers and steam are used to kill green shoot growth. Steam is also used for killing buried weed seeds and subterranean organs of perennial weeds, particularly in greenhouse operations. Fire may be used for selective weed control in onions, cotton, and corn (Knake et al., 1965) and in castor beans (Peacock et al., 1965), since the young plants of these crops are more resistant to fire than most weed seedlings. Flaming has the advantage that no chemical residue is left in the crop. It is, however, not widely used in areas where preemergence herbicides and cultivation give satisfactory control. Development of new and lightweight burning equipment that permits good control of speed and temperature may lead to more widespread use of this technique (Figure 5-1).

Nonselective applications of fire have been made where eradication of small infestations of weeds, such as dodder in alfalfa, is desirable. The flame in this case destroys both the weed and the crop; therefore it is used only to eradicate small weed patches. Fire seldom does more than kill the tops of the plants, although, according to some reports, death of certain portions of the roots—presumably due to toxic substances produced in the tops—may occur under certain conditions. Fire is, however, much more effective with annual weeds than it is with perennial weeds.

Although burning is not usually considered an effective method of selective weed control in most crops, it is often desirable for other reasons, such as removal of fire hazard, clearing of waterways, killing insect and fungus pests, lessening the amount of trash in plowing or discing, and the removal of unsightly debris. Burning is, of course, hazardous, since it may set fire to adjoining fields or trees; or smoke may be a hazard to traffic under special conditions; and allergies are sometimes carried in smoke. Moreover, it has been shown that burning reduces the amount of humus in the soil, leaving a deposit of ashes which may soon be washed away or made unavailable to the crop. Fire is also used to destroy the dry tops of weeds that have matured or been killed by mowing or spraying. Russian knapweed and morning-glory retain their seeds better than other species so that burning may destroy a large percentage of the viable weed.

Under primitive methods of tropical agriculture, burning is done every year. This practice has been followed for many centuries. The land, however, is generally on a 7- to 10-year rotation. During the fallow period second-growth timber and shrubbery grow on the land. This regrowth is cut down, allowed to dry, and then burned to make the land available for

(a)

(b)

Figure 5-1 *Weed control by flaming. Burning when weeds are small can give good results in certain crops. (a) Preplant application to young weeds. (b) Same field 4 weeks later: treated area at left, untreated plot at right. (Photo courtesy of D. V. Peabody.)*

planting. Also the low nutrient content generally found in tropical soils makes the addition of these ashes very desirable in the early growth of the crop.

MULCHING

The effect of mulching may be attributed to various physical aspects, especially the preventing of light from reaching the weeds. The covering must be light tight since it is mainly by hindering photosynthesis that the weeds under the material are killed and new growth prevented. Many nonliving materials have been used to cover the soil and thus prevent weed growth in the rows between the crop plant, or around trees and shrubs. Among these are straw, hay, manure, and rice hulls. The layer on the soil must be thicker for perennials than for annuals. For morning-glory and other deep-rooted, vigorous perennials it must be at least 3 to 4 feet thick. Obviously, the cost is too high for large infestations of weeds. Sawdust has been used quite widely in pineapple plantations.

Paper and plastic have also been used commercially. Paper mulch is used in sugarcane and pineapples in some tropical areas. The paper may be laid down in broken or solid strips or in squares. Agricultural plastic is a relatively recent innovation and appears to have many desirable characteristics from the standpoint of weed control, water retention, and protection from freezing. Both the cost of these materials and the cost of applying them in the field are generally too high to permit their use in anything except small areas or high-value crops. Weeds will grow through any holes in the paper or plastic, including those in which the crop is planted. Improved water retention with these materials, particularly the agricultural plastic, may be of some value in areas where water supplies are scarce. More roots tend to grow near the surface of the ground in the more fertile, better-aerated portion of the soil. In shallow soil this can be of critical importance. Many home gardeners could make better use of mulches (see also Chapter 10).

COMPETITION

Some vigorous and tall-growing crops can compete with many weeds. Through rapid growth, especially in the seedling stages, they rapidly shade and thus kill the slower-growing weeds. Vigorous crops are also good competitors for most of the available nutrients and moisture, thus inhibiting weed development. Some crops that are good competitors are barley, alfalfa, sorghum, sugarcane, Sudangrass, buckwheat, sweet clover, and millet. In many crops a single cultivation or single spray treatment is sufficient to enable the crop to compete successfully with the weeds. Thus, the same weed pest may be handled quite differently in different crops, depending upon the competitive ability of the crop species. For example, in one experiment by the author at Pullman, Washington, wild oats were seeded to make a dense infestation. Barley, wheat, peas, and lentils were planted in the spring and treated with various wild oat herbicides. Marked differences in competitive ability were clearly visible. The untreated barley grew so vigorously that it competed successfully with the wild oats. Wheat, peas, and lentils followed in competitive ability with correspondingly increasing yields in the treated plots over the controls as a result of reduction in the wild oat stand. Many more wild oats grew in the lentil plots than in the others despite the application of the chemicals at the same time and rate.

This increase of weeds was, of course, due to the relatively poor competitive ability of the lentil. This led to the apparent anomaly that the greatest improvement in yield due to the control of the weeds occurred in the crop with the poorest apparent weed control. In the plots where the weeds were not controlled, the lentils were nearly completely choked out. Most of the oats probably germinated after the dissipation of the herbicides. In vigorous crops like cereals the weeds were shaded out and could not compete, whereas in the weaker legumes, more space moisture and nutrients were available for the weeds to use.

In attempting to establish perennial turf grasses in rows for seed production, the lack of competition in the first year is especially evident. In experiments with short-lived herbicides which disappear from the soil quickly, it is often impossible—8 to 10 weeks after the chemicals were sprayed—to distinguish the plots in which the weeds were controlled from the untreated plots, because of the rapid growth of the late-germinating weeds. Nevertheless, marked improvements in the growth of the grasses in the treated plots show up in the following year, demonstrating the importance of controlling weeds early in the life of the crop.

Lack of competition in crops which have been injured by winter killing, diseases, or insects usually leads to infestation by weeds. Once established, the weeds may successfully compete with the crop. For example, downy brome frequently infests large patches of bluegrass grown for seed where the grass has been damaged by wireworms. The downy brome severely reduces growth and seed production of the desirable grass. Unless the weed is controlled the bluegrass may take years to recover. Certain perennial weeds with deep root systems, e.g., bindweed, can grow vigorously after the surface moisture is exhausted. Such weeds frequently appear in crops late in the season and make their best growth if other weeds are eliminated by cultivation or chemicals.

NURSE CROPS

Nurse crops are sometimes used to prevent weed growth. These are species which can be controlled fairly easily with chemicals, or are annuals in a perennial crop. They are usually quicker to germinate and are rapid in early growth. Annual rye, for example, is sometimes planted with lawn grasses or in orchards. It restrains the weeds and permits the crop to become established. Since the rye is an annual, it does not usually present much of a weed problem itself, especially if it is mowed to prevent seed production. Clover is sometimes planted with oats as a nurse crop.

TIMING OF OPERATIONS

The date of seeding should be selected for the best growth of the crop. This will often depend on whether summer or winter annuals are more serious. For example, fall-planted alfalfa usually competes well with spring-germinating annual weeds, whereas spring-planted alfalfa might be crowded out. Spring planting may be preferred where winter annual weeds are more serious.

Weeds which germinate before the crop sprouts can be killed by cultivation or by chemicals. Sometimes it is desirable to delay planting until most of the weeds have germinated. Land may be prepared for planting and the weeds allowed to germinate. The weeds are sprayed with a foliar-active herbicide, and the crop is then planted with minimum disturbance of the soil to avoid bringing buried seeds to the surface where they may germinate.

Herbicides can be used effectively to make farm operations more flexible. By appropriate manipulation of herbicides and machinery, the farmer can take advantage of good weather conditions. Weed competition can be effectively reduced prior to or following planting, if necessary, by aerial application of herbicides when the soil may be too wet for cultivation but excellent for weed and crop growth (see also Chapter 4).

QUESTIONS

1. Why are crops cultivated?
2. What is the main aim of cultivating annual weeds?
3. What is the influence of cultivation on seed germination? Will this affect seeds with innate, induced, or enforced dormancy?
4. What is the aim of cultivating perennial weeds?
5. How do temperature and day length affect the amount of food storage in underground roots?
6. Why does mowing induce tiller formation?
7. How does flooding kill plants?
8. What is the mechanism by which fire may be used selectively?
9. What are the disadvantages of fire for weed control?
10. Why do you suppose burning is so popular in primitive agriculture? Think of this in terms of available energy sources.
11. How does smothering with nonliving materials reduce weed growth?
12. How does the selection of a crop affect weed control practices? That is, in densely weeded areas consisting mainly of broadleaves, would you plant barley, lentils, peas, or wheat? Suppose the area was known to be heavily infested with (1) wild oats, (2) downy brome; how would this affect your choice of crop?

REFERENCES

Bruns, V. F., and L. W. Rasmussen. 1957. The Effects of Fresh Water Storage on the Germination of Certain Weed Seeds. *Weeds*, **5**:20–24.

Knake, E. L., F. W. Slife, and R. Seif. 1965. Flame Cultivation for Corn and Soybeans. *Weeds*, **13**:52–56.

Peacock, J. F., O. C. Burnside, T. L. Lavy, D. G. Hanway, and D. L. Kittock. 1965. Flaming, Intertillage and Chemical Weed Control in Castorbeans. *Weeds*, **13**:290–292.

Robbins, W. W., M. K. Bellue, and W. S. Ball. 1956. Weeds of California. California Department of Agriculture.

Robinson, D. W. 1964. Non-Cultivation Systems for Small Fruits and Vegetables. *Weeds*, **12**:245–251.

Shaw, W. C., and A. J. Loustalot. 1963. Revolution in Weed Science. *Agr. Sci. Rev.*, 1–10.

CHAPTER SIX
SELECTIVITY

The principles involved in the selective action of chemicals on plants apply equally to any chemical or to any species. The aim of this chapter is to develop in the student an understanding of these principles.

One of the most curious characteristics of herbicides and growth-regulating chemicals is their selectivity. A selective herbicide is one which acts only on certain plants and not on others (Figure 6-1). Thus certain chemicals may kill one plant but hardly affect another; defoliate one variety of several; or control weeds at one time but not a few weeks later. Some of the most fascinating research of the present day is directed toward elucidating these factors of selectivity.

The success or failure of an attempt at chemical regulation depends on the ability of the operator to distinguish the factors affecting herbicidal action and to take advantage of them (Figure 6-2).

The first question the investigator should ask is, "What plant do I want to grow in this place?" The second question is, "What do I need to do to control the weeds most effectively and economically to achieve the growth of the desirable plant?" This applies as much to noncropland as it does to cropland unless complete sterility is the aim. The combination of selective chemical treatment and the planting of competitive plants of appropriate growth habit would be of much value in maintaining rights-of-way, firebreaks, highways, and other public utilities.

Thus it is important to know the relative susceptibilities of the crop and weed to different herbicides, as well as the influence of stage of growth on this relative susceptibility.

Figure 6-1 *Selective control with simazine in a conifer nursery. Treated plot in foreground, untreated plot at left rear overgrown with weeds. Survival and growth of six conifer species were excellent in the treated plots and very poor in the unweeded plots.*

Selective action of an herbicide may be achieved by taking advantage of the following differences in growth and development of the crop and weed:

1.   Age or maturity: The desired plant has not emerged or is at a different age from the weed and so is less susceptible.

2.   Morphological differences: The desired plant may be so structured as to prevent contact of the chemical with its growing points as compared to the exposed growing points of the weed, e.g., the protective sheath around the apical meristem of a monocotyledon as compared to the exposed buds of a dicotyledon.

3.   Physiological differences: The desired plant may not translocate the chemical to the "susceptible" cells or it may be capable of inactivating the chemical after it is translocated, as with corn removing a chlorine atom from simazine to detoxify it. In some instances, the desired plant may lack an enzyme needed to modify the chemical, as alfalfa with 2,4-DB, which is harmless until it has been converted to 2,4-D (see also Chapter 8).

RULES FOR HERBICIDAL ACTION

Three rules govern generally the response of plants to herbicides: (1) Susceptibility often decreases with age or maturity. Some species remain

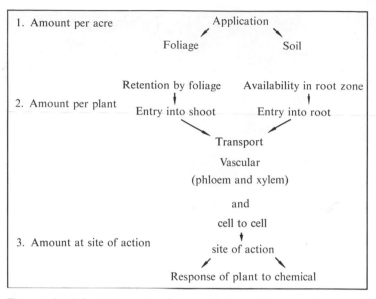

Figure 6-2   *Selectivity may be due to a number of factors as shown in the above diagram. An herbicide may be blocked in its action at several possible points.*

susceptible throughout their life cycles, while others develop resistance very soon. (2) Plants that grow rapidly—i.e., those that grow under optimum conditions of adequate moisture, warmth, and nutrients—are most susceptible. (3) Mature perennial plants are best treated with 2,4-D when carbohydrate reserves are low. Seedlings of perennial weeds should be treated within a few days after germination before the plant has begun to compete seriously with the crop or before it has established an extensive root system that will enable it to withstand cultivation or chemical treatment.

1.   Many examples can be given of weeds which rapidly gain resistance with age or maturity. The coast fiddleneck (*Amsinckia intermedia*) is very sensitive to 2,4-D in the rosette stage but becomes resistant as soon as the plant starts to flower (Figures 6-3 and 6-4). Tansy ragwort (*Senecio jacobaea*), a biennial, is moderately susceptible to 2,4-D in the first year. In the second year, when it begins to flower, it is much more difficult to kill. Unfortunately, in the first year, or rosette stage, it is relatively inconspicuous and may escape notice. In the second year, when it is conspicuous because of its bright yellow flowers, it is then recognized as a serious problem but it is too late to spray effectively. Other plants such as mustard, fanweed (*Thlaspi arvense*), or dandelion remain sensitive to 2,4-D for nearly the whole season of growth.

Plant responses may differ between chemicals also. For example, pepperwort becomes decreasingly susceptible to MCPA as the growing season progresses, yet shows an increasing susceptibility to 2,4-D until flowering time, followed then by decreased susceptibility (Blackman, 1950).

Crop plants also follow a similar pattern of changing response to herbicides. For example, it is possible to kill young plants of cabbages, soybeans, and tomatoes with concentrations of 2,4-D that have little effect on older plants of the same species (Weaver et al., 1946).

Wheat and other cereals have two periods of relative susceptibility

(a)

(d)

(b)

(c)

(e)

Figure 6-3 *Stages in growth of Coast fiddleneck* (Amsinckia intermedia). *Plant is sensitive to 2,4-D in (a) seedling, (b) rosette, and (c) prebolt stages but is resistant in (d) bolting and (e) flowering stages. Resistance rapidly increases as the plants mature. (From doctoral dissertation, W. G. Mauldin, Washington State University, 1963.)*

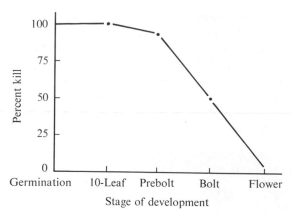

Figure 6-4 *Percent control obtained from spraying Coast fiddleneck* (Amsinckia intermedia) *with 1 pound 2,4-D per acre at stages of growth shown in Figure 6-3. (From doctoral dissertation, W. G. Mauldin, Washington State University, 1963.)*

to 2,4-D between germination to tiller stage and during early boot stage. Spraying at either time may cause severe loss in yield although reduction in stand may occur only from the early spray, i.e., before tillering. Later sprays reduce seed set but do not kill the plants. Small grains are very resistant to 2,4-D from the time of tiller formation to early flowering (boot stage), and again after flowering from soft dough stage to maturity (see also Chapter 9). Oats are more sensitive to 2,4-D than are the other small grains. In general, the ester form of 2,4-D causes more damage than the amine form.

2.   Plants growing under conditions which cause them to be stunted—such as dry, hot weather or low temperatures—are likely to be less affected by herbicides. This lack of effect may be partially due to the increase in cuticle formation caused by exposure to sunlight and dry weather and the consequent lack of entry of the herbicide into the plant, or to the presence of relatively few young active cells which are the most responsive to 2,4-D. The changes in susceptibility from one stage of development to another may thus be due in large part to the differences in growth rate and the associated proportions of young actively growing cells. Seedlings are made up mainly of meristematic and young expanding tissues with a rapid growth rate. Plants which have completed flowering are primarily made up of mature, well-differentiated tissues in a static condition in respect to growth and are generally quite resistant to herbicides such as 2,4-D.

3.   Perennial weeds, such as bindweed, Canada thistle, etc., are usually most susceptible at the early bud state, i.e., just prior to flowering. A combination of cultivation, to reduce the food reserves, and herbicides is likely to be most effective. For example, Canada thistle may be readily

killed by a combination of cultivation and 2,4-D but is resistant to either chemical or cultivation alone. The thistle is cultivated during the early summer months, until July or early August, then permitted to grow and come into the early bud stage, i.e., when the flower buds are visible but not open. At this time 2,4-D is sprayed at about 2 pounds per acre and a good kill is obtained. A similar spray of 2,4-D without cultivation is not as effective. Similar results have been obtained on certain other perennial weeds (Chapter 10).

IMPORTANCE OF PREVIOUS HISTORY

The susceptibility of plants to herbicides may be affected by their previous history in such areas as (1) cultivation, (2) damage from equipment, (3) other chemicals, (4) weather, and (5) diseases, insects, and animals (Aberg, 1964). Insects or animals may injure sprayed plants more than untreated plants.

1. Cultivation to weaken perennials should be timed to cause maximum depletion of food reserves prior to herbicide application. For example, with Canada thistle (*Cirsium arvense*) a good schedule is to cultivate until late summer, allow the plant to form flower buds, and then spray.

2. Wheel damage from tractors, sprayers, and other equipment increases with the lateness of the spraying. Plants growing in the wheel tracks often show more damage than those growing outside; these plants are bent over and may absorb more of the chemical than if they were upright. In addition, chemicals enter the leaves and stems more readily through wounds caused by the wheels.

3. Pretreatment with dalapon reduces leaf waxes, making both crop and weeds more susceptible.

4. Hail and high winds make plants more susceptible by causing injury and consequently easier penetration of the herbicide.

5. Plants infested with virus may be more susceptible to herbicides; e.g., tobacco plants and chickweed infested with tobacco mosaic are more sensitive to simazine than healthy plants (Ulrychova and Blattny, 1961). Plants damaged by insects or animals may suffer more from the spraying than undamaged plants.

6. Plants treated with herbicides may be made more attractive to insects or animals. Beans treated with 2,4-D are more susceptible to aphids (Maxwell and Harwood, 1960), and corn more attractive to mice (Chapter 13).

Genetic Differences

Many crops, such as wheat, corn, oats, barley, flax, potatoes, and grapes, have varieties which vary in response to herbicides.

Differences in response to herbicides have also been found in various naturally occurring ecotypes and biotypes of weeds, such as bindweed to 2,4-D (Muzik and Whitworth, 1959; Whitworth and Muzik, 1967), wild oats (*Avena fatua*) to IPC (Rydrych and Seeley, 1964), Canada thistle to 2,4-D and amitrole (Hodgson, 1964), and barnyard grass (*Echinochloa crusgalli*) to dalapon (Roché and Muzik, 1964).

FOLIAR-APPLIED CHEMICALS

Morphological factors

The amount of chemical remaining on the plant after a spray is applied to the leaves is affected by the angle of presentation and the shape of the leaves. If the leaves are erect and narrow, they will retain less chemical than if they are broad and horizontal. Drought may cause leaves to wilt or roll and thus affect retention and penetration.

Wettability of the leaves is reduced by waxiness. Young leaves are more easily wetted than mature leaves, probably because the wax and cuticle are thinner and may not form a complete layer. As a leaf grows older, the wax continues to be extruded from the epidermal cells—permeating the cell walls—and on the surface of the cuticle.

The exposed location of growing points of dicotyledons at the ends of aerial branches makes them more sensitive to contact chemicals than grasses with protected buds, which are often below the ground level.

Hairs and spines on leaves and stems prevent intimate contact with the leaf surface. Some plants, such as the mullein *(Verbascum)* or the water fern *(Salvinia)*, are so closely protected by stiff leaf hairs that ordinary aqueous sprays make poor contact with the leaf, unless wetting agents are added to the solution. On the other hand, if the spaces between the hairs are large and if the hairs are weak, forming a sort of mesh, then they may serve to hold the solution on the leaf.

Retention of the herbicide may be obtained by changing the volume of application. Too much may result in excessive runoff from the leaf surface and too little may result in poorly wetted leaves. Retention may also be varied by the addition of wetting agents (Holly, 1965). Wetting agents may help to prevent rapid drying out of the solution, thus improving the toxic action. Herbicides may be greatly reduced in effectiveness if they are precipitated as dry crystals or powders on the leaf.

Entry into leaves

Leaves are not well adapted to absorb and translocate foreign substances. The cuticle is probably the most important barrier to exogenous chemicals. It is thicker on the upper surface than on the lower surface and thus the latter is more easily penetrable. The primary cuticle is a varnishlike layer formed by oxidation of plant oils upon exposure to air. It is not attacked by wax solvents. Deposition is continuous until maturity. The cuticularized layers of leaves consist of this layer plus various surface and subsurface wax deposits.

Surface waxes are extruded through the intact cuticle by the epidermal cells. The outer cell walls contain cutin, cutin wax, pectin, and cellulose.

Production of the surface waxes continues until leaf expansion has ceased. Various factors influence the quantity and quality of these surface protrusions: (1) wind, (2) temperature, (3) moisture, (4) light, and (5) compounds in the soil. In general, strong winds, high temperatures, and high light intensity cause increased production of leaf waxes. Certain compounds such as dalapon are known to inhibit wax formation on leaves when the chemical is applied to the roots.

The evidence against cuticular diffusion includes the following: (1) Internal injury is frequently localized below stomates, (2) cuticle in vitro is impermeable to certain salts, (3) greatest effectiveness coincides with the periods of the day when stomates have the widest opening (Dybing and Currier, 1961; Sargent and Blackman, 1962).

On the other hand, evidence that entry does occur through the cuticle is shown by experiments with plants which have stomates on only one surface or in localized areas. Drops of liquid held on surfaces without stomates do penetrate effectively into the leaf.

Recent work suggests that entry through stomates is increased as the amount of surfactant in the formulation is increased (Currier et al., 1964). Entry is facilitated if the chemical is not allowed to dry out. The vapors of volatile chemicals enter the stomates readily.

Physiological factors

Translocation of foliar-applied herbicides downward and upward in the plant is accomplished in the living cells of the phloem (Figure 6-5). The major avenues of movement appear to be in the sieve tubes, although diffusion in parenchyma cells may also play a minor role.

Lateral translocation from cell to cell occurs by diffusion, as does movement through the mesophyll of the leaf. Transport of foliar-applied herbicides occurs along the cell walls of the leaf—rather than through the cells—until they reach the vein, i.e., vascular tissue, and enter the phloem sieve tubes. Translocation of 2,4-D out of the leaves occurs with the photosynthates and does not occur in the absence of photosynthesis.

The plant may conveniently be considered to consist of two

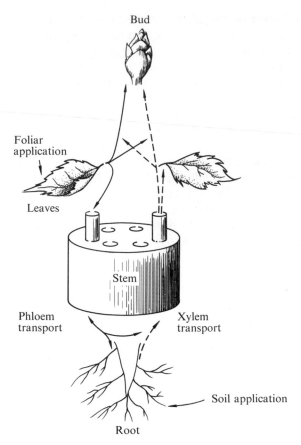

Figure 6-5 *Transport of foliar-applied herbicides occurs with sugars in the phloem in both upward and downward directions. Herbicides applied to the soil are translocated upward in the xylem with the transpiration stream. (Redrawn from Shaw et al., 1960.)*

phases: (1) symplast, the living cells with protoplasm, (2) apoplast, the nonliving cells. Both systems are continuous. The systemic foliar-applied chemicals translocate downward in the symplast along with the photo-synthates, and the soil-applied chemicals translocate mainly in the apoplast along with water and minerals.

If the chemical fails to translocate out of the leaf, it will have no systemic action although it may injure the leaf. Contact herbicides that cause death of the foliage and stems are often quite successful in killing young annual plants, but seldom cause serious injury to mature perennials which make new growth from protected buds under the soil.

SOIL-APPLIED CHEMICALS

Like foliar-applied chemicals, selectivity in soil-applied chemicals is conditioned on many factors (Shaw et al., 1960). The herbicide must reach the absorbing portions of the root and remain long enough in sufficient quantities to be absorbed in effective amounts. If it is a systemic chemical, it must enter the root and be translocated to the sensitive cells. Entry into the root is with the water and follows the same pathway as the transpiration stream (Figure 6-5). Injury to roots may affect uptake also, depending on the nature of the injury.

Placement

Some chemicals, such as simazine and 2,4-D, are held in the upper layers of the soil by adsorption on the soil colloids or soil organic matter or by forming insoluble salts with soil elements (such as calcium), and thus fail to reach the deep roots of perennial plants although they may be very effective on germinating seeds or seedlings.

Leaching

Other chemicals move readily with water in the soil and may be leached out of the root zone very rapidly. Dalapon even at very high rates (100 pounds per acre) may disappear from tropical soils within 2 weeks during the rainy season, but persist in the same region for months during the dry period.

Decomposition

Destruction of the soil-applied chemical by microorganisms may occur rapidly if conditions are proper for the growth of the bacteria and fungi in the soil. Adequate warmth, moisture, and organic matter are necessary for rapid growth and activity of the microorganisms. Therefore, very cold or very dry conditions or low humus content will tend to increase the persistence of chemicals in the soil by decreasing the rate of decomposition.

Some chemicals must be modified by microorganisms before they are toxic. For example, sesone, 2,4-dichlorophenoxyethyl sulfate, must be changed by a bacterium to 2,4-D before it will injure plants. In soils where this bacterium is absent, the chemical is ineffective.

Photodecomposition, or disappearance of the chemical from the surface in regions of high light intensity, may occur (Comes and Timmons, 1965; Day and Clerx, 1964). Their work showed that monuron or simazine applied to soils exposed to bright sunlight and little rainfall might be reduced in effectiveness due to photodecomposition of the chemical before sufficient rain occurred to leach it into the soil.

Volatility

Volatility is an important factor in the selective action of many soil-applied chemicals. Covering with a layer of plastic, paper, soil, or water, or cultivating to incorporate the chemical in the soil within an hour or less after application, is essential for the effective action of many very volatile chemicals, such as the fumigants, and EPTC, SMDC, diallate, etc. Volatility may be a serious problem in areas where circulation is restricted, as in greenhouses. Application of a volatile chemical to one plant may damage several others. The application of the isopropyl esters of 2,4-D, for example, to a single tomato plant may severely damage all the tomatoes in the greenhouse. Damage to orchards from volatile esters of 2,4-D have been reported over a distance of more than 30 miles (Chapter 8).

BIOCHEMICAL SELECTIVITY

Physiological responses

Systemic chemicals are those which translocate freely throughout the plant. They tend to accumulate in meristematic areas or in tissues with high oxidation-reduction activity.

Even if the chemical is translocated freely, it may not affect the plant. This lack of effect may be due to the presence of certain enzyme systems which detoxify the chemical and make it innocuous. For example, corn detoxifies simazine by removing a chlorine atom from the molecule.

On the other hand, other enzymes may make nontoxic chemicals toxic. Certain plants apparently change 2,4-DB or MCPB (which are relatively harmless) to 2,4-D or MCPA, respectively, which are toxic. These plants are subsequently injured, but other plants which lack the necessary enzyme systems do not make this change and remain unaffected by the chemical (Wain, 1965; Brian, 1965). Many legumes, such as alfalfa, do not have this enzyme system and therefore 2,4-DB and MCPA may be sprayed with relative safety. Unfortunately, many weeds are also resistant to these chemicals, presumably because they too lack the enzyme system to "toxify" the 2,4-DB or MCPB.

Many growth regulators accelerate either directly or indirectly the activity of some enzymes in plants. It is not clear how much the effect on enzymes represents a primary toxic effect or whether it is merely a reflection of generalized growth responses. For example, starch hydrolysis is accelerated and there is an increase in sugar content in the stem and leaves following application of IAA or 2,4-D. This is usually followed by a decrease of starch in the leaf and stem tissue.

As discussed elsewhere in this chapter, the growth rate, carbohydrate levels, and balance between the endogenous hormones may affect the response of the plant to the herbicide.

Morphological responses

Many growth-regulating herbicides interfere with the orderly progression of cellular development in stem, root, and leaf. This interference is marked by a typical series of cellular responses to growth regulators. First is (1) an increase in water content of the cells, (2) cell enlargement followed by (3) cell division, (4) differentiation, and (5) orientation into root primordia, and finally (6) death. This chain of responses may be stopped at any point depending on the amount of chemical applied and the sensitivity of the plant. Sensitivity will vary with the species, age, and growing conditions.

Living cells high in oxidation-reduction activity are most affected. In the mature stem these are the cambium, phloem parenchyma, and to some extent, the xylem parenchyma. In the very young stem tip, even the cortex, pith, and epidermis may be affected. Apparently these tissues age rapidly, because a few centimeters below the apex they may show no response.

Other chemicals, such as the triazines and ureas, have relatively little effect on cell enlargement and division but seem to act on photosynthesis (Brian, 1965; Van Overbeek, 1965; Chapter 8).

Shifts in plant constituents

Many growth-modifying chemicals bring about an increase in minerals, protein, and amino acid content of stems and a decrease in the roots. It is likely that some of these materials, such as potassium and the amino acids, are used in the structure of the new cells proliferating as a result of the treatment. Others, such as copper, magnesium, and iron, are essential to enzyme systems, some of which are affected by the chemical. Thus elements accumulate in tissues where meristematic activity has been induced by the herbicide, and play a part in building the new cells or in the increased enzyme activity.

It has been shown that protein shifts of the same or greater order than the shifts occurring in plants treated with 2,4-D may occur in plants dying of desiccation. Therefore one must be careful, following herbicide application, in interpreting the results of analysis of plants as being indicative of direct cause-and-effect relationships (Muzik and Lawrence, 1960). Because a change in a constituent of a plant occurs after treatment, it does not necessarily follow that the herbicide acts to kill the plant by affecting the metabolism of this particular component. The action of an herbicide may be compared to pulling a trigger in a gun. The plant is a complex system and a change in any one component will affect many others. The difficulty comes in determining which is the primary or trigger reaction. The mode of action of 2,4-D, which has probably received more attention than any other herbicide, is still obscure for this reason.

The action of amitrole and dalapon is apparently mediated through riboflavin and pantothenic acid, respectively. The addition of riboflavin to amitrole-treated corn plants resulted in recovery of green color. Pantothenic acid aided plants to recover from dalapon (Hilton et al., 1959). The addition of thiamin to a 2,4-D spray improved the herbicidal action of 2,4-D on coast fiddleneck during cold weather, due apparently to a lack of thiamin production in the plant at low temperature. The added thiamin induced rapid root elongation and better kill with the herbicide (Mauldin et al., 1966).

These examples serve to demonstrate the variety of effects that herbicides have on plants. Most of the herbicides act on more than one aspect of plant metabolism, having primary and secondary sites of action. It is not clear in most instances which of the effects play a primary role in death and which merely follow as a result of death.

HORMONES AND THEIR RELATION TO HERBICIDAL ACTION

The regulation of orderly growth and organic development in plants is apparently controlled by a complex system of checks and balances. The growth and development of all cells appear to be under the control of certain endogenous chemicals, the plant hormones. Interference with the natural processes whereby these phytohormones control plant growth is probably a major means by which the applied growth regulators and herbicides produce their effects.

Hormones are substances which are produced by the organism and are capable of inducing profound physiological effects in very minute quantities. They play a prominent role in the metabolism and growth of plants influencing stem and root growth, cell elongation, production of flowers, movements of organs, dominance of one part over another, and the production of abnormal growths such as galls or tumors.

Native and synthetic auxins

Three main groups of these chemicals occur naturally in plants. They are auxins, gibberellins, and phytokinins.

The natural auxin is indoleacetic acid (IAA). Many synthetic auxins such as 2,4-D have been developed with chemical structures similar to IAA. Both the natural and synthetic auxins are characterized by their stimulation of stem cell elongation and their ability to induce curvature responses in growing stems. In the growing plant the highest content of auxin is found in the most rapidly expanding tissues such as young stems and leaves, but falls to very low levels in mature or senescent organs. It is synthesized in buds and young green leaves in the light and transported downward, resulting in a falling gradient in auxin concentration from the young to the mature tissues. Movement occurs by diffusion in the parenchyma cells. The young stems and leaves, of course, show greatest epinastic responses to synthetic auxins such as 2,4-D and dicamba. When IAA or 2,4-D, dicamba, etc., is applied to plant foliage, the plant twists and bends as a result of the growth stimulus caused by unequal concentration of auxin on different parts of the plant. The plant recovers quickly from external applications of IAA because the system in the plant is adapted to controlling concentrations of IAA at safe levels. It does not recover as well from 2,4-D or dicamba or other "foreign chemicals" to which the plant enzyme system is not well adapted.

Straitjacket effect

The naturally occurring plant hormones control the growth and differentiation of every cell from birth until death. The levels of the different hormones change as the cells age, and the cells become confined in special areas within the plant. Thus the age response of a tissue to auxin is determined by a change in sensitivity of the cells to the hormone and by a "straitjacket" effect of the surrounding tissues which restricts growth in these cells. One of the most striking effects of 2,4-D application to dicotyledons is the rapid division and proliferation of the parenchyma cells leading to swollen and split stems, and permanent stunting and malformations. This does not occur nearly to the same extent in monocotyledons because of the differences in the stem structure, although individual cells may show similar sensitivities to auxin.

Since the balance between the endogenous plant hormones changes both with the age of the cells and with the environment in which the plant grows, it is not surprising that variable responses to chemical weed killers and growth regulators are frequently found in practice. Recent discoveries of biotypes of weeds resistant to 2,4-D, amitrole, and dalapon point to the importance of the basic genetic endowment. Nutrition, light, temperature, and moisture prior to, at time of, and following treatment affect the response of the plant. Generally speaking, a plant growing under optimum conditions of warmth, ample moisture, and nutrients is most sensitive to 2,4-D. Stunted plants growing under low moisture or cold conditions are more resistant.

METABOLISM

In all living organisms there is an unceasing flow of energy, ebbing and flooding with the level of activity of a particular organ or tissue. Living substance is constantly being formed and destroyed, new tissues are formed, cells elongate and differentiate, wastes are excreted, and general protoplasmic activities are induced.

The working materials for these activities are the carbohydrates, fats, proteins, and minerals. Interference with the metabolic processes at many different sites is a feature common to many herbicides.

The proteins are the protoplasm building materials and are present in every living cell. Indeed, there can be no life without protoplasm. The proteins are always found in abundance where there is active cell division and growth. Shifts in protein concentrations in the plant following 2,4-D applications are very common. Generally the move is toward the stem and out of the roots. Similar shifts occur in plants dying from desiccation (Muzik and Lawrence, 1960).

PHOTOSYNTHESIS

Carbohydrates are made by the plant in the chloroplasts. These may occur in many parts of the plant but are by far most common in the leaves, which are particularly adapted for photosynthesis.

Movement of most foliar-applied chemicals out of the leaves apparently does not occur in the absence of photosynthesis. In addition, one of the earliest effects of many herbicides, such as 2,4-D, substituted ureas, triazines, etc., is a reduction in photosynthesis (Van Overbeek, 1965). When this is combined with an increase in respiration, as with 2,4-D, it has the effect of rapidly reducing food reserves. Certain herbicides such as paraquat (Chapter 8) are made toxic to the plant only during photosynthesis. Therefore the action of this chemical is affected by the time of spraying. Applied in the late afternoon, the chemical enters the plant and is freely distributed during the night. When dawn arrives and the plant resumes photosynthesis, the chemical is changed to a free radical, becomes toxic, and kills the plant. A spray application during bright sunshine will have a more rapid effect but may not give as good a kill because the chemical is made toxic before it translocates very far into the plant (Slade and Bell, 1966). Certain herbicidal oils apparently are affected in a similar way by light.

QUESTIONS

1. What is *selectivity*?
2. When are all plants most susceptible to herbicides?

3. Why are plants that grow under optimum conditions generally most susceptible to herbicides?
4. How does cultivation affect susceptibility?
5. How does damage from machinery affect selectivity?
6. What effect does pretreatment with dalapon have on selectivity?
7. What is the relationship of viruses and insects to selectivity?
8. What is meant by *wettability*?
9. Why are dicotyledons more sensitive to contact herbicides than grasses?
10. Does volume of carrier affect selectivity?
11. Define *cuticle*.
12. What factors affect surface wax production?
13. What is the relationship between surfactants and entry through stomates? Why?
14. What is the main reason that chemicals held in the upper layers of the soil attack seedlings and not mature plants?
15. Would you expect an herbicide to disappear more rapidly from a sterilized soil or an unsterilized soil?
16. What is *biochemical selectivity*?
17. Which tissues are most affected by growth-regulating herbicides?
18. What is the effect of 2,4-D on starch and sugar content of leaves and stems?
19. Why do many minerals move from leaves and roots to the stems following 2,4-D treatment?
20. What is meant by a *primary site of action*?
21. What are the natural growth-regulating chemicals?
22. What is an *auxin*?
23. What usually happens to the starch content of a plant following growth-regulator treatment?
24. What is the relationship of photosynthesis to translocation of herbicides out of leaves?
25. What would happen to the effectiveness of paraquat if you applied it following a treatment with a substituted urea?

REFERENCES

Aberg, E. 1964. Factors in the Plant Modifying the Response of a Given Species to Treatment, in "The Physiology and Biochemistry of Herbicides," L. J. Audus (ed.), pp. 401–419, Academic Press, Inc., New York.

Blackman, G. E. 1950. Selective Toxicity and Action of Selective Herbicides. *Sci. Progress,* **152**:637–651.

Brian, R. C. 1965. The Classification of Herbicides and Types of

Toxicity, in "The Physiology and Biochemistry of Herbicides," L. J. Audus (ed.), pp. 1–33, Academic Press, Inc., New York.

Comes, R. D., and F. L. Timmons. 1965. Effect of Sunlight on the Phototoxicity of Some Phenylurea and Triazine Herbicides on a Soil Surface. *Weeds*, **13**:81–83.

Currier, H. B., E. R. Pickering, and C. L. Foy. 1964. Relation of Stomatal Penetration to Herbicidal Effects Using Fluorescent Dye as a Tracer. *Weeds*, **12**:301–303.

Day, B. E., and W. A. Clerx. 1964. Photodecomposition of Triazine. *Weeds*, **12**:5–6.

Dybing, C. D., and H. B. Currier. 1961. Foliar Penetration by Chemicals. *Plant Physiol.*, **36**:169–174.

Hilton, J. L., J. S. Ard, L. L. Jansen, and W. A. Gentner. 1959. The Pantothenate-Synthesizing Enzyme, A Metabolic Site in the Herbicidal Action of Chlorinated Aliphatic Acids. *Weeds*, **7**:381–396.

Hodgson, J. M. 1964. Variations in Ecotypes of Canada Thistle. *Weeds*, **12**:167–170.

Holly, K. 1965. Herbicide Selectivity in Relation to Formulation and Applied Methods, in "The Physiology and Biochemistry of Herbicides," L. J. Audus (ed.), Academic Press, Inc., New York.

Mauldin, W. G., T. J. Muzik, and W. C. Robocker. 1966. Influence of Thiamin on Response of Coast Fiddleneck to 2,4-D at Low Temperature. *Weeds*, **14**:1–3.

Maxwell, R. C., and R. F. Harwood. 1960. Increased Reproduction of Pea Aphids on Broadbeans Treated with 2,4-D. *Ann. Ent. Soc. Am.*, **53**:199–205.

Muzik, T. J., and J. M. Lawrence. 1960. A Method To Aid in Separating Specific and Non-Specific Effects of Chemicals on Plants. *Nature*, **183**:482.

———— and J. W. Whitworth. 1959. Effect of Herbicides on Root Morphogenesis in *Convolvulus arvensis*. *Proc. Ninth Intern. Botan. Cong.*, 216.

Roché, B. F., and T. J. Muzik. 1964. Ecological and Physiological Study of *Echinochloa crusgalli* L. (Beauv.) and the Response of Its Biotypes to Sodium Dichloropropionate. *Agron. J.*, **56**:155–160.

Rydrych, D. J., and C. I. Seeley. 1964. Effect of IPC on Selections of Wild Oats. *Weeds*, **12**:265–267.

Sargent, J. A., and G. E. Blackman. 1962. Studies on Foliar Penetration I. Factors Controlling the Entry of 2,4-Dichlorophenoxyacetic Acid. *J. Exp. Bot.*, **13**:348–368.

Shaw, W. C., J. L. Hilton, D. E. Moreland, and L. L. Jansen. 1960. Herbicides in Plants, in "The Nature and Fate of Chemicals

Applied to Soils, Plants and Animals," U.S. Dept. of Agriculture Publication ARS 20–29.

Slade, P., and E. G. Bell. 1966. The Movement of Paraquat in Plants. *Weed Res.*, **6**:267–274.

Ulrychová, M., and C. Blattný. 1961. Synergistic Action of Simazine and of Plant Viruses as a Method for the Possible Selection of Viral Diseases. *Biologia Plantarum* (*Prague*), **3**:122–125.

Van Overbeek, J. 1965. Survey of Mechanisms of Herbicide Action, in "The Physiology and Biochemistry of Herbicides, L. J. Audus (ed.), pp. 423–463, Academic Press, Inc., New York.

Wain, R. L. 1965. The Behavior of Herbicides in the Plant in Relation to Selectivity, in "The Physiology and Biochemistry of Herbicides, L. J. Audus (ed.), pp. 465–479, Academic Press, Inc., New York.

Weaver, R. J., C. P. Swanson, W. B. Ennis, and F. T. Boyd. 1946. Effect of Plant Growth Regulators in Relation to Stages of Development of Certain Plants. *Bot. Gaz.*, **107**:563–568.

Whitworth, J. W., and T. J. Muzik. 1967. Differential Response of Selected Clones of Bindweed to 2,4-D. *Weeds*, **15**:275–280.

CHAPTER SEVEN
METHODS OF
APPLYING CHEMICALS

This chapter describes the various ways of applying chemicals to plants and how differences in formulation and method of application may modify the activity of the chemical.

KINDS OF APPLICATION

Applications made before the crop emerges, but after it is planted, are called *preemergence* applications. Those made after emergence of the crop are called *postemergence.* Preplanting or presowing applications are made prior to planting the crop. Some other types of application are:

Band: herbicide is applied in bands over the rows and not over the entire area.

Directed: herbicide is directed toward the ground or weeds to minimize contact with the crop.

Overall: spray is applied uniformly over the whole area, as opposed to band applications.

Overhead: spray is applied over the crop as opposed to application directed specifically to weeds.

Contact preemergence: a contact herbicide is applied to weeds that have developed before the crop emerges.

Residual preemergence: a residual herbicide treatment is applied to the soil before the crop emerges.

Spot: application is directed to patches of weeds.

Basal bark: to kill trees and shrubs, treatment is applied by sprayer or paintbrush to a bank of bark encircling the basal foot or two of the stem.

FORMULATIONS

Chemicals may be dissolved or suspended in water, or in various oils such as diesel oil, or emulsified in water and oil. Selectivity may be changed somewhat as a result of the carrier used. Granular formulations for most chemicals are available and are used mainly in horticultural crops and for general vegetation control. Herbicides are no longer available as dusts because dusts are too liable to drift.

Herbicides are usually sprayed on either the foliage or the soil, and should be applied as evenly as possible over the surface. The degree of evenness obtained will depend on the quality and suitability of the equipment, the skill of the operator in using the equipment, and the effect of environmental factors such as wind. The majority of agricultural usage involves spray applications of aqueous solutions, suspensions, or emulsions.

A solution is a stable, physically homogenous mixture of two or more substances. It does not settle out or need agitation. The dissolved constituent is called the *solute*, and the substance in which the solute is dissolved is the *solvent*.

An emulsion is a mixture of two liquids (stable or unstable) held together by a third chemical or emulsifier. Emulsions are usually either (1) oil in water (o/w)—the more common type, or (2) water in oil (w/o), called *invert emulsions*. When the oil droplets are dispersed in the water, the water is referred to as the *continuous phase*, and the oil droplets as the *discontinuous phase*. The converse is true with the invert emulsions. The latter have been used in special applications such as by airplane where they are particularly suitable. Special equipment is needed to spray the invert emulsions, but they have the advantage of relatively little danger of drift.

A suspension is a dispersion of finely divided solid particles in water. These particles tend to settle out unless they are agitated. Many of the new chemicals are *wettable powders* which are insoluble in water or oil and must be sprayed as suspensions.

Oil may be used as a carrier for other chemicals or as an herbicide in its own right. Nontoxic or chronic toxic oils are usually used as carriers. Chronic toxic oils are saturated oils which cause a chlorosis and slow death to the foliage over a period of weeks. Unsaturated (acute toxic) oils cause a rapid "burning," wilting, and death of the foliage, often within a few hours after application. These are unsuitable for general carriers of systematic herbicides because they kill the conducting tissues before the chemical can be thoroughly distributed.

In most emulsions and suspensions, the water tends to be repelled by the other liquid or solid, thus producing surface tensions or interfacial tensions. Such a tension is created because the water molecules are attracted to each other and toward the center of the body. For those molecules at the surface, there is an unbalanced force pulling them toward the interior causing the surface to assume a shape with the smallest possible area. Water is not compatible with many surfaces; when this is so, it tends not to adhere uniformly but to form droplets, as on the waxy surface of the plant.

SURFACTANTS

A surfactant (surface active agent) is a material that exhibits activity at surface or interfaces; examples are detergents, wetting agents, spreaders, sticking agents, and emulsifiers. They are frequently added to herbicide and growth-regulator formulations to increase their effectiveness (Behrens, 1964), and they may affect the activity of herbicides in oil sprays as well as in aqueous sprays (Jansen, 1964). All surfactants lower the surface energy of their solvents.

Surfactants may: (1) increase total spray retention, (2) decrease total spray retention, (3) increase spray retention at key sites, (4) increase penetration by increasing area of contact with the leaf by greater droplet spread, (5) increase penetration by eliminating air film between droplet and leaf surface, (6) act as humectants, or (7) solubilizing agents, (8) increase direct entry through stomates by lowering the surface tension of the spray solution, (9) facilitate movement along cell walls after entry by lowering interfacial tensions, and (10) aid in redistribution of chemicals upon rewetting.

A surfactant is a molecule with two opposing characteristics, termed *hydrophilic* and *lipophilic*. The hydrophilic (H) group is attracted to water and the lipophilic (L) group is attracted to oil. In an o/w emulsion, a drop of oil can be visualized as surrounded by a film of closely packed surfactant molecules with the L portion oriented toward the oil and the H portion attracted to the water (Figure 7-1).

There are two major classes of surfactants, the *ionic* and the *nonionic*, depending upon their ionization or dissociation in water. The nonionic group has no particle charge and does not ionize in water. These surfactants are classed as nonelectrolytes and are chemically inactive in the presence of salts. Some of the emulsifiers used with herbicides fall in this group.

The ionic group of surface active agents ionizes in water and has two main divisions. *Anionic* agents are those in which the anion portion of the molecule exerts a dominant influence. The *cationic* agents form a cation (positive charge) when they become ionized in water. Anionic surfactants

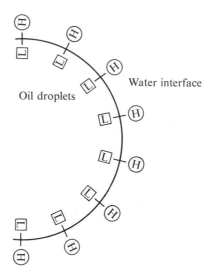

Water interface

Oil droplets

Figure 7-1 *Surfactant films form at interfaces of oil and water emulsions. The surfactant molecule is composed of a lipophilic (L) portion and a hydrophilic (H) portion. The presence of a surfactant reduces surface tension, thereby causing the emulsion to spread uniformly over the leaf.*

(detergents, wetting agents, emulsifiers) are more commonly used in agriculture. They are less useful in hard water than the nonionic surfactants, and the two are frequently mixed for commercial usage.

GRANULES

Granules are particles made of inert materials, such as clay, plastic, or vermiculite, mixed with the herbicide to provide enough bulk for even distribution. They are usually spread by hand or with mechanical spreaders. Their effectiveness depends on future wetting to dissolve and carry them into the soil.

Granular materials are sometimes easier to use than liquid sprays for small infestations, but application is seldom as uniform. Other advantages are that no spray equipment or water is needed to apply the material, and placement of granules is easier than placement of sprays. The weight and bulk increase the cost of application. Granular herbicides have been most widely used in horticultural crops and for vegetation control.

MIXTURES OF HERBICIDES

One of the most effective ways to increase the number of weed species killed selectively in a crop is to mix appropriate herbicides. Two precautions must be followed: (1) The herbicides must be compatible—that is, there must be no undesirable change in their physical properties, such as forming a precipitate; (2) the interaction between the chemicals must be beneficial. Particular mixtures are usually selected because of the individual properties of each herbicide. For example, a weedkiller which is effective against grasses but nontoxic to maize might be combined with one which is primarily effective on broadleaf weeds and also selective on maize. Generally, mixing herbicides does not change their selectivity, but this is not always true.

Most commonly, a mixture in which each component must be used at the full rate gives an additive effect. When the activity of the combination is less than additive, the combination is said to be *antagonistic*; when it is greater than additive, it is said to be *synergistic*.

In addition to broadening the spectrum of weed control, another advantage of mixtures is that sometimes the dosage of any one herbicide can be reduced. This is possible even without a synergistic action because the recommended rates of a chemical are based on the dosage required to give good control of a wide range of species. Usually the dose required to kill the most susceptible species is considerably less than the dosage required for the most resistant species. By combining compounds that are effective on different species it is possible to use the minimum amount of each that kills the most sensitive species. This is especially important when one of the chemicals is very expensive or when either persists long in the soil. When these soil-residual chemicals are used in dosages high enough to kill most weed species, they may cause damage to the following crop or leave undesirable residues in the foliage or fruit.

Combinations of various chemicals are made to broaden the spectrum of activity without increasing toxicity to the crop, as well as to reduce fire hazards. Certain combinations may be antagonistic, while others appear to give a synergistic response (Colby et al., 1965). For example, mixing an herbicide like paraquat (which is dependent on photosynthesis to become toxic) with an herbicide like diuron (which reduces photosynthetic activity) will reduce the effectiveness of the paraquat. A combination of a foliar-active compound such as 2,4-D or amitrole with a residual chemical such as atrazine may be useful where it is desired to kill existing vegetation and prevent later seed germination as in certain chemical fallow practices. The fire hazard of sodium chlorate is reduced by mixing it with borates and urea herbicides.

Some examples of well-known mixtures which have been found effective are 2,4-D and 2,4,5-T for brush control, and IPC and CIPC with DNBP for selective control of both broadleafs and grasses in many crops. A more recent mixture which is gaining in popularity is the combination of 2,4-D with dicamba. Dicamba does not control cruciferous weeds, but it is more effective than 2,4-D against certain broadleaf weeds such as coast fiddleneck and gromwell. Atrazine and linuron are used together for selective weed control in maize (corn), along with several other mixtures such as DNBP and Falone, CDAA and 2,4-D, EPTC and 2,4-D.

MIXTURES OF HERBICIDES WITH FERTILIZERS OR OTHER PESTICIDES

Herbicides for selective weed control are often mixed with fertilizers or other pesticides, thus saving both time and labor. Lawn chemicals are frequently sold as single-treatment applications for insects and weeds. If the chemicals are compatible, there is no objection to this practice. Generally, however, the best time for weed control is seldom the best time for fertilizing or controlling other pests so that it is usually more effective to spray the pesticides and fertilizers separately. Phytotoxicity may be greater when certain insecticides and herbicides are applied jointly, as in the case of monuron and disyston on cotton (Hacskaylo, Walker, and Pires, 1964).

EQUIPMENT FOR APPLYING CHEMICALS TO PLANTS

Requirements

Machines for applying chemicals should (1) dispense material at a uniform rate, (2) distribute this material uniformly over a given area, and (3) be readily calibrated to apply a desired quantity. Desirable features to increase the flexibility and utility of the apparatus are: hinged booms which are adjustable for height; pressure regulators; and strainers to prevent clogging.

A good sprayer usually has the following components: (1) tank, (2) strainer between tank and (3) pump, (4) pressure regulator, (5) line strainer, (6) boom, and (7) nondrip nozzles. Each of these has a special function: the tank holds the liquid, the strainer keeps large particles from going into the pump or clogging the nozzles, the pump develops the pressure to force the material out of the tank, the pressure regulator maintains the pressure at the desired level, the strainer in the line helps to keep small particles from entering the boom or clogging the nozzles, the boom distributes the chemical to the nozzles, and the nozzles break the liquid into the right sized particles so they can be spread properly. The strainers in the system also prevent wear on the pump, the pressure regulator, and the nozzles.

Many of the materials now used for herbicide spraying are wettable powders which are likely to cause considerable wear on the softer parts of the sprayer.

Factors of choice

The type of sprayer to be chosen for a particular operation depends upon a number of factors. One is the type of job to be performed, particularly the amount of acreage involved and the kind of crop. Another is whether a dual-purpose sprayer is required or one designed especially for herbicides. Herbicide spraying is done at low pressures on the order of 30 to 40 pounds per square inch, whereas many farm operations such as orchard spraying or spraying cattle with insecticides require a pressure of several hundred pounds per square inch. For safety's sake, it is advisable to have a separate sprayer set aside for herbicides to preclude the possibility of damage to sensitive crops as a result of using a contaminated sprayer.

Mounting of ground sprayers

Ground sprayers may be mounted on either a tractor or a trailer. Tractor mounting is less expensive and more maneuverable than trailer mounting (Figure 7-2). On the other hand, it has two disadvantages: it limits the size of sprayer that can be used, and the tractor may be busy on other work during the spraying season. Trailer mounting can accommodate a large tank with high clearance, and it is convenient to use (Figure 7-3). Its disadvantages are high cost, lack of maneuverability, and often excessive wheel damage to the crops.

Size and kind of tank

The size of the tank depends on the number of gallons to be sprayed. Also important is the distance from the water supply to the field

Figure 7-2 *Tractor-mounted sprayer, front view. Boom is permanently attached to tractor, giving greater maneuverability than trailer mounting, but tractor is not so readily available for other work.*

Figure 7-3 *A trailer-mounted field sprayer. Large tank, long boom, and high clearance are advantages of this type of mounting. Lack of maneuverability is a disadvantage. (Photo courtesy of S. McGregor.)*

of operation. For small acreages, a 50-gallon tank is often sufficient, whereas a 1000-gallon tank may be necessary for large acreages or where high gallonages are sprayed. The tank may be made of wood, metal, or plastic. Metal tanks are easy to clean and are less apt to retain and absorb toxic chemicals than the wooden tanks. Some tanks are made entirely of stainless steel, or with stainless steel or plastic coatings on the inside. These, however, tend to be more costly than either the straight metal or wooden tank. The bottom of the tank should be sloped so that it will drain completely. Removable tank liners of synthetic rubber or plastic have given excellent results. They are convenient to use, very inexpensive, and they save time in cleaning.

Tractor-operated machines

The majority of machines in use are mounted on the tractor three-point linkage, but this system places a limit of about 100 gallons on the tank capacities (Figure 7-2). Where larger capacities are required, either the machine is trailed or saddle tanks are mounted on each side of the tractor. The tank capacity of a sprayer is often an indication of the maximum volume rate for which it is suitable. Generally a machine should be capable of carrying sufficient material to spray at least 1 acre at its highest volume rate (i.e., a 40-gallon tank is suitable for volumes up to about 40 gallons per acre). The pressure at which the sprayer is operated is usually in the region of 30 pounds per square inch but ranges from 10 pounds per square inch, for low-pressure nozzles, up to 45 pounds per square inch.

The pump capacity (i.e., the gallons per minute output) in relation to the boom length is the main factor in deciding the volume per acre which the sprayer can apply. As a rough guide, an application rate of

10 gallons per acre (with nozzles set 18 inches apart and a forward speed of 4 miles per hour) will require a pump capacity of 1/10 gallon per minute per nozzle. The approximate pump capacity (in gallons per minute) required to spray at a given number of gallons per acre can be calculated by multiplying the gallons required per acre by the number of nozzles and dividing by 100. This capacity will need to be increased by 10 to 20 percent to allow for recirculation of the liquid necessary for agitation within the tank (Woodford and Evans, 1965).

Boom lengths vary from about 21 feet up to about 40 feet, although longer booms are sometimes used. The advantage of a long boom is, of course, a high rate of work. Its main disadvantage is that it tends to "whip" or "flap" more than a similar boom of shorter length. Unless the boom is fitted with some device such as outrigger wheels or skids, when the tractor tilts on uneven ground the distance that it moves vertically is greater with a long boom than with a shorter one. This is a serious disadvantage on uneven ground.

Mixing and agitation

Chemical spray materials must be mixed thoroughly with the proper dilutions of water and/or oil before they are applied. These materials are formulated as solutions, emulsions, or wettable powders. Only a mild agitation is required to mix and maintain solutions and emulsions containing adequate surfactant. However, the powders of wettable suspensions readily "settle out" if not continuously agitated, and an emulsion without sufficient emulsifiers will separate if agitation is stopped. Tanks can be agitated by mechanical paddles or by hydraulic jets.

Agitation of the contents of the tank is usually accomplished by returning part of the output from the pump back to the tank. This recirculation system, which is often referred to as the *hydraulic method*, has in many instances superseded mechanical agitation. Hydraulic agitation can be the simple return of the spray fluid to the top of the tank. Such a system is, however, ineffective for sprays containing suspended particles and is liable to give rise to foaming. Suspensions are best agitated by agitation jets or nozzles fitted near the bottom of the tank in such a way as to scour the bottom and resuspend any material that has settled out.

Volume rate

The volume of liquid needed per acre is determined mainly by the type of herbicide but to some extent also by the density of the foliage. Herbicides applied to the soil must be distributed evenly over the soil surface, and the actual volume of liquid in which they are applied is unimportant as long as this objective is achieved. With spraying machines in good order, volume rates of 20 to 30 gallons per acre are normally satisfactory. Contact herbicides are efficient only when the spray thoroughly wets the foliage. To help achieve this, volume rates of 40 gallons or more per acre are usually employed. In addition, some contact herbicides (e.g., DNBP) form a satisfactory suspension only when applied in a high volume rate of 50 to 100 gallons per acre. When using translocated herbicides it is not necessary to wet the foliage quite so thoroughly, and volume rates of 10 to 20 gallons per acre are usually satisfactory for weed control but with correspondingly greater danger of drift as the volume is reduced. Where dense crop and weed foliage is present, however, a minimum volume rate of 20 gallons per acre may be necessary.

The following definitions of volume rates have been adopted:

Very low volume: Up to and including 5 gallons per acre
Low volume: Over 5 and up to and including 20 gallons per acre
Medium volume: Over 20 and up to and including 60 gallons per acre
High volume: Over 60 gallons per acre

Some sprayers are capable of operating only in one or two of these ranges (at normal forward speeds of 3 to 5 miles per hour). Because of this, such terms as *low volume*, *low/medium volume*, and *high volume* are often applied to the machines themselves.

Band sprayers

Band sprayers apply the spray liquid in a narrow band—usually 5 to 7 inches wide—over the rows of the crop. They are used mainly to conserve the chemical and thus reduce the cost of application. It is often convenient to apply the herbicide at the same time that the crop is sown, and thus some band sprayers are made for attachment to seed drills. For this purpose the nozzles, which may be either the fan or the hollow-cone type, are specially designed to give an even application of liquid across the band, or a substantially rectangular pattern of the required width. It is not satisfactory to simulate band spraying by simply blocking off nozzles on an ordinary sprayer.

Special sprayers

Sprayers have been specially designed for the application of weed killers to roadsides, railway tracks, ditches, and canals. Other special designs cover such uses as directed application between rows of crops or around the bases of young trees by means of shielded nozzles.

The *dribble-bar* is a type of spray boom which largely eliminates spray drift. It consists basically of a perforated pipe which is fed with liquid at a low pressure, 2 pounds per square inch (psi) or less. The holes in the tube may be up to 0.5 inch apart, the actual spacing depending on the degree of cover required. A suitable size for the holes is $^1/_{32}$ inch in diameter. With such a machine the minimum volume of spray required for effective cover is 60 gallons per acre, but up to about 100 gallons per acre may be needed. The swath width and the degree of cover are both relatively unaffected by the height of the boom above the crop. The dribble-bar may be used in conjunction with hand-operated equipment (e.g., as a watering-can attachment) or with tractor-mounted equipment providing that the correct pressure can be obtained.

The *vibro-boom* is a tractor-mounted dribble-bar which has been modified for use at low volume rates of application. The perforated pipe has holes spaced at up to 2.5 inches apart; it is vibrated transversely to the direction of travel of the outfit and at a rate of about 1000 vibrations per minute. Application rates as low as 15 gallons per acre have been reported to be effective.

The *logarithmic sprayer* is designed for experimental work (Figure 7-4). It applies a steadily decreasing rate of chemical as it moves

Figure 7-4 *Tractor-mounted logarithmic sprayer designed to spray a steadily decreasing rate of chemical. The two cylindrical tanks in foreground hold water which feeds into the spray tank, steadily diluting the solution as spraying continues. This versatile sprayer, which was built at Washington State University, can also be used to spray a uniform rate of chemical by bypassing the spray tank and spraying directly from one of the cylindrical tanks containing the desired solution.*

Figure 7-5 *Knapsack sprayer is useful for small areas or where unevenness of land or irrigation pipes precludes use of wheeled vehicle. Operator is spraying a small patch of bamboo in Puerto Rico.*

across a field. Thus one is able to determine rather quickly the effective limits of application to a particular crop or weed. A single application can give rates from a fraction of a pound per acre to hundreds of pounds per acre.

Knapsack sprayers

Knapsack sprayers are slung on the body of the operator who directs the lance or boom delivering the spray to the soil or foliage (Figure 7-5). The contents may be pumped out by an attached hand pump or by a charge of pressurized air above the liquid in the container. In the latter type the air capacity is usually adequate to discharge the liquid contents without repumping and, if pressure-regulating valves are fitted, the liquid may be sprayed out at constant pressure. Such machines can operate at pressures of 20 to 80 pounds per square inch. With a single nozzle or with three or four small nozzles on a short boom, they are very useful where only a small area is to be treated and only a few gallons have to be applied. They are also useful where the unevenness of slope of the land or the presence of irrigation ditches or pipes precludes the use of a wheeled vehicle.

Nozzles

The most commonly used hydraulic nozzles for herbicide application in agricultural sprayers are the *fan* and the *hollow-cone* types.

Flat-fan nozzle

This is essentially a low-pressure (30 to 50 psi) nozzle and is most suitable for low or medium volume work. The spray from this type of nozzle is usually more forceful than that produced from a hollow-cone nozzle of similar output. At low to medium volume rates it is thus better able to penetrate dense foliage. These nozzles are designed to give a higher rate of deposit in the center of the spray, thus giving uniform application when the nozzles are properly spaced on the boom for overlapping.

Swirl or hollow-cone nozzle

With this type nozzle the liquid is forced through a swirl plate and enters a small chamber tangentially. The rotating liquid escapes through a central hole in the nozzle disc and its rotation causes it to expand to form a cone of liquid which then breaks up into droplets. Swirl plate design and chamber depth can alter performance. In practice the common method is to change the nozzle disc and vary the pressure. There is now a range of specially designed low-pressure hollow-cone spray nozzles which are suitable for low-volume machines. They operate at pressures of 10 to 15 psi and are capable of delivering 10 to 35 gallons per acre at 5 mph. These nozzles produce droplet sizes of a high degree of uniformity, and have almost eliminated the very small drift-prone droplets which are a weakness of both flat-fan nozzles and high-pressure hollow-cone nozzles. These nozzles will probably become more popular as their advantages are more widely recognized.

Wear in nozzles is an important factor, since the output of the nozzles will increase with use and the spray pattern may change. The rate at which nozzles wear will depend on the material used in their construction, the abrasiveness of the spray, and the operating pressure. Generally speaking, solutions such as many of the 2,4-D types of herbicides cause very little wear, while wettable powders such as diuron cause a higher rate of wear. Hardened stainless steel tends to be resistant to wear, and ceramic fairly resistant, while brass wears a little more rapidly than either. The outputs of the nozzles should be checked at least once per season. Wire should never be used to unblock clogged nozzles since it may enlarge the orifice. Use a toothpick or straw, or remove the nozzle and rinse it in water. If a nozzle cannot be easily cleaned, replace it with a new one.

Pressures

Pressure of operation affects the nozzle output, the spray pattern, and the droplet size. The output is approximately proportional to the square root of the pressure and thus doubling the pressure will increase the output by about 40 percent. An increase in pressure will increase the proportion of small droplets and therefore the amount of potential spray drift. Because a change in pressure can affect the size and velocity of the droplets, the width of the spray pattern is likely to change with a marked change in pressure. It is thus better to operate a nozzle at its recommended pressure. Change in application rates should preferably be obtained by using different sizes of nozzles rather than by changing the operating pressure or changing the speed of the spray rig.

Aerial sprayers

Various types of aircraft are used for aerial spraying, some of them specially designed for chemical application. Many of the planes, however, have been adapted from surplus war equipment and are not necessarily well designed for these operations. The single-engine biplanes and monoplanes are most widely used, while the multiengine planes, such as the DC-3, are used for longer hops and larger areas where a bigger payload is needed. Light planes are best in farming country because their cost is low and they are highly maneuverable—both in the air and for making emergency landings.

The rotary wing or helicopter is also widely used for spraying. The initial investment is much higher than for the fixed-wing planes. Nevertheless, the helicopter has many advantages. No runway is needed for takeoffs; it is very maneuverable and thus much better in fields hemmed in by trees or hills; it is less handicapped by poor visibility; and there may be some gain in wetting leaves with the downwash pushing the spray down among the leaves.

Selection of a plane for a particular job depends on the size of the fields, the nearness to a landing strip, the kind of country, the cost-payload ratio, and the type of equipment the plane carries.

The boom on an airplane, usually attached a foot or more below the wings, is approximately three-fourths as long as the wing. This design reduces vortices at the wing tips. Hollow-cone nozzles are preferred over the flat spray type because they exhibit less wear from wettable powders and produce more uniform droplets. The nozzles are spaced progressively closer from center to tip of the boom with a few nozzles grouped at the right of the center of the plane. A space without nozzles to the left of the center, about 3 or 4 feet from the center, helps to reduce distortion from the propeller slipstream. In certain instances, nozzles have been dispensed with and it is reported that the naked orifices produce large droplets which help to avoid drift. For a given airplane, the strength of the vortex is a function of the plane's weight and its flight velocity. Reduction in flight velocity results in a stronger, more turbulent vortex system, plus a marked increase in downwash in the central section. Similar tests with helicopters revealed essentially the same situation. At low forward speeds a violent turbulent wake is produced. The actual air currents near the end of the boom are outward and up as the helicopter produces a trailing vortex, similar to the fixed-wing aircraft. Likewise, in the central portion of the boom, there is a pronounced downwash which accompanies the strong free vortices. The strength of the vortices and downwash is materially reduced when the forward speed is increased.

For minimum drift with hazardous sprays it is desirable to (1) fly low, (2) keep the nozzle out of the wing tip area, at least 3 feet from the wing tip, and (3) keep the boom as far from the wing as practical.

Swath width

The swath width depends on the altitude of the plane at the time of spraying, the wind velocity, the type of plane, and the equipment it carries. Field measurements are required to determine a swath width accurately. The part of the swath width that receives a recommended dosage rate is called the *effective swath width*. Once the effective swath width has been determined by measurement, calibration of the equipment is very simple. For example, the number of acres per minute sprayed may be calculated by a simple formula:

$$\text{APM} = \frac{2\text{SW} \times \text{MPH}}{1000} \text{ and GPM} = \frac{2\text{SW} \times \text{MPH} \times \text{GPA}}{1000}$$

where APM = acres per minute
      SW = swath width in feet
      MPH = miles per hour
      GPM = gallons per minute
      GPA = gallons per acre

Flight height for agricultural spraying should seldom exceed 5 to 10 feet. The accepted flight pattern is a grid in which the operator flies crosswind and moves upward on each pass. This avoids flying into the spray. On irregular areas most pilots fly the contours on the down slope.

HAZARDS

Damage from herbicides generally results from: (1) direct application to sensitive crops as a result of misuse or faulty equipment, (2) vapors arising from volatile formulations, (3) physical drift of sprays or dusts, (4) careless storage and handling, (5) improper disposal of empty containers, (6) multiple use of sprayers without proper cleaning, and (7) contamination of irrigation water.

Prevention of aerial damage

Damage to sensitive neighboring crops is almost always caused by aerial contamination. Herbicides may become air contaminants either as gases or vapors or as small particles (aerosols). Movement of airborne spray particles is called *spray drift* (Figure 7-6). *Vapor drift* is the movement of vapors or fumes given off by the chemical. *Blowoff* is the movement, by high wind, of dried spray particles or of soil impregnated with the herbicide away from areas originally treated. Movement of herbicides down steep slopes in water or with soil may occur.

Spray drift is likely to be more troublesome in areas where there is a mixture of agronomic and horticultural crops. It is by far the most important cause of damage and results from the dispersion of the material at the spray nozzle. Further dispersion is affected by the nature of the carrier, the wind velocity, and air turbulence (Adams et al., 1964). Amount of drift will depend on the size of the droplets, the amount of wind, and the height above the ground that the spray is released (Figure 7-6; Brooks, 1947). Small droplets result from the application of a small quantity to a

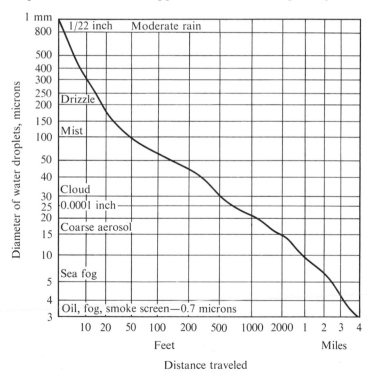

Figure 7-6 *Chart showing distribution of various size droplets while settling 10 feet in a 3-mph wind. (From Brooks, 1947.)*

large area or from application under high pressure. The particle size is also affected by the carrier. Water is very volatile, particularly in a dry atmosphere. Consequently, large droplets may rapidly evaporate and become small droplets which remain suspended. Oil is less volatile than water but it has a very low surface tension and consequently the droplets are small when they leave the nozzle. Both oil and water have some undesirable features as media for herbicide dispersion. Water tends to evaporate too fast and oil tends to break up into very small particles.

Increasing the pressure increases the proportion of smaller droplet sizes. As a rule, pressures above 30 to 40 psi should not be used.

Damage from spray drift can be reduced by the use of suitable equipment and by proper timing. The following precautionary measures should be observed before spraying herbicides in the vicinity of susceptible crops:

1.   Spraying should be performed only when wind velocity is less than 10 mph and temperatures are moderate, and preferably before the susceptible crops appear above the soil. That is to say, there should be little or no movement of air (wind, convection current, etc.) toward these crops.

2.   Nozzles should be fitted so as to produce a minimum proportion of small droplets (e.g., low pressure nozzles) and use as high a volume of spray per acre as is consistent with good weed control and sound economics.

3.   The boom should be as near the target as is consistent with obtaining an adequate distribution of the chemical on the weeds. In this respect close spacing of the nozzles and/or the use of wide-angle nozzles enable the boom to be brought close to the target.

4.   Where a susceptible crop has emerged and is on the downwind side of a crop requiring treatment, the operator should leave an untreated strip along the edge. This should never be less than 10 yards wide and should preferably be much wider when conditions are adverse. The actual width must be determined by individual judgment. This treated area should be sprayed later when there is no wind or when the wind is blowing away from the susceptible crop.

5.   Spraying downwind causes slightly less drift than spraying upwind or crosswind, and will reduce widespread drift when treatment is necessary in windy weather or in exposed positions. This method, however, must not be used when spraying hazardous materials, such as DNOC or DNBP, as the toxic risks to the operator are greatly increased.

Drift hazards with herbicides applied from aircraft are more serious than from ground-spraying machines. Chemical formulations are being modified in order to reduce the formation of small droplets liable to drift. The use of invert emulsions and particulating agents may be helpful in this regard.

With machines that do not possess an antidrip device, damage can sometimes occur through drip from the nozzles while the machine is traveling over susceptible crops on its way between the filling point and the field being sprayed. Where the intervening crop is grassland, danger arises mainly from the herbicides which are poisonous to stock or from chemicals which have not been cleared for use on pastures and which may lead to undesirable residues in meat or milk. The machine should be routed to avoid as much damage as possible.

Crops particularly susceptible to MCPA and 2,4-D are tomatoes, beets, brassicas and other crucifers, lettuce, tree fruits, and many flowers.

Volatile chemicals should not be sprayed in the vicinity of sensitive crops. The high molecular weight esters are less volatile than the low molecular weight esters, but care should be used in their application. Salts of 2,4-D (sodium or amine) have little or no volatility hazard. Volatile impurities in herbicides may also be a danger. For example, the aerosols that may occur as impurities in 2,4-D or MCPA can cause taint in tomatoes as a result of vapor drift.

CALCULATIONS

To obtain maximum effectiveness with a minimum of chemical, it is necessary to determine the exact amount of chemical applied. Since this involves the application of a very small amount of chemical to an acre, it is sometimes difficult to determine how much should be applied (Maletic, 1949). Whatever type of sprayer is used, the operator should ensure before beginning to spray that the machine is applying liquid at the correct rate. The rate of application for a particular nozzle spacing depends on three factors, namely, the speed of the sprayer, the operating pressure, and the size of the nozzles. Most manufacturers supply a table correlating these factors with the quantity of spray applied per acre.

Most liquid forms designate the number of pounds of active chemical per gallon on the label, whereas most powders or granules designate the percentage. This information is used in the calculations. Liquids, powders, and granules are considered separately.

The content of active ingredients in an herbicide may be expressed in different ways depending on the nature of the formulations.

Weight/weight (wt/wt or w/w)

For solid formulations such as dusts or wettable powders the active ingredient (ai) is usually expressed as a percentage of the weight, e.g., 3 percent wt/wt = 3 pounds in each 100 pounds of material.

Volume/volume (v/v)

When a liquid formulation has a liquid active ingredient the latter is usually given as a percentage of the volume and is written as percent volume/volume.

Weight/volume (wt/vol or w/v)

This term is used for liquid formulations which have a solid active ingredient. It is an abbreviation for weight per unit volume as grams per cubic centimeter. Since 1 gallon of water weighs approximately 8 pounds, a concentration of 25 percent w/v of active ingredient contains about 2 pounds of active ingredient in each gallon. Some herbicides, particularly the growth regulators, are compared on an acid equivalent (a.e.) basis, which is the content of active ingredient in the concentrate expressed as the free acid. The acid equivalent of a concentrate is always less than its content of active ingredient unless the active ingredient is itself an acid, and the extent of the difference depends on the molecular weights of the acid and salts in the concentrate; for example:

Molecular weight of MCPA   = 200.5
Molecular weight of MCPA, sodium   = 222.5
Molecular weight of MCPA, potassium = 238.5

If, therefore, we have a sodium MCPA formulation containing 22.2 percent w/v of sodium MCPA, this formulation would contain 20 percent w/v of acid equivalent. Alternatively, this could be expressed as 1.6 pounds (or 25.6 ounces) of acid equivalent per gallon. Similarly, in a formulation with a potassium MCPA content of 23.8 percent w/v, the acid equivalent content would be 20 percent w/v or 1.6 pounds (25.6 ounces) per gallon.

Usually governmental (state or Federal) recommendations for the amount of herbicide to apply are given in ounces or pounds of acid equivalent per acre, while those of manufacturers are usually given in pints per acre of their particular product. When the required amount of acid equivalent per acre is known, the quantity of the weed killer formulation in pints per acre can be calculated.

Liquid chemicals

Three steps are involved in determining the amount of chemical to be applied in liquid form. The same calculations can be used for mixtures if the total amount of the two chemicals is used in the calculations.

Step 1

Determine the number of pounds of acid in 1 pint of chemical with the following formula:

Number of pounds acid equivalent in container ÷ number of pints in container = pounds of acid in one pint.

Example

The label on a 1-gallon container states that there are 3 pounds acid equivalent in the container. Since 1 gallon contains 8 pints, the number of pounds per pint is calculated as follows:

$3 \div 8 = 0.375$ or $\frac{3}{8}$ pound acid equivalent per pint

Step 2

Determine the number of pints to be used per acre with the following formula:

Pounds of acid equivalent to be applied per acre ÷ number of pounds of acid equivalent per pint = number of pints per acre.

Example

Suppose you wished to use $\frac{1}{4}$ pound of the above-mentioned chemical per acre. The calculation is as follows:

$\frac{1}{4} \div \frac{3}{8} = \frac{2}{3}$ pint per acre

For ease in calculation the fraction may be converted to decimals and calculated as follows:

$0.25 \div 0.375 = 0.67$ or $\frac{2}{3}$ pint per acre

Step 3

Determine the amount of chemical needed for each sprayer load. Use the following formula:

(Gallons in sprayer ÷ gallons per acre) × number of pints per acre = number of pints per sprayer load.

Example

Suppose the sprayer holds 100 gallons and has been set to deliver 20 gallons per acre. Then suppose that $\frac{1}{4}$ pound of the chemical mentioned above is to be used. The calculation is as follows:

$100 \div 20 = 5$ acres sprayed with one load
$5 \times \frac{2}{3}$ or $0.67 = 3\frac{1}{3}$ pints per sprayer load

Powdered chemicals

The amount of powdered chemical needed for each sprayer load of water can be calculated as follows:

Step 1

Using the following formula, determine the number of pounds of chemical needed per acre.

> Pounds of acid per acre ÷ percent of acid = pounds of powder per acre.

Example

Suppose a powdered chemical containing 80 percent acid is to be applied at the rate of 40 pounds of acid per acre. The calculation is as follows:

> 40 ÷ 80 percent = 50 pounds of powdered chemical per acre

For ease in calculation, the percent may be changed to a decimal as follows:

> 40 ÷ 0.80 = 50 pounds of powdered chemical per acre

Step 2

Using the following formula, determine the number of acres that one sprayer will cover.

> Gallons in sprayer ÷ gallons per acre = acres per sprayer load.

Example

Suppose that the sprayer holds 100 gallons and has been set to apply 40 gallons per acre. The calculation is as follows:

> $100 \div 40 = 2\frac{1}{2}$ acres per sprayer load

Step 3

Determine the amount of chemical needed for each sprayer load. Multiply the pounds of powder per acre (step 1) by the acres per sprayer load (step 2) in the following formula:

> Pounds of powder per acre × acres per sprayer load = pounds of chemical per load.

Example

In step 1, 50 pounds of chemical is needed per acre; and in step 2, 2.5 acres can be sprayed with one sprayer load. Therefore, $50 \times 2.5 = 125$ pounds of powdered chemical per sprayer load.

After the amount of powdered chemical needed for each sprayer load has been determined, it is advisable to select a container that will hold the exact amount needed and use one full container for each sprayer load. In the example above, two and a half 50-pound drums would be needed.

Granules

The amount of granules required to apply a certain amount of acid per acre may be determined as in step 1 of the calculation for powdered chemical.

Example

Suppose that a granular formulation containing 5 percent acid is to be applied at the rate of $\frac{1}{4}$ pound of acid per acre. The pounds of granules needed per acre would be figured as follows:

$$\frac{1}{4} \div 5 \text{ percent} = 5 \text{ pounds of granules per acre}$$

When changed to decimals, the calculations would be:

$$0.25 \div 0.05 = 5 \text{ pounds of granules per acre}$$

Spray calculations

To apply a given quantity (x pounds) herbicide to an acre requires consideration of (1) the relationship between sprayer speed, nozzle delivery, and nozzle spacing; (2) the relationship between nozzle delivery, pump pressure, or pressure at the nozzle; (3) calibration of the spray equipment in accordance with these relationships; and (4) the preparation of the herbicide solution (Maletic, 1949).

The calibration formulas are based on (*a*) spray swath = number of nozzles on the boom (equally spaced) × space between nozzles; (*b*) acres per hour = spray swath in feet × speed sprayer in feet per hour ÷ 43,560; (*c*) gallons per hour = number of gallons delivered per nozzle per hour; (*d*) gallons per acre = gallons per hour ÷ acres per hour.

Symbols: GPA = Gallons per acre
GPH = Gallons per hour per nozzle
GPM = Gallons per minute per nozzle

$$ZN = \text{Number of nozzles}$$
$$NSF = \text{Nozzle spacing in feet}$$
$$NSI = \text{Nozzle spacing in inches}$$
$$MPH = \text{Sprayer speed in miles per hour}$$
$$FPH = \text{Sprayer speed in feet per hour}$$

Using the symbols we substitute into (*b*), (*c*), and (*d*) above,

$$GPA = (ZN \times GPH) \div (ZN \times NSF \times FPH) \div 43,560$$

By rearranging terms we can write:

$$GPA = \frac{ZN \times GPH \times 43,560}{ZN \times NSF \times FPH} \tag{1}$$

This formula now expresses the basic relationship between the variables. It can be used as given; or if other units of measurements are desired, simple substitutions can be made to take care of the conversion. The substitutions are made by use of the following equalities:

$$FPH = MPH \times 5280$$

$$GPH = GPM \times 60$$

$$NSF = \frac{NSI}{12}$$

An example follows. To express GPA in terms of GPM, MPH, and NSF we can substitute the required equalities in formula (1), obtaining:

$$GPA = \frac{(GPM \times 60) \times 43,560}{MPH \times 5280 \times NSF}$$

$$= \frac{GPM}{MPH \times NSF} \times \frac{60 \times 43,560}{5280}$$

Thus

$$GPA = \frac{GPM \times 495}{MPH \times NSF} \tag{2}$$

Similarly we could obtain:

$$GPA = \frac{GPH \times 8.25}{MPH \times NSF} \tag{3}$$

$$GPA = \frac{GPM \times 5940}{MPH \times NSI} \tag{4}$$

$$GPA = \frac{GPH \times 99}{MPH \times NSI} \tag{5}$$

Formula (5) is convenient to use but it is generally expressed in another form. If the reciprocal of the constant (99) shown in the numerator is placed in the denominator, the equality is not destroyed; hence:

$$GPA = \frac{GPH}{MPH \times NSI \times 0.01}$$

Since spray equipment calibration problems arise in which it is desired to know the MPH or GPH, the formula can be solved for these values obtaining:

$$GPH = GPA \times MPH \times NSI \times 0.01$$

$$MPH = \frac{GPH}{GPA \times NSI \times 0.01}$$

PROCEDURE IN THE FIELD

Filling

Use a clean water supply, preferably soft water, because with some herbicides more chemical is needed to obtain the same results from hard water. It is better to partly fill the sprayer with water before adding the chemical, then continue to add water until the tank is filled. All chemical and water should enter the sprayer through the filter basket provided. Wettable powders should be "creamed" first with a small amount of water in a clean bucket to ensure complete wetting. Soluble powders should be dissolved in a small quantity of water before adding to the tank.

Timing

Spray at the correct time. Foliar sprays should be applied during good growing conditions and only during suitable weather, not in strong winds or when rain or frost is imminent. Due regard must be made for climatic conditions when applying weed killers such as DNBP since they are greatly influenced by the temperature. For soil-applied herbicides the condition of the soil is important, but the efficiency of many of these herbicides is less dependent upon the weather, with the exception of rainfall, although cold weather may delay action for an extended period. Some rain after spraying is desirable for most soil-applied herbicides, such as the triazines, particularly where they are not incorporated into the soil.

Decontamination of sprayers

It is not advisable to use the same sprayer for applying both herbicides and insecticides. This is because it is difficult to clean out the last traces of some herbicides, particularly oil-based formulations. A minute amount of an herbicide such as 2,4-D sprayed as a contaminant in an insecticide spray could raise havoc with susceptible crops.

If, however, for reasons of economy, it is not possible to keep one machine for herbicides and a separate one for insecticides, some decontamination procedures are recommended at the end of the Appendix.

QUESTIONS

1. What are the disadvantages of oil and water as carriers for herbicides?
2. What is a *surfactant*?
3. How does the addition of a surfactant affect selectivity?
4. What are the advantages of granules?
5. What are the disadvantages of granules?
6. What is *preemergence application*?
7. How many pints of a 4-lb/gal formulation of 2,4-D do you put in a 50-gallon sprayer to achieve a rate of 1 pound per acre assuming that you spray 25 gallons per acre?
8. How many pounds of a 5-percent granular formulation do you put on an acre to achieve a rate of active ingredient of 3 pounds per acre?
9. An airplane sprays a swath width of 80 feet. At 80 miles per hour how many pints of a 4-lb/gal formulation should the pilot place in a 30-gallon tank to spray 1 pound per acre at the rate of 1.5 gallons of water per acre?
10. How is swath width of an airplane measured?
11. A farmer wishes to apply ½ pound active ingredient per acre of a 2 pounds per gallon formulation in 30 gallons of water per acre. He has a sprayer which holds 150 gallons, a spray boom with 16 nozzles spaced 18 inches apart, delivering 0.2 gallon per nozzle per minute. How fast should he drive his spray rig?
12. How many gallons per minute will an airplane spray if the swath width is 45 feet, assuming that gallons per acre equals 1.5 and miles per hour equals 90?
13. What is meant by *effective swath width*?
14. How many gallons per acre will be applied if a spray rig is driven at 4 miles per hour, with a boom 16 feet long, nozzle spacing 16 inches apart, each nozzle spraying 0.3 gallon per minute? How many gallons will be applied if the speed is slowed to 2 miles per hour?
15. Suppose with the conditions as in problem 14, it is necessary to put on the only available new nozzles which are found to spray 0.45 gallon per minute. What speed should be maintained to spray 30 gallons per acre?
16. You have a nozzle that delivers 3.8 gallons per hour. The nozzle will

treat a $3\frac{1}{2}$-foot band. Walking 3 miles per hour, 1.2 acres are treated per hour. _____ gallons of spray are applied per acre. If there are 4 pounds of 2,4-D per gallon, you'll need _____ liquid ounces of 2,4-D per gallon of spray to apply $\frac{1}{2}$ pound of 2,4-D per acre.

17. You have a sprayer that sprays a swath $16\frac{1}{2}$ feet wide. It sprays 80 gallons of water per hour. At a continuous 8 miles per hour, _____ acres are treated per hour and _____ gallons of spray are applied per acre.

18. Your sprayer tank holds 55 gallons. With only 6 gallons left, you need to refill the tank. You will add _____ pints of 2,4-D amine (4 pounds per gallon) to the tank prior to filling with water if you wish to apply 1 pound per acre acid equivalent in 10 gallons of water per acre.

19. You want to apply 4 pounds per acre active ingredient of IPC to bluegrass. The label states that it is 80 percent active. You will need to apply _____ pounds of the commercial material per acre.

20. Sketch and label the essential parts of a sprayer.

21. Sketch nozzle and boom placement on a fixed-wing aircraft.

22. How can spray drift be reduced (1) from aerial application, (2) from ground application?

23. How would doubling the pressure (i.e. from 20 to 40 psi) affect volume rate?

24. Define *acute toxic, chronic toxic.*

25. How would you double the volume rate by changing the pressure? Assume that you started at 25 psi.

26. Why is it not satisfactory to apply a band spray with the nozzles ordinarily used on a boom sprayer?

REFERENCES

Adams, D. F., C. M. Jackson, and W. L. Bamesburger. 1964. Quantitative Studies of 2,4-D Esters in the Air. *Weeds*, **12**:280–283.

Behrens, R. W. 1964. The Physical and Chemical Properties of Surfactants and Their Effects on Formulated Herbicides. *Weeds*, **12**:254–258.

Brooks, F. A. 1947. The Drifting of Poisonous Dusts Applied by Airplanes and Land Rigs. *Agr. Engr.*, **28**:233–239.

Colby, S. R., T. Wojtaszek, and G. F. Warren. 1965. Synergistic and Antagonistic Combinations for Broadening Herbicidal Selectivity. *Weeds*, **13**:87–91.

Hacskaylo, J., J. J. Walker, and E. G. Pires. 1964. Response of Cotton Seedlings to Combinations of Pre-emergence Herbicides and Systemic Insecticides. *Weeds*, **12**:288–291.

Jansen, L. L.   1964.   Surfactant Enhancement of Herbicide Entry. *Weeds*, **12**:251–254.
Maletic, J. T.   1949.   Handbook of Weed Control Calculations. Tech. Rept., Bureau of Reclamation.
Woodford, E. K., and S. A. Evans.   1965.   "Weed Control Handbook," Blackwell Scientific Publications, Oxford, 4th ed.

CHAPTER EIGHT
CHEMICALS USED
FOR WEED CONTROL

There are at present over 150 herbicides available to the agriculturist. The major groups and selective examples are described in this chapter to demonstrate the principles governing the application of these chemicals to plants and soils. A more complete listing is given in the appendix.

With each group of herbicides the characteristics common to all of the chemicals in the group will be discussed first, followed by specific characteristics that distinguish individual chemicals. The advantages and limitations and the forms of each herbicide available on the market, the carrier or carriers, method of application, volatility, and hazards to animals will be discussed. Mode of action of the individual chemicals will be stressed. For many of the chemicals in common use, the mode of action is still not clearly understood, but much evidence is being gathered and will be briefly summarized.

It will be easier for the student to gain a basic knowledge of the chemicals used in weed control if the chemicals are categorized in as large groups as possible, emphasizing mode of action, selectivity, carrier, and persistence. The technology of weed control is changing rapidly and local authorities should be consulted before making any applications.

CLASSIFICATION OF HERBICIDES

Herbicides may be classified into four general categories: (1) contact selective, (2) contact nonselective, (3) systemic selective, (4) systemic nonselective. Many of the newer organic herbicides may be either selective or nonselective depending on the amount applied (see also Appendix).

Contact herbicides kill tissues at or very close to the point of application. Foliar-applied contact herbicides must be thoroughly distributed over the surface of the plant in order to kill the meristematic tissues in the buds and leaves. Contact herbicides may be either selective or nonselective, depending mainly on differential wetting and based on differences in cuticle, leaf arrangement, and location of buds. Nonselective contact herbicides kill all vegetation with which they come in contact.

Grasses, which have their growing points below the soil, will frequently be more resistant to contact herbicides than broadleaf plants which have their buds exposed at the ends of the branches.

Translocated or systemic herbicides must enter the plant and move in the vascular tissues throughout the plant system. Selectivity is usually of the biochemical type, that is, it depends on some specific feature of the protoplasm, usually differences in enzyme systems. Penetration rate, dosage, and movement must be so regulated that adequate chemical is moved without the conducting cells and tissues being damaged. Sufficient chemical must reach the root or underground stems to bring about death of all cells capable of producing shoot buds.

The organic herbicides contain carbon and hydrogen. They are nearly all derived from acids. In many instances, the acid is insoluble in ordinary solvents and to meet this problem, salts, esters, or wettable powders are manufactured. The salts are made by combining the acid with a base, and the ester by mixing the acid with an alcohol. The salts are water soluble and the esters oil soluble. The esters are often sold as emulsifiable concentrates for mixing with water. Most of the organic herbicides are not considered toxic to animals.

In contrast to organic herbicides, the inorganic herbicides do not contain carbon and hydrogen. They are applied as water solutions or as granules. They are not volatile.

If the student will keep all these principles in mind, noting the exceptions, rather than attempting to memorize the characteristics of individual chemicals, it will be much easier for him to develop an understanding of herbicides which will be useful in the future as well as in the present.

Some of the most expensive literature in the world is that written on the labels of pesticide containers. It is worth reading *before* rather than after application. Great care is exercised by most companies to make the information given on their labels as factual and as complete as possible. Nevertheless, errors may occur, and in any event, it is impossible to cover all possible environmental variations, so that one is well advised to consult local authorities before applying a new chemical and then only apply it to 5 percent or less of his acreage as a test case.

THE INORGANIC HERBICIDES

Arsenic compounds

Arsenic is usually applied as sodium arsenite or arsenic trioxide in water or in pellet form. Applied to leaves, it has a contact effect; soil applications, however, are transported upward with the transpiration stream. The principal constituent of most arsenical weed killers is sodium arsenite.

Tests in many different soils have shown that textural grain of the soil is a very important factor in arsenic toxicity. This interaction between arsenic toxicity and soil texture can possibly be explained through the action of the soil colloids in fixing the arsenic in unavailable forms. In addition, the ability of the soil to retain arsenic against the leaching action of percolating water, but in a form available to plants, is important.

The plant's tolerance to arsenic in the soil depends on two factors:

1. *Depth of roots.* The absorbing roots of many weeds, particularly perennials, are located deep in the subsoil. Such roots are not killed by arsenic held in the surface layers.

2. *Susceptibility of protoplasm.* The protoplasm of weed species varies in resistance to arsenic poisoning. The mechanism of this tolerance is not well understood at the present time. Some of the more resistant species are summer annuals, particularly yellow star thistle, hayfield tarweed, and knotweed. These weeds, all of arid or desert origin, are able to tolerate high concentrations of salts in the soil. This characteristic may contribute to their ability to resist the action of arsenic.

Arsenic dosages for soil sterilization vary between wide limits. Recommendations can at best be only approximate because of the complex relations between toxicity as related to availability, permanence affected by leaching, and susceptibility as determined by the arsenic tolerance of the weed species concerned. In general, larger amounts of arsenic are required in heavier soils of the clay and adobe clay types and soils high in organic matter. On light and coarse soils 300 to 600 pounds of arsenic trioxide per acre will kill all vegetation; whereas as much as 1000 pounds may be required on heavy soils. Arsenic has not been used extensively in recent years because it is toxic to man and animals and because it may build up in the soil, thus injuring subsequent crops. Arsenic trioxide has, however, been used for aquatic weed control, and certain organic arsenicals have been used for crabgrass control in turf. The tendency for arsenic buildup in the soil makes establishment of seedlings difficult and limits its usefulness for control of weeds in lawns, golf courses, etc. It has some value as a desiccant.

The use of arsenic is banned in some countries because of its toxicity to man and animals, but it is not banned in the United States.

Certain organic forms of arsenic are less toxic to animals than the inorganic form (see Appendix).

Sodium chlorate

Sodium chlorate is one of the most widely used soil-sterilizing agents, although it is now banned for use in croplands. This chemical is a strong oxidizing agent and has many uses in industry, including the manufacture of matches and fireworks. When sodium chlorate is added to oxidizable matter, such as cloth or wood, it forms a combustible material that is dangerous to handle. Incidents are not uncommon where spontaneous fires ignite, severely burning users or animals. Clothing which has been wet with the solution may dry and then catch fire through friction. Careless use of sodium chlorate has caused more than one farmer to walk home in his underwear or in a barrel! To reduce this fire hazard, various chemicals such as borate salts and substituted ureas have been mixed with the sodium chlorate. Although the fire danger is usually the main hazard, sodium chlorate is toxic to cattle who will eat vegetation sprayed with it when they are salt hungry.

This chemical acts as a contact poison on leaves and it also serves as a translocated herbicide when applied to soil and absorbed by roots (Loomis et al., 1933). It is very soluble in water and is usually applied as a spray or as dry crystals. Soil treatment is the most reliable method of using sodium chlorate to kill deep-rooted perennial plants (Latshaw and Zahnley, 1927). The toxicity of sodium chlorate appears to be correlated inversely with the fertility of the soil. That is, chlorates are most effective in soils low in nitrates. It is for this reason that fall application is usually recommended because, in the fall, the plants have generally taken up a high percentage of the available nitrates in the soil. This reasoning can also explain why root responses vary according to the various soil horizons. (Although chlorate is mobile in soils, a given amount may be rather uniformly distributed when applied in solution in sufficient volume with the soil.)

The distribution in soil is a matter of leaching; therefore, in regions of restricted or seasonal rainfall the time of application as related to annual precipitation is very important. In order to control deep-rooted perennial plants, chlorate must be leached to a depth at which it can come in contact with the roots. Treated soils are more sensitive to erosion and therefore treatment of steep slopes should be avoided (Figure 8-1).

Chlorate injury to plants appears to be a direct reflection of absorption, and the chlorate absorption in turn is related to the relative availability of chlorate as compared with nitrate, sulphate, and other ions in the nutrient medium. Heavy nitrate applications after treatment will reduce the toxicity. Small grains vary in their tolerance to chlorate in the

Figure 8-1 *Erosion and bare spots in wheatfield due to excessive amounts of sodium chlorate. This chemical has a deleterious effect on soil structure, making the soil more susceptible to erosion. In addition, it may prevent growth of any plant for several years.*

following order of efficiency: (least tolerant) barley, rye, wheat, oats, and flax (most tolerant).

Sodium chlorate affects the plant metabolism in various ways. It depletes the food reserves, increases respiration rate, and decreases catalase activity; the exact killing mechanism, however, is not known.

Boron compounds

Boron compounds are newer in weed control than are the chlorates and arsenicals. They are obtained from desert lakes or ore deposits. It is the borate ion that injures the plants, and since it is toxic at low concentrations (but since it is a minor element necessary for plant growth, it is also valuable in extremely low concentrations), even relatively insoluble compounds of boron are useful herbicides. Boron compounds are not subject to the type of bacterial and fungal decomposition that tends to reduce the toxicity of other chemicals, partly because when used at rates large enough to be an effective herbicide, they are toxic also to most soil microorganisms. As a result the boron compounds persist for very long periods in the soil although they do diminish appreciably with time due to chemical fixation and leaching. The solubility of the various boron compounds is the principal factor governing their effectiveness. Sodium tetraborate and borax are the most common forms; they are nonflammable, noncorrosive, nonvolatile and nonpoisonous, and may be applied as a water spray or in granules.

Plants differ widely in their protoplasmic susceptibility to boron; however, differences in response also exist because of soil type, precipitation, and method of application. Severe injury from boron results from a concentration of the poison in the surface soil, where the young absorbing roots come in direct contact with it. A delay between application and seeding, or heavy rains immediately after applications, or a thorough mixing of the chemical with a large mass of soil all tend to reduce the boron toxicity. Although the toxicity of boron varies widely in different soils (it appears to be greater in the coarser-textured soils), applications of 1000 to 3000 pounds per acre are usually required to produce sterility. The main disadvantage of the boron compounds is that so much chemical must be used to obtain satisfactory kill that it may persist in the soil for several years.

Grasses are somewhat more tolerant of boron than are broad-leaved and woody species, and therefore tend to be the first plants to occupy treated areas. Mixtures of boron and numerous other herbicides are available. Boron is commonly mixed with sodium chlorate to reduce that chemical's flammability.

Calcium cyanamide

Calcium cyanamide ($CaCN_2$) is used as a fertilizer, an herbicide, and a defoliant. It is usually applied as dry granules at rates of about $1\frac{1}{2}$ pounds per square yard for turf or tobacco seedbeds and is mixed in the top inch of soil. Several weeks should elapse before seeding. The exact length of time for disappearance from the soil will depend on weather conditions, but factors which favor plant growth, i.e., moisture, warmth, and good aeration, also favor rapid decomposition. This chemical is non-toxic, nonvolatile, and nonflammable.

THE ORGANIC HERBICIDES

Chlorophenoxy herbicides

The chlorophenoxy herbicides are by far the best known and most widely used of all herbicides. Characteristic of the group is effectiveness against many broadleaves and consequent selective use in cereals and grasses. The chlorophenoxy herbicides all have similar basic effects; i.e., differences in molecular structure affect absorption, translocation, and degradation more than they do the ultimate mode of action. The parent acids are poorly soluble in common solvents and esters and salts are commonly marketed to fill this need. The esters, which are oil soluble and usually emulsified in oil and water for application, are made by combining the

2,4-D acid with an alcohol. The length of the alcohol portion (ester side chain) of the molecule determines the volatility. The shorter the side chain portion, the more volatile the ester, but there is no sharp line of demarcation. High volatile (HV) esters are methyl, ethyl, isopropyl, and butyl (1-5 carbon side chain). Examples of low volatile esters are the butoxyethoxypropanol and the iso-octyl esters.

The salts are made by mixing the acid with a base, such as sodium hydroxide, ammonia, etc. Amine salts are the most soluble in water and are the most widely used forms.

All the herbicides in this group are nontoxic to animals or fish and are nonflammable. They may be applied as granules, ground very fine and mixed with water to form pastes, or dissolved in special solvents and formulated into sprays.

2,4-dichlorophenoxyacetic acid

When 2,4-dichlorophenoxyacetic acid (2,4-D) was introduced in 1944, it heralded a whole new era of agricultural chemicals. In contrast to the herbicides known at that time, it was effective at low rates, selective in cereals and grass crops, nontoxic to animals, and both cheap and potent.

Some phases of the chemistry of the phenoxy acid types of herbicides are presented in the following paragraphs.

By mixing products from petroleum oil, table salt, and vinegar, a chemist could theoretically produce 2,4-D and other growth-regulator herbicides. Benzene, which serves as a basis for 2,4-D and other pesticides, is a fraction of petroleum oil, as are kerosene and gasoline. A part of 2,4-D is acetic acid, the compound which makes vinegar sour.

Chemical language and symbols sometimes require clarification. H_2O, of course, is readily recognized as water—a combination of hydrogen (H) and oxygen (O). Sodium (Na) and chlorine (Cl) join to make sodium chloride (NaCl), commonly known as table salt. Just as simple to the petroleum chemist is this six-sided benzene, which for convenience, we will call a *phenol ring*. Each point on this phenol ring represents a carbon atom and is designated with a number, thusly:

The 2,4-D is an abbreviation of the chemical name of 2,4-dichlorophenoxy-acetic acid. The *dichloro* indicates 2 chlorines attached to the 2 and 4 positions of the phenol ring. *Phenoxy acetic acid* indicates that acetic acid

(CH$_3$COOH) is attached to the phenol ring with oxygen as the connecting unit. Thus:

$$2,4\text{-}D = $$

2,4-D structure: benzene ring with O—CH$_2$COOH, Cl, and Cl substituents

The abbreviation 2,4,5-T stands for 2,4,5-trichlorophenoxyacetic acid with chlorine atoms at the 2, 4, and 5 positions.

2,4,5-T structure: benzene ring with O—CH$_2$COOH, Cl, Cl, and Cl substituents

SALTS. The most common salts of 2,4-D are the amines. Others, such as sodium salt, are less soluble in water and less effective.

The salts are ordinarily nonvolatile and may be sprayed in water solution or applied as granules. The amine is the most commonly used form of 2,4-D, although the salts are slightly less effective than the esters. Their lack of volatility and their low cost make them more practical for many purposes.

ESTERS. The esters of 2,4-D are oil soluble. They may be emulsified in water and oil or sprayed in pure oil. They are generally considered more toxic to plants than the amine salts. This greater toxicity is probably due to their compatibility with the cuticle and leaf waxes which they may be able to penetrate more readily. Also they have greater wetting ability because of the oil-like nature of the ester. The oil carrier may aid penetration of the stomates, and volatility permits entry of the vapors through the stomates.

The ester is identified by the alcohol used. The low-molecular-weight esters—methyl, ethyl, isopropyl, and butyl—are considered highly volatile. Longer chain esters are less volatile but more so than the salts or acid. These esters are often sold as HV and LV esters, respectively.

TRANSLOCATION. Entry and translocation occur readily in both leaves and stems, probably moving down the stem with food materials in the phloem. Translocation out of young leaves is very limited. During periods of rapid apical stem growth and flower development, movement may be upward in the phloem to the growing points. Translocation from the roots upward follows the transpiration stream in the xylem. Movement downward in the xylem occurs rarely and is apparently limited to severely moisture-stressed plants.

The stage of growth, i.e., maturity, influences the plant's susceptibility to 2,4-D. Plants are generally most susceptible at germination and gain tolerance as they grow older (Chapter 6). Some never develop tolerance; whereas others, such as the grasses and cereals, become resistant soon after germination. The cereals have another period of sensitivity during flower formation which is followed by increasing resistance (see Chapter 9). Weeds such as coast fiddleneck and gromwell are sensitive early in spring when fiddleneck is in the rosette stage, but gain resistance rapidly when bolting begins. This resistance is in part associated with a change in pattern of food translocation during bolting.

The effect of age may be obscured by environment, particularly temperature. Even in the sensitive rosette stage, coast fiddleneck showed little response to 2,4-D when treated at 50°F or less (Muzik and Mauldin, 1964).

EFFECTS ON METABOLISM.   When applied at lethal rates, 2,4-D upsets the balance between synthesis and use of food. Respiration is increased with the consequent breakdown of starches to sugars, and photosynthesis is reduced so that plants killed by 2,4-D show a marked depletion of carbohydrates. Proteins are more resistant and consequently the percentage of protein is increased because of the more rapid depletion of the other constituents of the plant. The increase in sugars apparently makes certain poisonous weeds more palatable to cattle so that care must be taken when applying 2,4-D to poisonous plants within the reach of livestock. Beans sprayed with 2,4-D are more attractive to aphids, due possibly to changes in amino acid content. Levels of certain toxic chemicals may be increased (Chapter 13).

The amount of 2,4-D applied per plant is critical. Sublethal doses may cause temporary increases in respiration and decreases in photosynthesis from which the plant recovers (Loustalot and Muzik, 1953). No definite relationship to particular enzymes has been established.

STRUCTURAL CHANGES.   Increased brittleness in plants following 2,4-D treatment usually occurs. This is related to an increase in turgor pressure in the cells. Sensitive plants also develop grotesque malformed leaves as a result of differential rates of cell division in the leaf meristems. Twisting and curvatures of the stem (epinasty) are due to differential turgidity and unequal rates of cell division and cell enlargement.

2,4-D is transported to tissues growing actively, such as embryonic and meristematic regions. Relatively inactive mature tissues are less affected. Depending on the age of the plant, the cambium, endodermis, pericycle, phloem parenchyma, and phloem rays show most response. In very young plants even the cortex and epidermis may be affected.

Typical responses of sensitive plants are (1) cell enlargement, followed by (2) cell division, (3) differentiation into abnormal tissue and elements, (4) the production of numerous root primordia in the stem, and finally (5) death.

Phloem translocation is blocked by the abnormal growth. Xylem formation stops so that not only is translocation of food downward blocked but also the movement of water upward is impaired. Depending on the amount supplied, these processes may stop at any point. With sublethal amounts the plant may recover and resume growth.

Root malformations in monocotyledonous and dicotyledonous plants are similar to those in the stem of dicotyledons. Cortical cells enlarge, abnormal cell division occurs in the pericycle and endodermis, and clusters of short, stubby lateral roots are formed. Root malformations in wheat and bindweed resemble each other very closely, much more so than the malformations of the stems. Elongation of the roots of bindweed and young wheat cease about 4 days after 2,4-D spray to the foliage.

The stems and leaves of grass plants show relatively little response to 2,4-D, although cereals sprayed in the boot stages exhibit many seed head malformations. Cell enlargement and root formation may occur in the regions of the intercalary meristems (Chapter 4).

Leaf malformations result from stunting of the lateral leaf meristems and continued growth of the vein meristems when light doses are applied (Figure 8-2). Consequently the blade area is reduced and the veins appear longer and abnormally close together. The mesophyll cells are replaced by "replacement tissue," which consists of closely packed round cells with few intercellular spaces. The sensitivity of some plants to

(a)   (b)

Figure 8-2 *Leaf malformation and epinasty caused by 2,4-D application to leaves of tomatoes. (a) Untreated plant; (b) treated plant.*

2,4-D is remarkable. For example, 1 ounce of 2,4-D will cause leaf malformations in 35 acres of cotton (Chapter 4).

PERSISTENCE. At sublethal rates 2,4-D persists at least 60
days in tomato plants (Muzik and Whitworth, 1963). Little is known about
its pathway of metabolism in plants, but it appears that 2,4-D may combine
with the proteins to form a number of chemical complexes.

2,4-D disappears, like most other chemicals in the soil, mainly
by decomposition by microorganisms. Decomposition is most rapid when
conditions are good for microorganism activity, with adequate moisture,
warmth, and organic matter. Dry, cold weather or sterilization of the soil
delays the disappearance. In heavy clay and high organic soils, 2,4-D is
held in the top inch or so of soil even after heavy rainfall, due to absorption
on the soil colloids or to the formation of insoluble salts (Muzik et al.,
1951). In lighter, sandy soils the movement is greater.

Other chlorophenoxy herbicides

MCPA. MCPA (2-methyl-4-chlorophenoxyacetic acid) is very
similar in action to 2,4-D. The chemical structure is the same except that
one chlorine is replaced with a methyl (CH_3) group. MCPA is less injurious
to oats and peas than 2,4-D and more effective on a few weeds such as
creeping buttercup (*Ranunculus repens*).

SESONE. Sesone (2,4-dichlorophenoxyethylsulfate) has two advantages over other phenoxy sprays: (1) safety from foliage application,
(2) safety from drift. It is not an effective herbicide until it has been in
contact with the soil where it is changed to 2,4-dichlorophenoxyethanol
by a bacterium, *Bacillus cereus* var. mycoides. When 2,4-dichlorophenoxy-
ethanol is oxidized, it changes to 2,4-D. Both are toxic to plants.

Sesone is applied in water, and is nonvolatile and nontoxic to
animals. It is most useful in crops like strawberries, peanuts, evergreens,
trees, and lawns which are moderately resistant to 2,4-D. Root absorption
by sensitive plants such as beans or tomatoes may produce 2,4-D-type
malformations.

2,4,5-T. 2,4,5-T (2,4,5-trichlorophenoxyacetic acid) has one
more chlorine atom in the phenol ring than 2,4-D. Its herbicidal properties
are very similar to 2,4-D except that it is much more effective on certain
woody species and in most soils is more persistent. The esters and salts
follow the same patterns of volatility and solubility as 2,4-D. 2,4,5-T acid
is more soluble in water than 2,4-D acid.

Mixtures of 2,4-D and 2,4,5-T are especially effective since
together they control a wider spectrum of weeds.

PROPIONIC ACIDS. The propionic acids, 2,4-DP and 2,4,5-TP have physical and chemical properties similar to their acetic acid equivalents. They are more persistent in soil.

2,4,5-trichlorophenoxypropionic acid (2,4,5-TP or silvex) has proven very useful as a turf herbicide and for brush and aquatics. It may be applied in combination with 2,4-D to control a broader spectrum of weeds.

BUTYRIC ACIDS. 4-(2,4-dichlorophenoxy) butyric acid, or 2,4-DB, is only slightly toxic to plants in its original molecular state. Many weeds apparently convert it to 2,4-D. Because legumes in general either lack the necessary enzyme system or convert it so slowly that they are not injured, it has been recommended for weed control in such legumes as peas, clover, trefoil, and alfalfa.

The acids, salts, and esters of this chemical have solubility and volatility characteristics similar to their 2,4-D counterparts.

Carbamates

The carbamate herbicides are derived from carbamic acid (NH_2COOH). Among the most effective are isopropyl N-phenyl carbamate (IPC); isopropyl N-(3-chlorophenyl carbamate) (CIPC); 4-chloro-2-butynyl N-(3-chlorophenyl) carbamate (barban): 2-chlorallyl diethyldithiocarbamate (CDEC); ethyl N,N-di-n-propylthiocarbamate (EPTC); 2,3-dichloroallyl di-isopropylthiolcarbamate (diallate), and sodium-N-dimethylthiocarbamate (SMDC or vapam). They are mitotic poisons that have their lethal action principally in the meristems.

IPC and CIPC

IPC and CIPC are the oldest of the carbamate herbicides. They are especially useful as preemergence herbicides, being particularly active against seedling grasses, although they do have some postemergence action as well, especially on small seedlings. CIPC has a somewhat longer residual life in the soil. They are frequently used in legume crops to kill annual grasses—wild oats in peas, annual grasses in alfalfa—and in established grasses for annual grass weeds. CIPC is useful for controlling dodder in alfalfa.

Application during cool weather and placement in the root zone increase effectiveness. Absorption is through roots, and the chemicals cause severe mitotic aberrations in the root meristems. They also interfere with photosynthesis.

Both IPC and CIPC are volatile and are rapidly decomposed by microorganisms so that they disappear rapidly from the soil. Both are more soluble in oil than water. They are sold as wettable powders, emulsifiable concentrates, and granules. They present no toxic dangers to man or animals under ordinary conditions of application.

Barban

Barban differs from the other carbamates in being a foliar-absorbed chemical. Selectivity is not due to differences in absorption or translocation but to inherent protoplasmic differences (Crafts, 1961). This chemical is particularly useful against wild oats in spring cereals and legumes. The stage of growth is very critical. The oats must be at about the two-leaf stage for best results, and the wheat at about the same stage. Oats become less sensitive as they grow older, but the cereal may be more severely affected. Some varieties of rye are sensitive.

Barban is sprayed in water, and low gallonage (5 to 10 gallons) per acre appears to be more effective than higher rates (20 to 40 gallons). There is no danger from volatility, nor is it toxic to humans.

CDEC

CDEC is a preemergence herbicide. It is selective against annual grasses and has been used in a variety of crops, among which are: nursery stock, cole crops, legumes, celery, lettuce, and corn.

This herbicide is most useful in areas of frequent rainfall and seems somewhat better adapted to sandy soils than to clay or organic soils. CDEC disappears from moist warm soil in 4 to 5 weeks at ordinary rates of application. It is sold as an emulsifiable concentrate to be mixed with water before spraying.

CDEC is very irritating. Applied to skin it causes a dull aching pain which lasts up to 4 hours. Cold weather increases the sensitivity. Vapors and spray mist may cause severe irritation and watering of the eyes.

EPTC

EPTC is a selective preemergence herbicide, which is very volatile and must be mixed with the soil immediately following application for best results. It is effective on a variety of weeds while they are germinating seedlings but has little effect on emerged weeds. It is absorbed through the coleoptile rather than by the roots. Selectivity depends on rapid detoxication by the tolerant species.

The chemical is only slightly soluble in water but is very soluble in most organic solvents and is available as an emulsifiable concentrate or as granules.

This compound normally decomposes in warm moist soils in 4 to

6 weeks and in dry soils in 12 to 16 weeks. The amount of moisture in the soil and the depth of incorporation are the most important factors affecting the loss of EPTC from soil (Gray and Weierich, 1965).

EPTC is a useful chemical in "chemical rotation" since it can be used on a number of crops which follow each other such as corn (maize) and beans with little danger of residual effect. It is quite safe to humans.

Diallate

Diallate (2-3-dichloroallyl di-isopropylthiolcarbamate) is a selective preplanting or preemergence herbicide. It is selective against wild oats in a number of crops, such as peas, wheat, barley, and lentils. Selectivity on cereals is marginal.

Entry of this compound is mainly via the coleoptile rather than the root system. Deep placement of the chemical in the soil therefore reduces its effectiveness and thus it should be incorporated shallowly. It is slightly volatile and must be incorporated for effective results.

Triallate has been more recently introduced. While not as effective against wild oats, it is safer to use on cereals (see Appendix).

SMDC (Metham)

SMDC or sodium N-methyldithiocarbamate is useful in limited areas such as gardens. When applied as a preplanting treatment to the soil, it releases a toxic vapor (methyl isothiocyanate) and will kill weed seeds, fungi, bacteria, nematodes, insects, and weeds. This herbicide does not require an elaborate sealing process, but the soil should be moistened with water immediately after application and kept moist for several days. It is most effective in light textured soils with a high moisture content. Seeds in manure may escape. Planting may be done about 2 weeks after application. SMDC is a water-soluble salt and should be applied with large amounts of water. No great toxic hazard exists.

Chloroacetamides

The chloroacetamides are contact toxicants that destroy weed seedlings in their germination stages. They inhibit respiration, cause disarrangement of cells, and inhibit cell division.

CDAA

In many respects CDAA (2-chloro-N,N-diallylacetamide) resembles CDEC except that it is better adapted to soils high in organic matter or clay content. It is easily leached from sandy soils and volatilizes readily from wet soil. This chemical, which is sold as an emulsifiable concentrate, is applied in the preemergence stage and is selective against grasses. Care must be taken in handling it, however, for it is irritating to skin and eyes.

CDAA + TCBC

CDAA is sometimes mixed with trichlorobenzyl chloride. The action of the trichlorobenzyl chloride is not clear but the combination appears to be a more effective herbicide in corn than CDAA alone. Under dry conditions, as in the irrigated areas of the West, residues have occurred which damaged potatoes in the following crop year. Under more moist conditions, this persistence does not occur (Crafts, 1964).

The combination is available in both liquid and granular form.

Triazines

The triazine compounds control a wide variety of weeds but are most effective on seedlings. The triazines are sold as wettable powders or granules and are nonflammable and nontoxic to animals. Selectivity is due to transformation of the molecule by resistant plants, partly by removal of a chlorine atom. Fixation of the chemical in the upper levels of the soil away from the absorbing regions of the deeper-rooted plants is also important in selective action.

The triazines disappear in soil mainly by decomposition by microorganisms and by removal by crops and weeds. Some photodecomposition may occur (Comes and Timmons, 1964; Day and Clerx, 1964). Among the more widely used triazines are simazine and atrazine, although many others are available (see Appendix). Differences in the response of corn varieties to atrazine and simazine have been reported (Eastin et al., 1964; Anderson, 1964).

Simazine

Simazine (2-chloro-4,6-bis (ethyl amino) s-triazine) must be applied preemergence and the application followed by moisture within a few weeks for effective action. It is absorbed by roots and not by the leaves. Some plants appear to be protected by having a deep root system. Others, like corn, sorghum, and sugarcane, have an enzyme which detoxifies the chemical. Simazine is applied at 1 to 6 pounds per acre to corn, strawberries, asparagus, sugarcane, orchards, woody ornamentals, and conifers for selective weed control, and along roadsides and in waste areas for non-selective control at higher rates of application.

Atrazine

Atrazine (2-chloro-4, ethyl amino-6, isopropyl-amino-1,3,5 s-triazine) is slightly more soluble in water than simazine and is more effective in low rainfall areas. It is more rapidly absorbed than simazine through the foliage and thus has some postemergence effects. It is also rapidly broken down in corn, sorghum, and sugarcane. It is less selective than simazine but appears to be a more active compound.

Atrazine shows promise for use as a "chemical fallow" in areas where a slightly residual chemical is desired. For this purpose it is applied at low rates, generally in the fall, in mixtures with 2,4-D, amitrole, or dalapon.

Both atrazine and simazine may cause residual effects in dry areas and it is recommended that corn be followed with corn in the season following application.

Either of these chemicals is a soil sterilant at high rates (10 to 40 pounds per acre).

Chlorinated aliphatic acids

The chlorinated aliphatic acids, TCA and dalapon, are strong acids that have powerful formative effects. Inside plants they are very persistent. TCA is the sodium salt of trichloroacetic acid. Dalapon is the sodium salt of 2,4-dichloropropionic acid. Both are selective against grasses. TCA is absorbed only through roots, but dalapon is absorbed by both roots and leaves. Lower rates are needed for annual than for perennial grasses. Dalapon is about twice as effective as TCA on most grass species.

Both TCA and dalapon are soluble in water and are readily leached from soil by heavy rainfall. In low rainfall areas they may persist for several months. Rates of 5 to 10 pounds are used for annual grasses, and 50 to 100 pounds for perennials. Breakdown is rapid in warm moist soil, slow in cold moist soil, and negligible in dry soil.

Dalapon and TCA have been used in crops such as alfalfa, beets, cotton, potatoes, flax, and sugarcane, as well as many others. Cultivation of perennial grass weeds, such as quackgrass (*Agropyron repens*) or Johnson grass (*Sorghum halapense*), about 2 weeks after treatment is recommended. The resultant breaking up of the underground system causes the dormant axillary buds to become active and the chemical is translocated to them. Neither TCA nor dalapon translocates well to the dormant buds; and without the disturbance of the plants, these chemicals may be relatively ineffective.

Chlorobenzoic acids

The chlorobenzoic acids produce many of the formative responses found with 2,4-D. They stimulate respiration and are more persistent in plants and soils.

The substituted benzoic acids can be formulated, like 2,4-D acid, into esters and salts.

TBA

TBA (2,3,6-trichlorobenzoic acid) is useful for the control of perennial weeds such as wild morning-glory, leafy spurge, blue-flowering lettuce, Russian knapweed, and Canada thistle. It is much more active on these weeds and more persistent in soil than 2,4-D. At 20 pounds per acre, it is a temporary soil sterilant, disappearing from most soils in about a year.

TBA is soluble in water and may be applied as a spray or in granules. It is absorbed through leaves and roots, but the major route of entry appears to be through the leaves. Malformations of stem tissues resemble those caused by 2,4-D. It is not toxic, flammable, or volatile, but it cannot legally be used on cropland.

Amiben

Amiben (3-amino-2,5-dichlorobenzoic acid) is selective as a preemergence application in a number of legume crops and vegetables against a variety of annual grasses and broadleaf weeds. It is widely used in soybeans. The activity of this compound, unlike most preemergence herbicides, is the same in muck soils as it is in mineral soils.

Amiben is sprayed in water solution and may be applied in granules. It is neither toxic, volatile, nor flammable. Application should be made at planting time when rain is expected in a few days. In the absence of rain, irrigation is desirable for best results.

Dicamba

Dicamba (2 methoxy-3,6-dichlorobenzoic acid) is satisfactory for selective weed control in turf and cereals, although it is not effective against mustards and therefore is usually combined with 2,4-D or MCPA for general purpose weed control. At higher rates, i.e., 4 to 16 pounds per acre, it has shown promise against various perennial weeds such as bindweed and Canada thistle. It is applied as an aqueous solution of amine salt or as granules.

Phenols

Phenol is also known as carbolic acid, a weak acid used in disinfecting or as a germicide.

Substituted phenols are used as contact herbicides or as preemergence herbicides. They are not effective on perennials. They have a great stimulating effect on respiration and deplete the plant of stored food by affecting the production of phosphates. They also have a coagulating effect on protoplasm.

Among the substituted phenols are pentachlorophenol and its sodium salt (PCP), and dinitrophenol (DNBP or dinoseb) and its salts. Dusts of PCP can irritate the nose, throat, and eyes but do not present any serious health hazard. DNBP and its salts are poisonous if inhaled or taken internally, or if large quantities are absorbed through the skin. With normal precautions the chemicals are readily applied without hazard to humans or livestock. Fish are sensitive. The salts of DNBP are more selective than DNBP and can be used in certain crops such as peas and seedling grasses. They are soluble in water and insoluble in oil, the opposite of DNBP.

The most favorable conditions for application are dry, sunny weather with temperatures of 70 to 85°F. Light rain following preemergence treatment is beneficial in carrying the chemical into the soil and preventing losses due to volatility. The substituted phenols do not persist long in soil.

DNBP is usually sprayed as an oil-water emulsion, and the salts as an aqueous solution. Below 60° the salts are only slightly toxic to plants, and above 85° they are extremely toxic.

DNOC or dinitro-o-cresol is similar in action to DNBP.

Substituted ureas

Urea is a common fertilizer. By replacing some of the hydrogen with other elements, effective herbicides are produced. No useful fertilizing effect has been reported.

The four oldest substituted ureas are fenuron, (3-phenyl-1, 1-dimethyl urea); monuron, 3-(p-chlorophenyl)-1, 1 dimethylurea; diuron, 3-(3,4-dichlorophenyl)-1,1-dimethylurea; and neburon, 1-n-butyl-3-(3,4-dichlorophenyl)-1-methylurea. Newer substituted ureas, such as norea, tenoram, cotoram, linuron, and siduron, have proven useful in a number of crops (see Appendix).

Most of the substituted ureas may be used as soil sterilants at high rates and selectively at low rates. They are absorbed by the roots and are transported upward in the xylem in the transpiration stream, and all act as inhibitors of photosynthesis. Persistence in soil is largely dependent on the action of microorganisms although photodecomposition of chemical on the soil surface may occur (Jordan et al., 1964; Comes and Timmons, 1964). Fenuron is the most soluble and neburon the least. The substituted ureas are nonvolatile, nontoxic, and nonflammable.

Fenuron

Fenuron is applied mainly as a soil treatment to kill woody plants. It may be sprayed or applied in pellets. It is readily leached into the soil and may be used for deep-rooted perennials in areas of moderate rainfall.

Monuron

Monuron at low rates (2 to 5 pounds per acre) has been used as a selective preemergence treatment in asparagus, mint, citrus, alfalfa, sugarcane, and pineapple. Asparagus appears to be especially resistant. It is used in cotton as a lay-by spray in regions of light to medium rainfall. At higher rates it is a soil sterilant. Persistence in soils is apparently dependent on the activity of microorganisms. It is especially persistent in dry regions with soils low in organic matter.

Monuron is rapidly absorbed by roots. Bean plants are killed by a 15-minute immersion of half the root system. Root tissues appear to be more resistant than stem tissues and translocate the monuron very freely. Trees have been seriously damaged from monuron applications 30 to 40 feet distant. Although leaves absorb monuron, there is no movement out of the leaf or down the stem (Muzik et al., 1954). The chemical is applied as a wettable powder.

Diuron

Diuron is less soluble than monuron and somewhat more persistent in soil, especially in areas of high rainfall. It is available as a wettable powder.

Like monuron, it is selective at low rates ($1\frac{1}{2}$ to 5 pounds per acre) on much the same species as monuron and is a soil sterilant at high rates. It is very toxic to most seedling weeds. A promising use appears to be the application of this chemical in the autumn or early spring on winter wheat. Its use for this purpose is questionable in regions low in organic matter or with low rainfall, where damage to the wheat is likely to ensue.

Neburon

Neburon is available as a wettable powder and is used as a selective herbicide in nursery plantings or woody ornamentals and in some turf areas. It has very low solubility, is strongly absorbed on soil colloids, and effectively resists leaching.

Miscellaneous chemicals

Amitrole

Amitrole (3-amino-1,2,4-triazole) is a very effective chemical. It is useful against perennial weeds like Canada thistle, quackgrass, Bermuda grass, poison ivy, and cattails, and is sometimes used as a defoliant, especially in cotton. In combination with 2,4-D it has proven satisfactory as a "chemical fallow" treatment for the control of volunteer wheat and annual grass and broadleaf weeds. If applied a few weeks before planting, the

combination of amitrole and 2,4-D leaves no residue problems for succeeding crops. Often a mixture of amitrole and ammonium thiocyanate
(amitrole-T) is more effective than amitrole alone.

Amitrole is more mobile in plants than 2,4-D. It is rapidly
absorbed and translocated through leaves or roots of many plants. It is also
rapidly broken down in soil but persists in an active form for several months
in plants. Seeds of treated plants sometimes produce seedlings with chlorotic
leaves.

The most striking morphological effect of this herbicide is that
it causes new growth to appear white due to the lack of chlorophyll (Figures
8-3 and 8-4). Chlorophyll in the old leaves is not destroyed, but plastids do
not develop in new growth. The chemical appears to accumulate primarily
in meristems. It affects the distribution of carbohydrates, stimulates respiration, and inhibits growth. Evidence is accumulating that it interferes with
purine metabolism. In certain species the effects of amitrole have been
overcome by adding substances such as riboflavin, histidine, or adenine.

Amitrole is soluble in water and is usually applied as a postemergence spray. It is not volatile and is not toxic to humans.

Diquat and paraquat

The toxic grouping of diquat (1,1-ethylene-2,2-dipyridilium

Figure 8-3 *Chlorotic leaves induced by amitrole treatment. New growth on
treated tomato plant at left is white compared to untreated plant at right.*

Figure 8-4 *White footsteps resulting from workmen walking through an area that has just been sprayed with amitrole. (Photo courtesy J. Gallagher.)*

dibromide) and paraquat (1,1-dimethyl-4,4-bipyridilium) is a base, in contrast to the great number of acidic compounds useful as growth regulators and herbicides. These chemicals must be reduced by the plant to a toxic form (free radical) in the process of photosynthesis. Action therefore is much more rapid in light than in darkness.

Apparently a slight injury improves translocation out of the leaves. Once the chemical has been absorbed into treated leaves, light-induced damage is required for significant movement through the rest of the plant, but the damage then inhibits further entry into the xylem. A period of darkness following application enhances the effect of paraquat (Slade and Bell, 1966).

These chemicals are water soluble, have a rapid contact action, and are nonselective. Paraquat is useful as a spray on weeds around fruit trees, and diquat may be used against aquatic weeds. Neither is volatile, flammable, or toxic.

Endothal

The mode of action of endothal (disodium 3,6-endoxohexa-hydrophthalate) is uncertain but it is known to cause pronounced mitotic effects. It has been used as a desiccant and defoliant, and as a selective foliage contact herbicide in many crops such as alfalfa and grass seed or as a preemergence herbicide. It is readily absorbed by roots and translocated upward. Adequate soil moisture is critical for effective action. Ammonium sulfate is sometimes added to increase effectiveness.

Endothal is soluble in water and is sometimes used to kill aquatic weeds. It is not harmful to fish but is toxic to mammals at rather low dosages. It is neither flammable nor volatile, and presents little hazard to the operator or consumer.

Trifluralin

Trifluralin (2,6-dinitro-NN-di-N-propyl-trifluoro-P-toluidine) is an effective chemical for selective weed control as a preemergence soil-incorporated treatment in many crops including cotton, peanuts, soybeans, safflowers, and others. It is absorbed by roots and is not flammable, toxic, or volatile. It is available as an emulsifiable concentrate or as granules.

Picloram

Picloram (4-amino-3,5,6-trichloropicolinic acid) is a persistent chemical which appears to be extremely effective against many annual and perennial broadleaves. Both Canada thistle and morning-glory seem very sensitive; in applying this chemical, however, care must be exercised to avoid contact with sensitive crops, shrubs, or trees. Picloram is available commercially in a mixture with 2,4-D and, in general, any plant sensitive to 2,4-D will be greatly affected by it.

This chemical shows great promise for use in pastures or turf areas since mature grasses are relatively resistant. It is not yet cleared for use in pastures or cropland, however, and its use in these areas may lead to confiscation of the harvested crop or of the meat from animals fed on the treated forage.

Picloram may be applied in water spray or as granules. It has a long residual life in soil, and it is nonflammable, nontoxic, and nonvolatile.

Fumigants

The fumigants have a number of common attributes: (1) they volatilize as gases which are heavier than air; (2) most of these chemicals have a multiple purpose—as well as controlling the weed, they control other pests, such as insects, fungi, and nematodes. They are too expensive and difficult to apply for large-scale use.

Carbon bisulphide

Carbon bisulphide (CS_2) is a chemical which has been used for many years. It is a clear, volatile liquid containing 84 percent sulfur. It was first used in 1854 as an insecticide. When injected into the soil and sealed in by tamping and moistening the surface layer, it kills all roots that come in contact with it. Consequently, it has proved to be a very valuable herbicide

for certain uses. Numerous factors influence the movement of carbon bisulphide vapors in soils. Among these are soil moisture, soil temperature,
compaction, and soil texture. The recommended rate is on the order of 20
pounds per square rod (3200 pounds per acre) or 2 ounces every 18 inches.

A moist or highly compacted layer of soil greatly restricts the
movement. Shallow hardpan layers or heavy clay pans always inhibit the
downward diffusion of carbon bisulphide vapor and, in some cases, may
limit the herbicidal action of the chemical. In the soil, the sulphur of the
carbon bisulphide is oxidized to sulphate which is itself a plant nutrient.
In addition, it gives rise by hydrolysis to sulfuric acid which dissolves
nutrients from the parent rock materials and makes nearly all the plant
nutrients more available. Soil alkalinity is often corrected, and crop yields
in carbon bisulphide-treated areas are usually increased.

This weed killer has no known deleterious effects on the soil, but
it does have two disadvantages: expense and fire hazard. The initial cost is
high, as is the expense of applying it, since it must be injected into the soil.
In addition, the vapor is inflammable and when mixed with air is explosive.
Even the flow of the liquid from the drum may generate enough electricity
to cause ignition by its discharge.

Chloropicrin

Another volatile soil sterilant is chloropicrin (CCl_3NO_2), the
"tear gas" of World War I. It is a colorless liquid which is slightly soluble
in water. Like carbon bisulphide this chemical controls a variety of pests in
the soil. It was used as early as 1908 as an insecticide and is toxic not only
to weeds but also to many insects, fungi, and nematodes. It has to be injected
into the soil, either by punching holes with a crowbar or using special soil
injection equipment. The main disadvantages of chloropicrin are the initial
cost and the large amount of hand labor involved in making the application.
Yields often improve as a result of killing of parasites, and it is frequently
used in greenhouses and compost soils as a substitute for stem sterilization.

Methyl bromide

Methyl bromide (CH_3Br) is another soil fumigant which has
been found useful under certain conditions. This chemical must be applied
under an impermeable cover such as brown paper or plastic. It was used
first as an insecticide in 1935. Cost weighs against this chemical, as well as
its toxicity to both plants and animals. The gas is odorless and is often
mixed with chloropicrin for commercial purposes. It is not flammable or
explosive.

In some areas where weeds have grown up through the black
top on roads, methyl bromide has been used successfully to kill these weeds

when ordinary chemicals could not be used. It has the advantage of very rapid penetration in the soil, as well as a very rapid disappearance.

Summary

An attempt has been made in this chapter to characterize families of herbicides and to briefly describe some of the more important herbicides within each family. Emphasis has been placed on mode of action, method of application, and hazards of use, rather than on an exhaustive discussion of the merits or faults of each chemical. The potential of herbicides has hardly been touched. In the rush to discover new agricultural applications, study of the mode of action of most of these chemicals has been neglected. New uses for these herbicides—either alone or in combination with other herbicides, fertilizers, insecticides, or fungicides—will be more effectively realized as we learn more about how they act within the plant system. Readers interested in further details and special uses should consult the Appendix.

QUESTIONS

1. Define *nonselective*.
2. Define *systemic*.
3. How must penetration and translocation be regulated to attain maximum effect?
4. Arsenic compounds were once very popular for golf course weed control but are seldom used at present. Can you tell why?
5. What is the relationship between the effectiveness of sodium chlorate and soil nitrogen?
6. What are the disadvantages of the borates as herbicides?
7. How could you explain the fact that both borax and calcium cyanamide contain essential elements for the plant's growth, but are used as plant killers?
8. Why may root responses to sodium chlorate vary in different soil horizons even though the herbicide is uniformly distributed?
9. What is the most volatile form of 2,4-D?
10. What are the typical cellular responses to 2,4-D?
11. What are the advantages of sesone?
12. How does 2,4,5-T differ from 2,4-D in structure and activity?
13. Why is 2,4-DB useful in legumes?
14. What characteristics do CIPC and IPC have in common?
15. How does barban differ from the other carbamates?
16. What characteristics of CDEC and CDAA make them unpleasant to use?

17. Why is simazine effective as a selective herbicide in corn? How does corn detoxify simazine?
18. How do simazine and atrazine differ in activity?
19. How do dalapon and TCA affect the response of plants growing in treated soil to other herbicides?
20. How does DNBP kill plants?
21. How is the persistence of monuron in soil affected by the environment?

REFERENCES

Anderson, R. N. 1964. Differential Response of Corn Inbreds to Simazine and Atrazine. *Weeds*, **12**:60–61.
Comes, R. D., and F. L. Timmons. 1964. Effect of Sunlight on the Phytotoxicity of Some Phenylurea and Triazine Herbicides on a Soil Surface. *Weeds*, **13**:81–83.
Crafts, A. S. 1961. "The Chemistry and Mode of Action of Herbicides," Interscience Publishers, New York.
————. 1964. Herbicide Behavior in the Plant, in "The Physiology and Biochemistry of Herbicides," L. J. Audus (ed.), pp. 75–108, Academic Press, Inc., New York.
———— and W. W. Robbins. 1962. "Weed Control," McGraw-Hill Book Company, New York, 3d ed.
Day, B. E., and W. A. Clerx. 1964. Photodecomposition of Triazines. *Weeds*, **12**:5–6.
Eastin, E. F., R. O. Palmer, and C. O. Grogan. 1964. Effect of Atrazine on Catalase and Peroxidase in Resistant and Susceptible Lines of Corn. *Weeds*, **12**:49–50.
Gray, R. A., and A. J. Weierich. 1965. Factors Affecting the Vapor Loss of EPTC from Soils. *Weeds*, **13**:141–147.
Jordan, L. S., C. W. Coggins, B. E. Day, and W. A. Clerx. 1964. Photodecomposition of Substituted Ureas. *Weeds*, **12**:1–4.
Latshaw, W. L., and J. W. Zahnley. 1927. Experiments with Sodium Chlorate and Other Chemicals for Field Bindweed. *J. Agr. Res.*, **35**:757–767.
Loomis, W. E., E. V. Smith, R. Bissey, and L. E. Arnold. 1933. The Absorption and Movement of Sodium Chlorate when Used as an Herbicide. *J. Am. Soc. Agron.*, **25**:724–739.
Loustalot, A. J., and T. J. Muzik. 1953. Effect of 2,4-D on Apparent Photosynthesis and Developmental Morphology of Velvetbean. *Bot. Gaz.*, **115**:56–66.
Muzik, T. J. and J. W. Whitworth. 1963. Growth Regulating Chemicals Persist in Plants. Qualitative Bioassay. *Science*, **140**:1212–1213.

Muzik, T. J., A. J. Loustalot, and H. J. Cruzado.   1951.   Movement of 2,4-D in Soil. *Agron. J.*, **43**:149–150.

———, A. J. Loustalot, and H. J. Cruzado.   1954.   Studies on the Entry, Transportation and Action of CMU. *Bot. Gaz.* **116**:65–73.

——— and W. T. Mauldin.   1964.   Influence of Environment on the Response of Plants to Herbicides. *Weeds*, **12**:142–145.

Slade, P., and E. G. Bell.   1966.   The Movement of Paraquat in Plants. *Weed Res.* **6**:267–274.

CHAPTER NINE
CROP-WEED-HERBICIDE
RELATIONSHIPS

The relationship of a plant's life cycle, taxonomy, structure, and response to chemicals is described in this chapter, with particular attention given to the most important annual and perennial monocotyledonous and dicotyledonous crops. Broad relationships are emphasized. An understanding of these relationships should help the student working on a previously untested crop or weed to determine what kinds of compounds are likely to be effective.

SIMILARITIES IN RESPONSE TO CHEMICALS WITHIN PLANT GROUPS

Approximately 150 herbicides are available to the farmer, and this number is constantly increasing. It has been calculated that there are about 600 species of important weeds in the world, although Fogg (1966) states that there are over 1200 weed species in Northeastern United States alone. The number of crop plants, including varieties of agronomic crops, shrubs, trees, and vegetables, is also of a large magnitude. When the complex relationship of these chemicals, weeds, and crops is further compounded by variations in climate and soil, the number of possible interactions becomes almost limitless.

Certain general relationships can be shown to exist between kinds of herbicides and groups of higher plants. The groupings presented here are partly based on taxonomic relationships and partly on ontogeny. As a general rule, the more closely a crop or weed is related to another

149

plant the more similar will be its response to chemicals. Thus all members of a species react about the same way, but as we progress through genus, family, order, etc., we find a steadily increasing diversity of response. In relation to response to herbicides, the major crop plants and weeds can be grouped into six classes, on the basis of taxonomy and ontogeny: (1) annual monocotyledons, (2) perennial treelike monocotyledons, (3) perennial herbaceous monocotyledons, (4) annual dicotyledons, (5) perennial herbaceous dicotyledons and ferns, and (6) woody dicotyledons and conifers.

The particular herbicide within each group to be used at a particular time will depend on the nature of the weed infestation, soil type, rainfall, and temperature. The close similarity between the response of the crops and that of the weeds in each group emphasizes the principle that the more closely related the crop is to the weed, the more difficult it will be to find an herbicide that will give selective control.

1.   The herbaceous annual monocotyledonous crops consist mainly of the small grains and corn (maize). Their response to herbicides is quite similar; i.e., they exhibit resistance to 2,4-D and related compounds, substituted ureas, triazines, and benzoic acids, and are easily injured by amitrole, dalapon, and TCA.

2.   The perennial treelike monocotyledons, palms, bamboo, bananas, etc., have not received as much attention as the cereals but their response appears to be of the same general order, i.e., resistance to 2,4-D, triazines, and substituted ureas and susceptibility to amitrole, dalapon, and TCA.

3.   The herbaceous perennial monocotyledons, the grasses, sugarcane, pineapple, asparagus, bulbs, etc., are fairly similar in response to herbicides with the exception that some of the lilies, such as the day flower *(Commelina* sp.), are very sensitive to 2,4-D. The chlorophenoxy herbicides, substituted ureas, and triazines are useful herbicides in most of these crops. TCA, dalapon, and amitrole kill or severely injure the grasses but are less toxic to asparagus and sugarcane.

4.   The annual dicotyledonous species form a very diverse group of several families. Nonetheless, these families possess many similarities in response to herbicides. The carbamates, phenols, and substituted ureas are useful in most of these crops, which are also sensitive to the chlorophenoxy herbicides, benzoic acids, and picloram.

5.   The herbaceous perennial dicotyledons are another very diverse group. Nevertheless, most of these crops respond to herbicides in a similar manner. The substituted ureas, carbamates, and triazines are useful, although the crops are readily injured by the chlorophenoxy herbicides, benzoic acids, and picloram.

6.   Perennial dicotyledons of woody habit, including many genera and families, are fairly alike in response to herbicides. They are

susceptible to chlorophenoxy herbicides applied to the foliage or bark and to the benzoic acids and picloram applied to foliage, bark, or soil. The triazines, substituted ureas, amitrole, and paraquat have proven useful, however.

The statement that, as a general principle, related plants of similar growth habit (crops or weeds) tend to respond similarly to growth-regulating chemicals and herbicides may seem contradictory in view of the emphasis already placed on variation within species, where ecotypes of perennial weeds or biotypes of annual weeds or varieties of crops have been shown to respond differently to chemicals. Nevertheless, some very broad basic classifications can be drawn which are helpful in understanding how these chemicals may be used most effectively and in predicting what chemicals are likely to be useful on a previously untested crop or weed.

These classifications are based on the range of responses found in a group. For example, most Cruciferae are susceptible to 2,4-D, with the responses ranging from that of Jim Hill mustard (*Sisymbrium officinale*), which is very susceptible, to blue mustard (*Chorispora tenella*), which is moderately resistant. No member of the family, however, shows the degree of tolerance to 2,4-D as that found in some members of the borage family or in the grass family.

Some of the broad relationships in the higher plants are illustrated in Table 9-1.

In view of the known variability within species and races, one should not expect to be able to transfer knowledge directly from one kind of plant to another, or even to the same plant growing in a different region. Nevertheless, it is true that if an herbicide works well on one kind of plant in one part of the world, it is well worth testing on a plant of similar characteristics growing elsewhere.

The value of this broad classification is that it enables the agriculturist to predict what types of chemicals are likely to be effective on previously untested crops or weeds. One can predict, for example, that a relatively new chemical like paraquat, which is widely used in orchards, will be equally useful in other parts of the world on other trees and shrubs. One can also predict that certain of these woody plants will be very tolerant and others rather susceptible but that the range of responses will be similar. Bromoxynil and ioxynil, which so far have been widely tested only on wheat, will undoubtedly be useful in other herbaceous monocotyledonous crops.

If the reader will keep these broad classifications in mind, we can proceed to discuss certain important crops which have been selected as examples in each category. These are crops on which the most extensive investigations have been conducted. The cereals have received by far the most attention, and 2,4-D is by far the most widely used herbicide.

Table 9-1   Plant Groupings in Response to Herbicides

All plants within each group respond in a similar way to herbicides

MONOCOTYLEDONS

Group I *Annual Monocotyledons*

A. Annual Crops

    1. Small grains, corn (maize), sorghum
    2. Herbicides used for selective control of weeds in these crops: chlorophenoxys, substituted ureas, triazines, benzoics

B. Annual Weeds

    1. Grasses (wild oats, foxtails, bromes, etc.)
    2. Susceptible to carbamates, amitrole, chlorinated aliphatic acids, substituted ureas

Group II *Perennial Herbaceous Monocotyledons*

A. Crops

    1. Grasses (sugarcane, turf, etc.), asparagus, pineapple, ornamental and edible bulbs
    2. Herbicides used for selective control of weeds in these crops: chlorophenoxys, substituted ureas, triazines

B. Weeds

    1. Perennial grasses (Johnson grass, canary grasses, *Agropyrons,* etc.)
    2. Susceptible to amitrole, chlorinated aliphatic acids

Group III *Perennial Treelike Monocotyledons*

A. Crops

    1. Palms, banana, bamboo
    2. Herbicides used in these crops: substituted ureas, triazines, chlorophenoxys, paraquat

B. Weeds

    1. Bamboo, palms
    2. Susceptible to amitrole, aliphatic acids

MONOCOTYLEDONS

Annual Monocotyledons

Small grains

Small grains include wheat, oats, barley, rye, and rice. Winter varieties are planted in the fall, live through winter, and are harvested the following summer; whereas spring varieties are planted in early spring and harvested in the late summer or early autumn of the same year. Rye is the most cold resistant and is grown the farthest north, followed by wheat, barley, oats, and rice in that order. Rice is almost entirely a spring crop

Table 9-1   (Continued)

DICOTYLEDONS

Group IV *Annual Herbaceous Dicotyledons*

A. Crops

   1. Beans, peas, lentils, peanuts, potatoes, tomatoes, cucurbits, cole crops, beets, cotton
   2. Herbicides used: carbamates, phenols, substituted ureas, toluidines

B. Weeds

   1. Pigweeds, knotweeds, nightshades, mustards, borages, mallows, dog fennel, etc.
   2. Susceptible to chlorophenoxys, benzoic acids, picloram

Group V *Perennial Herbaceous Dicotyledons**

A. Crops

   1. Mint, alfalfa, clover, strawberries
   2. Herbicides used: substituted ureas, triazines, carbamates, phenols

B. Weeds

   1. Bindweed, thistles, knapweeds, perennial nightshades, wormwood, perennial sow thistle, circle lettuce
   2. Susceptible to chlorophenoxys, benzoic acids, picloram

Group VI *Perennial Woody Dicotyledons†*

A. Crops

   1. Fruit trees, forests, rubber, tea, coffee, fruiting and ornamental shrubs
   2. Herbicides used: triazines, substituted ureas, phenols, amitrole (avoiding foliage)

B. Weeds

   1. Gorse, poison ivy, honeysuckle, blackberry, dogbane, brambles
   2. Susceptible to chlorophenoxys, picloram, benzoic acids

---

*Ferns respond to herbicides in about the same way as this group.
†Conifers have a similar response to herbicides as this group.

in the United States; in the tropics it is usually planted at the onset of the rainy season. Because of its special culture, it is discussed separately.

The majority of weeds in small grains are early maturing summer annuals or winter annuals. Spring varieties are primarily infested by summer annuals, and the winter varieties are infested by winter annual weeds or weeds that germinate in early spring. Wild oats (*Avena fatua* and *A. ludoviciana*) are a serious pest in most of the wheat-growing areas of the world. Downy bromegrass (cheatgrass) (*Bromus tectorum*), a winter annual, is especially pernicious in the drier regions of the Northwestern United States. Common perennials in the temperate zone are bindweed (*Convolvulus arvensis*), Canada (creeping) thistle (*Cirsium arvense*), and quackgrass (*Agropyron repens*) (Chapter 10). Since cultivation of the crop is very limited, good seedbed preparation, clean and vigorous seed, and the use of proper rotations are especially important. Wheat is grown in areas of rainfall ranging from 8 to 80 inches. The substituted ureas (diuron and linuron) appear to be most useful in areas of 10 inches of rain or more.

In the dry land regions (around 8 to 16 inches rainfall) where alternate cropping-fallowing is practiced, it is important to prevent weed seed production, moisture loss, and wind erosion in the fallow year. The practice of chemical fallowing, i.e., the use of chemicals instead of cultivation to kill the volunteer grain and weeds in the fall or early spring, is gaining acceptance. This practice has the advantage of maintaining a trash layer (the dead grain and weeds) on the soil, thus reducing wind and water erosion as well as helping to conserve moisture. Combinations of 2,4-D and amitrole, atrazine, and dalapon have been used for this purpose. The volunteer wheat and weed grasses are sensitive to amitrole and dalapon, while 2,4-D kills the young broadleaf weeds. Atrazine remains in the soil to kill the germinating seedlings. Generally a long-term residual effect is not desirable since replanting is usually done the following year.

CONTROL OF ANNUAL BROADLEAF WEEDS IN SMALL GRAINS WITH 2,4-D. By far the most widely used chemical is 2,4-D. Most of the common broadleaf weeds are susceptible to it, although its widespread use has already caused a shift of weed populations to the more resistant species or to grasses. Oats are more sensitive to 2,4-D than wheat, rye, or barley; therefore MCPA is sometimes used in this crop.

STAGES OF GROWTH AND SUSCEPTIBILITY OF CEREALS TO 2,4-D. The cereals have two periods of relative sensitivity to 2,4-D: between germination and tiller stage, and during the early boot stage (Figure 9-1).

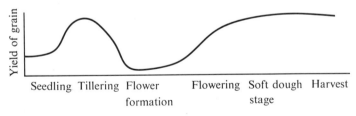

Seedling Tillering Flower   Flowering Soft dough Harvest
                     formation   stage

Time of spraying with 2,4-D

Figure 9-1 *Effect on grain yield resulting from spraying with 2,4-D at various stages of development. During the seedling stage, prior to tillering, the wheat may be severely injured by 2,4-D. It is resistant to 2,4-D while tillering but becomes very sensitive when flowering begins (boot stage). Plants with fruits in the soft dough stage and later are resistant.*

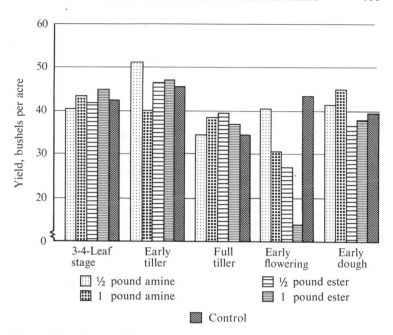

Figure 9-2 *Mean yield in bushels per acre of Brevor wheat treated with two, 2,4-D formulations at two rates compared to untreated checks. (From M.S. thesis, N. G. Johanson, Washington State University, 1960.)*

Spraying at these times may cause considerable (up to 100 percent) loss in yield.

Small grains are very resistant to 2,4-D from the time of tiller formation to early flowering. The best time to spray is immediately after tillering begins since at this stage the grain is tolerant and the weeds, which are usually small and easily killed, have not yet caused serious damage. In addition, the ground spray equipment causes little mechanical injury to the grain (Figure 9-2).

After flowering, from soft dough stage to maturity, small grains are again very tolerant to 2,4-D. At this stage, however, the ground spray equipment may injure much of the grain, and the weed competition has already damaged the crop yield. The main benefit obtained from such late spraying is a reduction in numbers of weed seeds and easier harvesting.

The ester forms of 2,4-D cause more damage to wheat in the sensitive stages than the amine salts, although they may be applied safely in the tolerant stages. Extensive damage to the root system of the young wheat plant by 2,4-D applied to the foliage or to the root may make the plant less able to withstand subsequent drought. Thus, when very young plants (before tiller formation) are sprayed prior to very dry weather, greater damage will ensue than if there is no moisture stress following application. Treatment during seedling stages may cause severe stunting, thin stands, seed-head malformations, and severe yield loss (Johanson and Muzik, 1961).

Sprays during early flowering also cause severe yield reductions and seed-head malformations, such as long internodes, twisted stem, onion leaf, failure of leaf to emerge from flag leaf, doubling of the caryopses, and abnormal branching (Figure 9-3).

In general, wheat is more tolerant to 2,4-D than barley, rye, or oats. Some varieties of wheat are more sensitive than others; e.g., Brevor wheat is more susceptible than Omar. 2,4-D is usually sprayed at rates from $\frac{1}{2}$ to 1 pound per acre and occasionally up to 2 pounds per acre. No more should be used than is required for good weed control.

INFLUENCE OF 2,4-D ON GERMINATION.   Treatments made at the proper time and rate do not reduce germination of wheat seed. Treatment during early flowering may cause a serious reduction in germination (Johanson and Muzik, 1961). Seedlings may be malformed and grow poorly.

INFLUENCE OF VIGOR ON RESPONSE OF CEREALS TO 2,4-D.   Very healthy cereal plants, if treated during a susceptible period, will be injured more than plants growing under low fertility or infested with rust. However, treatment of healthy plants during a tolerant stage will not reduce yields. Higher rates of fertility and freedom from disease would be expected to permit rapid and extensive growth, thus increasing the rate of meristematic tissue development and thereby making the plants more sensitive to the 2,4-D.

(a)   (b)

Figure 9-3 *Malformations in wheat heads caused by spraying in boot stage. (a) Bearded wheat and (b) club wheat are sensitive to 2,4-D in seedling and boot stages of growth. Head from unsprayed plant at left in each picture.*

CHEMICALS OTHER THAN 2,4-D FOR BROADLEAF WEED CONTROL
IN SMALL GRAINS. Other chemicals used in cereals for annual broadleaf
weed control are dicamba, diuron, linuron, bromoxynil, and ioxynil,
although clearances have not been obtained on all grains. Diuron and
linuron are applied as preemergence or early postemergence sprays and
appear to have greatest usefulness in areas of high winter or spring rainfall.
Application in soils low in organic matter or in areas with low rainfall may
result in damage to the grain. Dicamba does not control mustards and is
usually mixed with 2,4-D or MCPA to widen the spectrum of activity.
Both bromoxynil and ioxynil appear to have excellent potential for weed
control in wheat and barley. The safety margin appears to be much greater
than with 2,4-D, and sensitivity of certain weeds is much greater. These
chemicals appear to have excellent potential for use in other monocotyledonous crops but are not widely used at the present time, except in wheat.
Wheat exhibits some tolerance to various triazine herbicides.

CONTROL OF GRASS WEEDS IN SMALL GRAINS. Wild oats may
be successfully controlled in wheat and barley by preplanting soil-
incorporated treatments of diallate or triallate. The margin of safety to
the crop is greater with triallate, although wild oat control is not as good.
These chemicals are very effective in spring cereals or in the warmer winter
wheat areas where wild oat germination is in the fall. Spring-germinating
wild oats are not affected by fall applications since the chemicals do not
persist long in the soil.

Postemergence application of barban is also very effective for
wild oat control in spring wheat and barley. Application is most effective
when the grain crop and wild oats are small, preferably in about the one-
to two-leaf stage. Later applications cause more damage to the grain and
are less effective on the weed.

No effective selective control has been found in cereal crops
for many other grass weeds such as downy brome, darnel (*Lolium temulentum*), annual bluegrass (*Poa annua*), goatgrass (*Aegilops cylindrica*), and
foxtail (*Setaria* sp.). This difficulty is to be expected since, as previously
pointed out, the closer the taxonomic relationship, the greater the similarity
in physiology and morphology of the weed and the crop and therefore the
more difficult it is to find a chemical that will effectively control the weed
without injuring the crop. Reduction of seed population by crop rotation
of chemical fallow offers the best hope of success at present.

CONTROL OF PERENNIAL WEEDS IN SMALL GRAINS. Perennial
weeds in grain crops usually occur in patches but may cover several acres
in heavily infested fields.

Many of the perennial broadleaf weeds are moderately susceptible
to 2,4-D but are seldom killed by this chemical (Chapter 10). The food

reserves fluctuate, usually following a downward trend until bud stage—about midsummer. Spraying with 2,4-D is usually most effective at early flower bud stage. A combination of cultivation in spring to reduce the food reserves and 2,4-D sprays at early bud stage is more effective than either method alone.

Soil sterilants such as sodium chlorate or TBA at high rates are useful on small patches of perennial weeds although they also kill the wheat and force the land out of production. Sodium chlorate also has deleterious effects on the soil making it more susceptible to erosion. Mixed with organic matter such as dry weeds, it creates a fire hazard. Thus sodium chlorate, although widely used, has many disadvantages as compared to some of the newer herbicides (Chapter 8). Dicamba and picloram also appear to be very effective on many perennial broadleaf weeds. Of these chemicals, dicamba seems to disappear from the soil most quickly at the recommended rates of application. Full clearances for use in cropland have not been obtained for all these chemicals, and the land may have to be out of production for years following application.

Seedlings of these broadleaf perennial species will appear after the chemical has dissipated from the soil. For the first several weeks after germination, the seedlings may be treated as annuals and killed by cultivation or 2,4-D. If they are allowed to grow more than a few weeks, they develop perennial characteristics, among them the ability to regenerate from underground organs, and are thus more difficult to control.

RICE.   Rice responds to herbicides in much the same way as wheat, oats, barley, and rye. However, the culture of rice under flooded conditions makes for different weed problems. Early flooding tends to favor the broadleaf plants over the grasses. Certain varieties of rice (upland rice) may be grown without irrigation or submergence in regions of high rainfall where the soil is wet during much of the growing season. Different weed problems will, of course, be encountered than those found in flooded rice. The weed problems of upland rice resemble those of the other cereals.

Periods of susceptibility to herbicides are similar to those of wheat, oats, and barley. Treatment when rice is fully tillered (7 to 10 weeks after emergence) with either 2,4-D or MCP at $\frac{3}{4}$ to $1\frac{1}{2}$ pounds per acre causes only slight damage to the rice and gives good broadleaf control. 2,4,5-T may be used for weeds resistant to 2,4-D and MCP. Low rates of 2,4-D or MCP may be applied as early as 3 weeks after emergence if the weed problem is very serious, although there is more danger of damage to the rice at this stage of growth. Propanil, CIPC, and ordram appear to be suitable for weed control in rice. PCP is presently the most widely used herbicide in Japan and probably also in the rest of Asia.

Rice forms the staple diet for a large part of the world's population and development of herbicides for this crop offers much promise in increasing food production. As new dwarf varieties are developed which have high yield potential, the need for weed control will become even more critical. The varieties now grown in the underdeveloped areas of the world are tall and quick growing but not very high yielding. The early growth and height enables them to compete with the weeds. The dwarf varieties do not have this competitive ability.

Corn (maize) and sorghum

Corn (maize) and sorghum are grown in rows to facilitate cultivation and harvesting. Cultivation other than for weed control is of doubtful value, except to improve moisture penetration in certain soils and to provide a *dust mulch*. The dust mulch itself is of questionable value.

Both cultivation and herbicides are used in corn and sorghum. Cultivation kills the weeds between, but not within, the rows.

Preemergence chemicals such as simazine, atrazine, 2,4-D, diuron, or CDAA plus TCBC have given good results. 2,4-D is most effective on broadleaves, and CDAA plus TCBC on annual grasses. The triazines are effective on both kinds of weeds. These chemicals (other than 2,4-D) are not as useful in dry regions as they are in moist areas. Possible persistence of the triazines and CDAA plus TCBC makes it advisable to follow corn with corn when these chemicals are used. EPTC appears useful—especially in areas where there are many grass weeds and where many different crops are grown in rotation on the same land—for two reasons: it is more effective on grasses than 2,4-D, and it quickly disappears from the soil. 2,4-D also offers no problems from persistence in the soil under ordinary conditions.

2,4-D may be applied to corn at very low rates when it is small and at higher rates as the plants mature. The spray should be applied with nozzles dropped between the corn rows to reduce contact with the crop leaves. Corn varieties differ considerably in tolerance to 2,4-D (Figure 9-4), although corn is more tolerant than sorghum.

Postemergence application of atrazine may be made when the corn and weeds are very small. Rain or sprinkler irrigation within a few days after application makes the chemical more effective.

Witchweed (*Striga* sp.), a parasitic dicotyledonous plant in corn and other grasses, is presently limited in the United States to the sandy soils in North and South Carolina. This is a very serious weed of corn and sorghum in Africa and could become serious in this country. The plant reproduces by very tiny seeds, as fine as dust. These do not germinate until in very close proximity to a grass root. Present studies are devoted to discovering an economical method of control and to preventing the spread of this weed to other corn-growing areas. Witchweed appears to be susceptible

(a)   (b)

Figure 9-4   *Malformations in sensitive variety of young corn sprayed with 2,4-D. (a) Plant showing leaf and stem abnormalities; (b) root system of an untreated plant at left, root systems from two treated plants at right.*

to fenac and TBA at rates which corn tolerates fairly well (Sand et al., 1964; see also Chapter 10).

Quackgrass (couchgrass), a serious weed in many parts of the world, may be controlled by atrazine (see Chapter 10) and other chemicals. Both corn and sorghum are tolerant to this chemical. One of the more interesting techniques of use is the application of atrazine at rates sufficient to temporarily inhibit the quackgrass without killing it. The corn is planted directly in a furrow cut in the uncultivated sod with fertilizer applied over the furrow. The crop is harvested about the time the weed recovers. The quackgrass sod is not destroyed, and thus this method of weed control effectively prevents erosion.

Perennial monocotyledons

Treelike monocotyledons

This group of perennial monocotyledons consists of tall plants which have a persistent stem but which lack a true cambium. In this group may be placed the palms, banana, and bamboo. These plants are mainly tropical species growing in warm areas of fairly high rainfall. Diuron, simazine, and paraquat have been used for weed control in plantations of bananas, oil palm, and coconut palm. Relatively little work has been done for weed control in bamboo fields since the low-value bamboo crop is such an excellent competitor and may, in fact, frequently become a pest. Some of the thorny palms can also be quite a nuisance. Bamboo is susceptible to TCA, dalapon, and foliar-applied amitrole (Cruzado et al., 1961).

Herbaceous monocotyledons

Substituted ureas, triazines, and dinitros are widely used for weed control in the perennial herbaceous monocotyledons such as the perennial grasses, pineapple, asparagus, and bulbs. 2,4-D is widely used in sugarcane and asparagus but is less useful in pineapple because of its effect in inducing flowering in certain varieties of this plant, or in ornamental or edible bulbs because of damage to certain species.

Lawns and turf

Lawn weeds are usually low-growing, rosette, or prostrate types; in other words, plants which can withstand repeated mowings because the leaves and buds are close to the ground.

2,4-D, dicamba, or picloram will kill many broad-leaved weeds with no damage to most species of grass, if the grasses are well established. Bentgrasses are the most susceptible lawngrasses to 2,4-D. Application is effective in the fall or in the spring on the susceptible perennial weeds, but summer applications are preferable for most annual weeds. Combinations of 2,4-D, 2,4,5-T, and silvex have been more effective than 2,4-D alone on some broad-leaved weeds.

Annual grasses, such as crabgrass (*Digitaria* sp.) and annual bluegrass, are serious pests in many areas. Good control of crabgrass may be obtained through preemergence application of dacthal or certain soluble arsenicals. Various arsenicals have been used for this purpose but some have doubtful value because of the danger of accumulation of toxic residues in the soil making the establishment of new grass difficult. Annual bluegrass is best controlled by good management practices designed to make the lawn as good a competitor as possible. IPC is used to take downy brome (a winter annual) out of established bluegrass.

Perennial grasses frequently become established in new lawns and become difficult to eradicate. With large infestations, the householder is probably well advised to kill both weed and turf and then replant. As in other crops, the closer the relationship between the crop and the weed, the more difficult selective control becomes. A perennial grass weed in a perennial grass crop presents a very formidable problem.

Pastures and range

Many of the important weeds in pastures and rangeland are seldom found in cultivated land. Infestation will vary in relation to the amount of competition from the forage plants. The grazing animal's preference for the more palatable species acts as a constant pressure toward a less desirable mixture of species.

Pasture weeds include annual, biennial, and perennial broad-leaved plants and annual and perennial grasses. The severity of most pasture infestations is encouraged by overgrazing or poorly timed grazing. Grazing pressure, environmental factors (fluctuations in weather), and season of maximum usage will largely determine the rate at which the species composition changes, as the more palatable species are hindered in development or killed outright by overgrazing. The preferred species receives the greatest pressure. If it dies, the same pressure is diverted to another species, one previously considered inferior. Thus the desirable species are slowly replaced by weeds.

Low-value rangelands are seldom treated extensively with chemicals because it is not economically feasible. Biological control (Chapter 13) has been successful for cactus (*Opuntia* sp.) and St. Johnswort (*Hypericum perforatum*), and is being attempted for other weeds such as gorse (*Ulex europeus*), tansy ragwort (*Senecio jacobaea*), Canada (creeping) thistle, and halogeton (*Halogeton glomeratus*). The use of 2,4-D is a common practice for these weeds, but silvex, 2,4,5-T, and TBA have also been used.

Brush is frequently a problem on pastures, and 2,4-D, 2,4,5-T, silvex, picloram, and AMS are commonly used either as foliar sprays, basal treatments directly to the trunk, or cutting followed by stump treatment to prevent regrowth (Chapter 10). Removal of sagebrush with aerial sprays of 2,4-D is a common practice in the West (Alley, 1956).

In every instance it should be emphasized that where the problem arises from mismanagement or overgrazing, the application of improved control procedures will bring no permanent solution without an accompanying improved land use program. Reseeding may be necessary in some areas.

An interesting viewpoint is expressed by one writer who states that cows feeding in European pastures where weeds have been rigorously excluded give tasteless milk, and that to counteract this, certain weeds such as yarrow (*Achillea millefolium*), plantain (*Plantago* sp.), dandelion (*Taraxacum vulgare*), and others are planted along with the pasture grasses and legumes (Heeger, 1949). This problem (lack of weeds) has not yet arisen on most of the world's pastures.

DICOTYLEDONS

Annual herbaceous dicotyledons

Various carbamates, substituted ureas, and dinitro herbicides have been widely used in the annual herbaceous dicotyledons such as legumes (beans, peas, and peanuts), potatoes, tomatoes, lettuce, cotton, beets, etc.

Annual grasses are very serious in many of these crops. They may be selectively controlled by the use of various carbamates such as IPC, CIPC, diallate, and barban, or by diuron or monuron. Diallate and barban are especially useful for selective control of wild oats in peas and lentils. EPTC is widely used in beans.

TCA and dalapon have also been used for the control of annual grasses in many of the crops in this category. However, some of these species, especially the legumes, are moderately sensitive to these chemicals and thus low rates must be used to prevent injury. Dalapon in the soil at the time of potato tuber formation may cause bleaching in the tubers of the red-skinned varieties.

The amine salts of DNBP are used to control broad-leaved weeds in most of these crops, but they must be sprayed when the crop and weeds are very small or before the crop has emerged.

The legumes are tolerant of 2,4-DB and MCPB (Chapter 8), and these herbicides have found some usefulness for broad-leaved weed control in these crops.

Diuron, CIPC, trifluralin, herbicidal oils, or flaming are widely used in cotton. Hand labor in this crop has been reduced over 50 percent by the use of herbicides (Shaw and Loustalot, 1963). Trifluralin and related compounds have also shown promise in some of the other crops in this category.

Perennial herbaceous dicotyledons

Various substituted ureas, triazines, carbamates, and dinitro herbicides are widely used in the perennial herbaceous dicotyledons, among which are the perennial legumes (alfalfa, clover, lespedeza), mint, strawberries, etc. Although these crop plants occur in widely separated families, part of their similarity in response to herbicides is probably due to the possession of a perennial root system.

Legumes

Many perennial legumes are grown for hay, pasture, or soil-improving crops. Prevention of weeds by using clean seed and cultivation before seeding is very important since there is little opportunity for cultivation after seeding.

Date of seeding should be selected for maximum establishment of the crop and will depend on whether summer or winter annuals are more serious. For example, fall-planted alfalfa usually competes well with spring annuals in regions where spring alfalfa might be crowded out. Spring planting may be preferred where winter annual weeds are the main problem.

Weeds in established legumes may be treated by preemergence

(to the weed) or postemergence application. The preemergence sprays are usually applied when the crop is dormant or immediately after a hay crop is removed.

IPC, CIPC, and diuron have given good control of weedy grasses. CIPC controls dodder selectively in alfalfa when applied in spring before germination of the weed (Lee and Timmons, 1959; see also Chapter 10).

Postemergence applications of dinitros control many broad-leaved weeds. TCA and dalapon have been used to control grasses.

Some of the perennial legumes, such as ladino, white clover, and lespedeza, are fairly tolerant to 2,4-D, while the others are very sensitive. Applications should be limited to low rates, less than $\frac{1}{2}$ pound per acre, and made only to well-established healthy stands.

2,4-DB and MCPB may be used on legumes with more safety than 2,4-D. Sweet clover is sensitive to these chemicals, but most legumes lack the mechanism to toxify them by changing them to 2,4-D.

In some tropical tree crops, a perennial cover crop is sown to keep down the weed between the trees. These are usually species of legumes, either *Pueraria* or *Centrosema*. Certain substituted ureas have proven useful in helping these cover crops become established.

Strawberries

Strawberries are herbaceous perennials and therefore are handled differently than the other perennial fruits. Sesone and simazine are widely used as preemergence treatments, and 2,4-D as a dormant spray. Certain substituted ureas also show promise. Up to one-fourth of the production cost is associated with weed problems. This is due to the high cost of hand weeding, the difficulty and slowness of picking among weeds, and the loss of berries in the weedy growth. Some diseases, such as crown rot, are more severe under weedy conditions. Fruit ripening is likely to be uneven in weedy strawberries due to the uneven stand of weeds and consequent differences in light and moisture available to the strawberries. In fields where the weed competition is severe the grower may elect to accept a 10 to 12 percent loss of berries as a result of herbicide damage in order to avoid replanting and to facilitate harvesting.

Perennial woody dicotyledons

Tree crops

Weeds around trees have received less attention than in most herbaceous crops, with the possible exception of citrus and nuts. Of the tropical trees, rubber (*Hevea brasiliensis*) and coffee (*Coffea* sp.) have probably received the most attention. Chemicals used around trees include triazines, substituted ureas, dalapon, paraquat, weed-killing oils, dinitro herbicides, amitrole, and directed applications of 2,4-D to avoid contact with the foliage or stem (Figure 9-5).

Weed control practices in orchards are affected by many considerations. Among these are the following:

1. The need to reduce competition for water and minerals, to control obnoxious weeds such as thistle that interfere with harvesting, or ragweed that causes allergies, and to kill or inhibit blooming weeds which attract bees at a time when insecticides should be sprayed on the orchard.

2. Soil compaction problems. Heavy vehicles in orchards may compact soils so that movement of air and water is interfered with, thus hindering root development. Where plowing is part of the program, hardpans frequently develop and form a barrier to water and to growing roots.

3. Nitrogen and moisture control problems. In some orchards in areas of fall moisture, it is desirable to have a cover crop or weed growth to induce "hardening off" of the trees. The cover crop or weeds reduce the amount of water and nitrogen available to the trees, thus reducing late growth in the fall and making the trees more resistant to frost.

4. Erosion problems. Severe erosion in clean cultivated orchards can occur, especially where the trees are planted on slopes. The best defense against erosion is a plant cover, either sod or cover crop, or a mixture of weeds.

Chemicals are used mainly around the bases of fruit trees where cultivation is difficult and may cause harm to the delicate feeding roots

Figure 9-5 *Selective weed control in an orchard in Holland. A sod is maintained between the rows and a selective herbicide, which kills the weeds but is harmless to the trees, is sprayed next to the trees.*

which are often close to the surface. Either cultivation or chemicals may be used between the rows of trees. Generally cultivation is preferred at present. It is often desirable to develop a low-growing cover crop between the rows. Occasional mowing is enough to maintain the cover crop low enough so as not to interfere with operations. A cover crop offers competition to weeds like thistles, which can be a great nuisance especially at harvest time, as well as an opportunity to help regulate moisture and fertility. Some growers prefer a sod between the rows. Sod offers many of the same advantages as an annual cover crop and is perennial as well; it also enables the grower to enter the orchard for spray operations during rainy periods.

In certain periods of tree development, competition may be beneficial. In most orchards, nitrogen is most effective when it is available in spring. No cover crops should be competing with the trees for nitrogen at this time. A growth of sod may so reduce the supplies of water and nitrates available in spring that the size of the fruit is decreased. Rye, however, sown as a cover crop in late summer uses a large amount of water and nitrogen so that the growth of the trees is correspondingly checked. The trees are thus better prepared to withstand winter cold. The mulch of rye insulates the soil from rapid freezing and penetration of cold to the root zone. In areas of snow, it holds the fallen leaves around which the snow accumulates. The cover crop is plowed under in the spring and thus returns organic matter to the soil when it is needed.

In areas with frost, clean cultivation or good chemical weed control early in the season may lead to better frost protection because of increased radiation from the soil and more rapid development of shoots, blossoms, and fruits for earlier fruit maturity.

Variation in sensitivity to herbicides exists among the various types of fruit trees. This reflects not only a difference between species but also the difference between rootstocks. No one management system works best for all species or even for the same variety grown under different conditions or management programs. Any system will need to be modified from time to time.

Citrus trees are more susceptible to dalapon than other fruit trees but are very resistant to diuron. Oils, often fortified with DNBP, are widely used in citrus plantings.

In general, older trees are more resistant to chemicals than younger trees; nevertheless, the use of chemicals is usually more strictly regulated on bearing trees than on nonbearing trees because of possible uptake of the chemicals by the fruit.

In one experiment, the removal of plant growth adjacent to apple trees not only reduced competition but also reduced rodent damage due to the lack of cover (Holm et al., 1959).

Shrubs and vine fruits

Bush fruits (gooseberries, blackberries, currants, blueberries, raspberries) and grapes are woody perennials grown in dense plantings and are usually handled similarly to tree fruits. The triazines, substituted ureas, and dinitros are useful herbicides in this group of plants. The fruits of most of these crops ripen in midsummer, at the same time that vegetative growth takes place. These plants are shallow rooted, drawing moisture from the upper levels of the soil. This combination of vegetative growth and fruit production results in demand on limited moisture, thus the control of weeds to eliminate competition for moisture is very desirable. Cultivation is likely to injure the shallow roots.

The time of application is very important. Herbicides can have deleterious effects during bloom, fruit formation, and runner, shoot, or vine development, while the plants may be quite resistant at other times, i.e., during dormant periods in spring or after fruit harvest in the autumn.

Plantation tree crops

Rubber, cocoa, coffee, and tea are grown extensively as plantation tree crops in various parts of the tropics. 2,4-D, simazine, diuron, amitrole, paraquat, and dalapon are used for controlling weeds around the trees.

Low-yielding old trees have been killed with 2,4,5-T or arsenic to permit replanting with young, vigorous, high-yielding selections.

Atrazine and simazine are widely used to control annual weeds in conifer nurseries and field plantings.

QUESTIONS

1. Which four classes of herbicides appear to be most generally useful around dicotyledonous trees? Monocotyledonous trees?
2. If you were in the Peace Corps in the Tropics and were asked to initiate a program for selective weed control in cassava (*Manihot* sp., a shrubby dicotyledon), what sorts of chemicals would you test first?
3. If you were asked to develop a weed control program in millet (*Setaria italica*), what kinds of herbicides do you think might be effective?
4. What is chemical fallowing?
5. What are the two sensitive periods of wheat to 2,4-D?
6. Why is late spraying (after maturity) of doubtful value? What usefulness may it have?
7. How does rice differ from other cereals in its weed problems?
8. Which chemical would you recommend for weed control in corn in

the irrigated areas of the Columbia Basin if (1) the corn is followed with corn, (2) the corn is followed with potatoes?

9. What is witchweed?
10. What kinds of weeds grow in lawns?
11. Why are ranges seldom treated extensively with chemicals?
12. How does dry weather following treatment affect wheat's response to 2,4-D?
13. What is the best time to spray cereals with 2,4-D for weed control?
14. What application equipment and chemicals should a person be familiar with to develop an adequate program of weed control in (1) wheat, (2) peas, (3) corn, and (4) pastures?
15. Why do crops grown in primitive areas usually exhibit rapid early growth and develop considerable height?

REFERENCES

Alley, H. P. 1956. Chemical Control of Big Sagebrush and Its Effect upon Production and Utilization of Native Grass Species. *Weeds*, **4**:164–173.

Cruzado, H. J., T. J. Muzik, and W. C. Kennard. 1961. Control of Bamboo in Puerto Rico by Herbicides. *Weeds*, **9**:20–26.

Fogg, J. M. 1966. The Silent Travelers, Handbook on Weed Control. *Brooklyn Botanic Gardens Record*, **22**:4–7.

Heeger, W. F. 1949. Wertvolle Heilkräuterbeisaaten zu Wiesen-und Weidenmischungen (Medicinal Herbs for Seed Mixtures for Meadows and Pastures). *Dtsch. Landiv.*, 2, 116–117.

Holm, L., F. A. Gilbert, and E. Maltvick. 1959. Elimination of Rodent Cover Adjacent to Apple Trees. *Weeds*, **7**:405–408.

Johanson, N. G., and T. J. Muzik. 1961. Some Effects of 2,4-D on Wheat Yield and Root Growth. *Bot. Gaz.*, **122**:188–194.

Lee, W. O., and F. L. Timmons. 1959. Dodder and Its Control. *USDA Farmers Bull*, 2117, 1–20.

Sand, P. F., E. L. Robinson, and C. C. Dowler. 1964. The Effect of Several Herbicides on the Control of Witchweed in Corn. *Weeds*, **12**:37–39.

Shaw, W. C., and A. J. Loustalot. 1963. Revolution in Weed Science. *Agr. Sci. Rev.*, 1–10.

CHAPTER TEN
SPECIAL PROBLEMS
IN CONTROL

Certain specialized areas of weed control deserve particular mention. Among these are aquatic weeds, general vegetation control (soil sterilization), woody species, parasitic weeds, and certain perennial herbaceous weeds which because of their wide distribution and pernicious habit have received much attention. The species discussed in this chapter were chosen as representative of these various types of weed problems. Other species might equally well have been selected but these few serve to illustrate some of the problems and techniques in the field.

AQUATIC WEEDS

Aquatic weeds are those which start in water and grow at least part of their life cycle in water. They have various undesirable effects: choking lakes and irrigation and drainage ditches; interfering with swimming, fishing, and boating; and sometimes causing undesirable odors and flavors in the water. On the other hand, they may help prevent erosion along shorelines, and provide cover and food for fish, fowl, and game. Some of these aquatic weeds spread very rapidly. Single plants of sago pondweed (*Potamogeton pectinatus*), for example, grown from a tuber and a seed in 6 months, developed over 36,000 tubers and 63,000 seeds, respectively (Yeo, 1965).

Rapid killing of dense weedy growth may kill fish as a result of the decomposition of the dead plants. As decomposition proceeds, oxygen is used and is thus unavailable to the fish which may then die of asphyxiation. This may be avoided by treating only a part of the area at a time.

Vascular aquatic weeds are of three general types: submersed, emersed, and floating. Submersed weeds, such as the sago pondweed, are attached to the bottom and grow mostly or entirely beneath the surface. Emersed aquatics, such as the water lilies, are attached to the bottom but produce a majority of their flowers at or above the water surface. Floating aquatics, such as the water hyacinth, have true roots and leaves but are not anchored and thus float freely in the water. The algae make up another group of highly important aquatic plants, and in fact, are the original source of food for nearly all fish.

Shorelines or ditchbanks may also become infested by weeds such as willows, cattails, and perennial grasses that necessitate treatment.

Irrigation canals in the arid regions of the world present some interesting ecological problems. Within the space of a few feet, growing conditions change from very wet at the bottom of the ditch to very dry at the top. Various grasses have been planted in an effort to develop a sod which will protect against erosion and reduce invasion of undesirable species; several grass species are usually planted in order to take advantage of the varying habitat of the ditchbank.

Although chemical methods are the most popular, mechanical methods such as drying, pasturing, mowing, chaining, dredging, and burning are sometimes used to control aquatic weeds. These methods are relatively slow and often expensive as compared to the use of the newer herbicides.

Drying is an effective method of controlling many submerged aquatic weeds, especially in hot, arid regions. The water must be completely withdrawn from the pond or ditch. The stems and leaves of the submerged weeds will be killed after several days exposure to the sun and air. This method is not effective against emersed weeds which are rooted in the bottom. It must usually be repeated to control regrowth from the roots or propagules. A serious objection to drying is that it interrupts the use of the ditch, often during critical periods of need.

Pasturing is effective in controlling some of the marginal grasses and shrubs. A good legume-grass combination planted on the ditchbanks may be grazed if properly managed. A disadvantage of pasturing is that excessive trampling may destroy the banks and muddy the water.

Hand cleaning may be effective in small lightly infested areas where a few hours spent pulling out weed invaders may prevent the weed from spreading.

A heavy chain towed between two tractors on opposite sides of the ditch may be used to pull out or break off the weeds. If all the vegetation is not broken off in the first pass, pulling the chain back in the opposite direction is advisable. After chaining, it may be necessary to remove the loosened plant debris from the canal so that it will not collect in one area and obstruct the water. Weeds torn loose by chaining may drift downstream and cause new infestations.

Dredges specially equipped with weed forks rather than the usual bucket are sometimes used for aquatic weed control. Dredging appears equally effective against all types of aquatic weeds, but it has certain disadvantages: (1) it tends to remove mud along with the weeds and thus enlarge or deepen the ditch, thus changing its carrying capacity, (2) it usually leaves a bank of mud and weed growth which must be leveled out if the land is to be used, and (3) it is slow and expensive.

Burning, as previously discussed (Chapter 5), is most effective on young succulent plants and least effective on established perennials. Usually green plants are given a preliminary searing and a repeat application 10 to 14 days later when the plants may be dry enough to burn. This method is used to control ditchbank weeds. It may be combined with other methods to help dispose of the debris left by dredging, chaining, mowing, or chemical treatment.

Mowing of the ditchbank weeds may be practiced if the banks are fairly smooth and not too steep. Underwater power-driven weed saws and weed cutters are sometimes used. The effects are usually of short duration.

Chemicals may be applied as sprays or granules, or in porous bags dragged behind boats. Application may also be made on the frozen edges of lakes in winter, applying directly to the ice, treating the surface like a field area. When the ice melts in the spring, it releases the chemical into the water.

Copper sulfate is useful against algae, and is applied as a spray or in cloth bags (towed behind a boat in lakes and ponds) until the chemical has dissolved.

Sodium arsenite is sometimes used for the control of algae, submersed weeds, and floating weeds, but must be used with care since water with more than 0.05 ppm arsenic is hazardous to humans. From 2 to 4 grams will kill a cow, and therefore all grazing animals should be removed from the area. Rice is extremely sensitive to arsenic.

Aromatic oils are used for weed control in irrigation canals. These are very toxic to fish but have not caused injury to irrigated crops when used as recommended (Bruns et al., 1955).

Acrolein kills many water weeds and snails. It is becoming widely used in irrigation ditches although it is toxic to fish. Water treated at recommended rates has not harmed crops. This chemical is very irritating to the eyes and is usually applied with special injecting equipment. It may be effective up to 50 miles from the point of application (Bruns, 1965).

Endothal is useful for controlling many aquatic weeds in lakes and ponds without harming fish or wildlife. It is applied as a liquid or as granules sprinkled uniformly over the surface. Diquat shows promise for the control of several submersed weeds (Hiltibran, 1965).

The emergent weeds may be killed by spraying the parts above the water with phenoxy herbicides for broadleaves and dalapon or amitrole for grasses. The phenoxy herbicides are sometimes dissolved in the water but present no hazard to fish.

The use to be made of the water will largely determine the treatments that can be made for weed control. Irrigation requirements are different from recreation, swimming requirements are different from fishing, and so on. In many waterways, transportation is seriously hampered by such weeds as water hyacinth and water fern, and all other considerations are secondary.

Certain fish, especially carp and sunfish (*Tilapia* sp.), which feed on aquatic weeds have virtually eliminated aquatic weeds in ponds containing only these species. When stocked into established populations of bass and bluegill, the results were less encouraging (Shell, 1962). Manatee have been introduced into Florida waterways for the control of weeds.

A large freshwater snail (*Marisa cornuarietis*) shows promise for the control of aquatic weeds in Florida (Seaman and Porterfield, 1964) and in Puerto Rico (Radke et al., 1961).

IRRIGATED CROPS

A special note on irrigated crops is included here to emphasize the importance of the type of irrigation on water movement (Figure 10-1).

Weed control in furrow-irrigated crops is affected by the pattern of water movement which tends to be upward at the sides of the furrow, thus failing to move the chemical out of the surface of the soil. Special consideration must be given to this problem because soil-applied chemicals which work well in other areas may be useless under these conditions. Persistence in the soil is likely to be longer, with consequently greater danger to subsequent crops.

Sprinkler irrigation is frequently used in herbaceous and woody crops in dry areas, such as the Columbia Basin. The weed problems in

Furrow irrigation   Sprinkler irrigation

Figure 10-1 *Direction of water movement (shown by arrows) from rill or furrow irrigation (at left) or from sprinkler irrigation (at right).*

sprinkler-irrigated crops are different than in rill-irrigated crops because the pattern of moisture movement is more like that of rainfall, i.e., downward, and distribution is more uniform.

GENERAL VEGETATION CONTROL

Nonselective or general vegetation control is primarily useful in noncrop areas, where permanent control of all plant growth is desired. It is also utilized for the control of perennial weeds in cropland when the farmer is willing to accept the loss of yield due to leaving his land out of production for a few years in order to get rid of the weed.

The term *soil sterilization* designates the process whereby soil is so altered by the addition of chemicals that it no longer sustains plant growth. Microorganisms may or may not be affected. If the effect lasts more than a year it is called *permanent sterilization*. If the period of sterilization is a year or less it is termed *temporary*. In this process it is essential that (1) the chemical be distributed throughout the strata of soil in which the root and underground stems are growing, (2) it be present in these strata in lethal concentrations, and (3) it remain in the soil long enough to kill all the roots and rhizomes before it is decomposed or leached out.

Soil sterilization differs from foliage applications in that the herbicide is usually not sprayed directly on the plant. The chemical is applied to the soil and then leached by the action of water to the root systems of the plant. Temporary soil sterilization is used primarily to kill perennial weeds on agricultural lands. Permanent sterilization is used to suppress all vegetation, as on railroad rights-of-way, lumberyards, and waste areas where any plant growth is undesirable.

Some factors that decide the herbicidal effect of any nonselective chemical include (1) its inherent toxicity, (2) adsorption by the soil, (3) rate of decomposition, (4) leaching, (5) fertility, salt concentration, or reaction of the soil, and (6) species tolerance. The interplay of these various factors determines whether a specific chemical will be fixed in the topsoil in an available form where it may kill annual or shallow-rooted plants, or whether it will leach to deeper layers where it may kill deep-rooted perennials.

Both volatile and nonvolatile chemicals are widely used as soil-sterilant herbicides. The volatile chemicals, such as carbon bisulfide, chloropicrin, ethylene dibromide, and methyl bromide, are used mainly under greenhouse conditions or in very small areas of land. The major nonvolatile chemicals utilized as soil sterilants are various salts of arsenic and boron, chlorates, substituted ureas, triazines, and the benzoic acids, or mixtures of these compounds. These chemicals have been discussed in some detail in Chapter 8.

The choice of chemicals depends on a number of factors. First, and probably the most important, is the initial toxicity of the chemical to both the weed and the crop. Also critical is the rate of disappearance of the chemical in relation to the factors that affect persistence, such as leaching and decomposition. Soil moisture, amount of clay and organic matter, compaction, fertility, and reaction also affect the persistence and movement of the chemical. Adequate moisture and warmth are necessary for microbial action. With a low rate of microbial activity, as may occur in very dry or cold areas, herbicides may persist for years; whereas at the same rates of application, they may disappear within a few weeks or months in areas of high rainfall and warm weather conditions. For example, dalapon sprayed in an area of low (8 inches) rainfall in eastern Washington persisted for almost a year when sprayed at the rate of 4 pounds per acre. Under high rainfall conditions in Puerto Rico (80 inches annually) the herbicide disappeared within 2 weeks at rates as high as 100 pounds per acre. All these factors, as well as cost, will affect the choice of the chemical. In every instance the user would be wise to look ahead to the possible consequences of use, such as soil erosion, long-term sterility, and damage to desirable plants.

Bare land on hillsides or roadsides is very susceptible to erosion. Before using any chemical it is wise to ask "What plant do I want to grow in this place?" Something will grow there sooner or later. Using low rates of chemical and planting well-adapted and competitive low-growing grasses or shrubs is frequently cheaper, more aesthetically appealing and effective, as well as offering less risk of erosion, than using high rates of chemical in an effort to prevent the growth of all vegetation.

WOODY SPECIES

Woody weeds are primarily a problem in forestry and range management, but may be serious in orchards, pastures, roadsides, fence lines, ditchbanks, firebreaks, railway embankments, and the environs of buildings.

Various mechanical methods used to control these weeds include cutting, burning, and grubbing by heavy machinery. With certain woody weeds mechanical damage will increase the problem, as severed stems may sprout vigorously. Chemicals such as picloram, 2,4-D, 2,4,5-T, silvex, and ammonium sulfamate are effective both for initial control and to prevent sprouting.

Herbicides can assist in controlling woody growth at several stages in forest management: (1) complete or partial control of vegetation prior to planting, (2) selective weeding in early stages of establishment, and (3) in cleaning and thinning operations.

Large trees can be (1) killed by foliage spray applications, "basal" treatment, or soil sterilants and then left standing, or (2) they can be cut, followed by stump treatment to prevent regrowth or spraying to kill regrowth.

Basal bark treatment consists of spraying the lower foot or so of the tree trunk and wetting it to runoff, usually after slashing or "frilling" the bark to the depth of the cambium; this is generally done during the dormant season. If the trees and brush are cut, the regrowth foliage can be sprayed with 2,4,5-T, silvex, picloram, or ammonium sulfamate in early summer, or the stump can be treated to prevent resprouting. It is desirable to loosen the bark around the edges to aid penetration and to wet thoroughly. Chemicals may be "injected" into holes made in the trunk by chisels or special tools. Damage to adjacent trees may occur through root grafts or through actual soil contamination by the chemical passing through the root system and out into the soil, although most herbicides do not exude from the roots in amounts sufficient to cause damage to nearby trees.

In certain situations, the use of soil sterilants may constitute the easiest way of eliminating unwanted brush. Herbicides such as fenuron and monuron may be applied to the soil either as sprays or as pellets.

Of course, the destruction of woody plants does not always produce an acceptable change in vegetation. Weed problems frequently arise as a consequence of mismanagement or overgrazing. The application of control procedures without an accompanying improved land use program will lead only to reinfestation by other weed species.

PERENNIAL HERBACEOUS WEEDS

Often complete adherence to procedures for most quickly repressing a particular perennial weed is impractical. Weed control is ordinarily geared to cropping methods, and management should be based upon a total weed situation rather than a single kind. However, infestations of certain perennial herbaceous weeds sometimes become so critical that specific action is desirable. Economic considerations relating to annual weed control differ to some extent from those pertaining to major perennial weeds. Annual weeds are usually considered primarily on a seasonal (one-crop) basis, and the question is asked, "Will increased benefits (this year) justify the cost of treatment?" With persistent perennials the problem is viewed from a longer range. An established stand of a noxious weed may materially reduce soil productivity as well as reducing cash value of the land. Therefore, weed control may sometimes be given first priority, with crop yield receiving secondary consideration.

The general rule with perennial herbaceous weeds is to initiate treatment at a stage of growth when storage reserves are the lowest. With most perennial weeds this is at an early stage of flowering (early bud stage).

Seedlings

Even though an infestation of a perennial weed has been eradi-
cated, the soil will probably contain numerous seeds that will continue to
emerge in subsequent years. Up to a few weeks after germination, these
seedlings behave like annuals, and may be controlled with relative ease.
After this time the root systems build up reserves and become capable of
sending up new sprouts, and the plants can no longer be destroyed by
merely cutting off the tops, or by a single spray with a contact herbicide.

Canada or creeping thistle

Canada (creeping) thistle (*Cirsium arvense*) is a deep-rooted
dioecious perennial growing from 2 to 7 feet in height. Ecotypes may
exhibit leaf forms that vary from plants whose leaves are almost entirely
without spines to plants with deeply lobed, very spiny leaves (Figure 10-2).
Flower color also varies from purple to white. These differences appear to
be genetic in character.

Differential susceptibility to herbicides such as 2,4-D and
amitrole is exhibited by certain ecotypes of Canada thistle and may be a
factor in the variable responses achieved in the field (Hodgson, 1964). This
weed is a serious pest of pastures, grainfields, cultivated fields, cutover
woodlands, roadsides, and waste areas (Figure 10-3). It spreads rapidly
from roots which may readily produce new shoots or remain dormant for
many years if deeply buried. Seeds are not regarded as important means
of propagation because they are rarely shed from the flowering head and
few fertile seeds are carried by the thistledown which blows around in great
abundance (Woodford and Evans, 1965).

In grassland, Canada thistle is most common in pastures that
are overgrazed. In established grassland, the ratio of shoots to roots is

Figure 10-2 *Variation in plants of Canada thistle* (Cirsium arvense).
*Ecotypes vary not only in leaf shape and growth habit but also in response
to herbicides.*

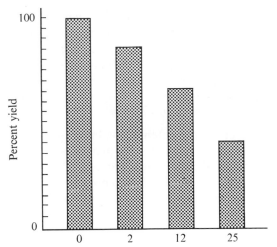

Figure 10-3 Cirsium arvense, *a widespread perennial weed, causes severe losses in many crops around the world. (From U.S. Dept. of Agriculture. Canada Thistle and Its Control. Leaflet no. 523.)*

likely to be low. Herbicides like 2,4-D and MCPA seldom achieve complete kill of the root system and gradual reinfestation occurs; whereas on recently reseeded grassland the disturbance of the lateral roots by cultivation usually leads to an abundant emergence of shoots, the ratio of the number of shoots to the amount of lateral roots is high, and the weed is more vulnerable to these herbicides.

2,4-D is widely employed and gives best results when sprayed at early bud stage, i.e., when the food reserves are lowest. Cultivation of the thistle from early spring until the middle of summer, followed by spraying in the early bud stage, has given the most consistent results. For small patches, various nonselective chemicals may be applied as previously discussed in this section and Chapter 8. Amitrole usually gives good control although it is not very selective and will severely injure other plants, such as cereals. For this reason it is usually applied a few weeks before planting the crop or is applied only to small patches of the weed.

Picloram at 1 pound per acre is very effective but presently may not be used on cropland. This will probably be the chemical of choice in the future where economically feasible if clearance can be obtained.

In using any herbicide, care must be exercised to avoid damage to desirable species, especially when using a potent chemical like picloram which will severely injure many broadleaf species. This is particularly important on mixed vegetation or along roadsides where the roots of trees may extend many feet beyond the periphery of the branches.

The flea beetle (*Haltica carduorum*) has recently been introduced into the Pacific Northwest as a possible biological control for thistle (Chapter 13).

Competitive crops for Canada thistle

Competitive crops are often recommended in various regions where they are adapted; these include solid planted soybeans, alfalfa, or, if land is subject to erosion, sudan or forage sorghum. Alfalfa seems especially effective, particularly if the thistles have already become somewhat weakened. This is probably because the legume recovers from cutting more quickly than the thistle. If a vigorous stand of alfalfa is maintained for 2 or 3 years, satisfactory control of the thistle will usually be obtained. Reasonably satisfactory results have sometimes been obtained with bromegrass as a perennial smother crop, with the areas being treated twice a year with 2,4-D.

Field bindweed

Field bindweed (wild morning-glory, creeping jenny—*Convolvulus arvensis*) is a serious weed in both cultivated and uncultivated land. It is a trailing vine with stems from 3 to 9 feet long. Much variation exists in flower color, leaf shape, pubescence, and response to 2,4-D (Whitworth, 1964; Whitworth and Muzik, 1967). When propagated vegetatively, ecotypes maintain these differences in growth habit and response to 2,4-D.

Bindweed reproduces by underground roots and seeds. Even small root fragments may give rise to aerial shoots. This makes the weed difficult to eradicate by cultivation. Roots have been reported at depths of 15 to 30 feet. Even though the tops of the plant may be destroyed, fresh sprouts eventually arise from deep in the ground to reestablish the weed. New shoots may arise from root tips no more than a few millimeters long (Torrey, 1958). Bindweed tolerates very close mowing and will set flowers and viable seed when mowed at $\frac{1}{2}$ inch. The tops are readily killed with 2,4-D, but portions of the underground system usually survive. Best control is achieved by sprays just prior to flowering.

In cereal crops, bindweed generally emerges too late to be sprayed with 2,4-D without damage to the cereal. Good results have been obtained from spraying after harvest when the bindweed is making new growth.

Bindweed has been implicated in poisoning of hogs (Kingsley, 1964), possibly due to a high level of nitrates. Distress may be mild to severe but is seldom fatal.

Cultivation for field bindweed control

Cultivation should begin no later than bud stage. After cutting, the loss of food from the root system continues at least 2 weeks before the new leaves are big enough to begin to send food back to the roots. Subsequent cultivations should, therefore, be at approximately 14- to 18-day intervals after shoot emergence. Cultivation followed by 2,4-D treatment at early bud stage is usually more effective than either cultivation or 2,4-D alone. Several years of careful cultivation, properly spaced for greatest effectiveness, are necessary for control of old and well-established infestations (Phillips and Timmons, 1954).

Competitive crops and pasturing for bindweed control

A number of crops are capable of some smothering action on field bindweed. Annuals like sorghum, sudan, or soybeans, or perennials such as alfalfa, may be employed. In some areas, a spring and fall grain combination has been recommended. The spring crop should be removed as hay or silage and the ground worked several times before replanting. The fall planting can be allowed to mature and can be harvested or, perhaps better from the standpoint of weed control, pastured. Following removal, the area should be fallowed and subsequently reseeded to winter rye or wheat. Alternately, sudan can be employed as a summer forage. Pasturing sheep in these crops is said to be particularly effective in weakening bindweed. In subsequent seasons, the land should be planted with alfalfa or perennial grass (Isely, 1960).

Chemicals for bindweed control

Soil sterilants (sodium chlorate, monuron, boron, fenac, TBA) can be used for small areas. TBA, at moderately high rates, has a considerably shorter residual effect in the soil than other sterilants and is usually the chemical of choice. Picloram and dicamba appear to be very effective and may supplant the older chemicals in many regions. These herbicides are not toxic to established grasses but will severely injure most broad-leaved species.

Diverse results have been reported from the use of 2,4-D. Its employment appears to have been more successful in the humid portions of the country rather than in drier areas. In general, $\frac{1}{2}$ to 1 pound per acre acid equivalent of this chemical, first applied at bloom stage and repeated several times, will hasten elimination of the bindweed. 2,4-D works best when it is employed in conjunction with cultivation, competitive cropping, and pasturing sequences. Silvex has been recommended in a few areas, often in combination with 2,4-D. Even though the mature plants have been destroyed, the soil will contain numerous long-lived seeds which will continue to germinate for many years. Up until about the five-leaf stage, these may be easily destroyed by cultivation or a single 2,4-D spray. As the seedlings mature, they develop the ability to send up sprouts from the root system and control becomes progressively more difficult.

Quackgrass

Quackgrass (couch grass) (*Agropyron repens*) is a perennial which spreads rapidly by means of abundant seed and rhizomes. It is relatively shallow rooted compared to other perennial weeds. Aggressive growth takes place mainly in the spring and fall. It is a cool season plant, doing best in moist soils. The seed may be spread in crop seed, straw, and manure. It is serious in wheat, peas, corn, and alfalfa, especially in irrigated areas, and is common in nursery-grown ornamentals.

Cultivation should be designed to break up the rhizomes and kill the resulting fragments by exhausting their food reserves. The first cultivation should be deep and carried out slowly to obtain maximum fragmentation. Later cultivations may be shallow and more rapid. The most common reasons for lack of control are too long an interval between regrowth and cultivation, allowing new rhizomes to be formed, and failure to persist in the treatment until all the fragments are dead.

The rhizomes appear to have an inhibiting effect on surrounding vegetation, due to the production of toxic substances.

Quackgrass is a fairly good foliage and cattle like it.

Chemicals for quackgrass control

A number of chemicals are available for controlling quackgrass. In many instances, particularly in extensive infestations, first considerations should be given to other methods (cultivation, pasturing, smother crops), since the use of herbicides may be an expensive alternative. For best results, the recommended cultural techniques should be used in conjunction with the herbicides.

In small areas or in nonagricultural soil, the best control may be by means of soil sterilants such as substituted urea compounds or aliphatic acids (dalapon or TCA) in high dosages ($\frac{1}{8}$ to $\frac{1}{4}$ pound per square rod). If resprouting occurs, a second application may be desirable.

For extensive stands in cultivated land, dalapon, TCA, and amino triazole are possible choices. The use of these chemicals has been discussed previously (Chapter 8). They may be applied early in the season, with the plants allowed to stand for about 2 weeks and then plowed. A late planted crop, preferably a smother crop which is resistant to the particular chemical, can then follow. A second year's treatment may be necessary.

Applications in the fall can be followed by normal cropping in the spring.

Heavy applications of atrazine or simazine at 6 or more pounds per acre have been shown to be capable of eliminating quackgrass, although lighter dosages may give adequate control. These treatments of atrazine and simazine may be applied directly over the tops of young trees without damage to many woody species, including most conifers and ornamentals.

Atrazine has been used to inhibit quackgrass without killing it (Lilly, 1965). Corn may be planted directly into the dormant sod and a crop harvested before the quackgrass recovers, thus reducing erosion and conserving moisture since the dormant quackgrass sod acts as a mulch (Chapter 8).

Horsetail rush

Horsetail rush (*Equisetum* sp.) is one of the fern allies with perennial rhizomes and annual stems. The fertile stems, which appear in spring, are erect, 8 to 25 centimeters high, unbranched, and terminated by a score of sporangia. The green sterile stems may be erect or prostrate, 10 to 50 centimeters high, with whorled branches and small scalelike leaves.

The plant reproduces by creeping rhizomes and by spores. It does not produce seed. The shoots are readily killed by 2,4-D but the rhizomes survive. Horsetail rush is most serious in moist fields, meadows, and strawberries. This weed is poisonous to some stock, particularly horses and sheep, and it presents a particular hazard when cut with the hay or silage. Application of 2,4-D a week or so before the grass is cut usually kills the shoots so that a crop may be taken.

Amitrole has shown promise for the control of horsetail rush. It is most effective when sprayed a few weeks after the sterile shoots have appeared. Dichlobenil has given good results in some areas.

PARASITIC WEEDS

Parasitic weeds such as the mistletoes, orobanche, birdvine, dodder, and witchweed attack other plants by making an organic connection with the conducting tissues of the host and deriving part or all of their food from the host. They either have no connection with soil or quickly lose it and are therefore difficult to control. Some may begin growth high in the branches of trees. According to Loomis and Wilson (1953) there are some 2500 species of parasitic flowering plants. The degree of parasitism varies a great deal. Some genera such as mistletoe (*Phoradendron*) derive only minerals and water from the host, whereas others such as dwarf-mistletoe (*Arceuthobium*) in the same family (Loranthaceae) can carry on only limited photosynthesis and must derive much of their energy requirements as well as water and minerals from their host (Gill and Hawkesworth, 1961).

The two largest families with parasitic weeds are the Loranthaceae and the Scrophulariaceae. The most destructive genera are the stem parasites such as *Phoradendron* and *Viscum*, *Arceuthobium*, *Loranthus*, and *Cuscuta*, and the root parasites *Orobanche* and *Striga*.

Attempts at chemical or biological control have met with only partial success. The margin of selectivity with most chemicals appears to be fairly limited. These parasites may be attacked by other parasites (hyper-parasitism), as well as various fungi and insects; however, these only serve to reduce a portion of the flowering plant and have not been successful in control.

Mistletoes

Phoradendron

This mistletoe produces large-leafed forms which attack numerous species of woody plants but seldom kill the host although they may cause severe yield reductions. The plant is used for decoration at Christmas as the traditional mistletoe.

Members of this genus are semiparasitic since their foliage contains chlorophyll and they can manufacture carbohydrates; the host, however, supplies all minerals, water, and possibly some carbohydrates.

The seeds are distributed by birds which carry the sticky seed on their beaks or feet and deposit it on branches where it takes root. The young radicle grows into the cortex of the host tree where it enlarges and forms an attachment disk and a haustorium, a rootlike structure which grows through the cortex to the cambium. Later, *sinkers*, which also resemble roots, penetrate the xylem tissue. The first leaves and sprouts are produced the following year from buds on the attachment disk.

Viscum

The European mistletoe consists of three races, two of which attack conifers while the third attacks various dicotyledons. Seed spread and growth characteristics are similar to those of *Phoradendron*.

Viscum is also used for Christmas decoration. In fact, it is sometimes propagated deliberately for this and other ceremonial purposes. In a method analogous to grafting used on old apple trees in England, the stem of the apple tree is gashed down to the wood and a branch of mistletoe placed in the wound and tied firmly. It is harvested by cutting off some of the branches with fruits attached. The widespread use of this plant in ceremonial functions is due to the ancient belief in its power to ward off evil.

Arceuthobium

The dwarf-mistletoes are serious parasites of conifers, especially in the Western United States. There are numerous species which vary in size from nearly microscopic to species with stems about 7 centimeters long. One species, *A. minutissimum*, a native of India, is the smallest dicotyledonous plant known (King, 1966).

The genus is dioecious and the berries take about 14 months to mature. Upon maturity, they explode, sending the seeds through the air for distances up to 45 feet. The seeds are sticky and adhere readily to bark or needles. They usually germinate the following summer and grow until they encounter a suitable host or exhaust their food supply. The plant forms a wedge-shaped holdfast at the base of the apical meristem which forces its way into the bark. Fingerlike cells intrude between cortex cells where they divide, enlarge, and crush the host cells. The parasite maintains itself in the active phloem tissue and puts out sinkers which enter the xylem tissue. The aerial shoot system is a leafless segmented perennial which has a xylem but lacks phloem (Gill, 1935).

Injury to the host is in reduction of growth and life-span. Common symptoms of infection are (1) witches'-broom, a mass of abnormal branches with dense foliage, (2) increase in diameter of branches, (3) swellings or cankers on stems and branches, (4) spike-topped trees formed as a result of reduction of carbohydrate supply to the crown. The host is reduced in size and may be killed.

Silvicultural control, i.e., pruning infected branches or removal of diseased trees, is the only satisfactory means of control at present.

Quick (1964) reported some success with chemical control with certain phenoxyacetic acids but found that any concentration killing the parasite also damaged the tree.

Birdvine

Birdvine (*Loranthus* spp.) is semiparasitic on trees in tropical regions on a wide variety of hosts. There are numerous species of this vine, some of which are hyperparasites. It has caused serious damage to tea, citrus, mango, teak, etc. The sticky seeds are attractive to birds and are spread by them as well as by natural fall from higher to lower levels of the host tree. $CuSO_4$ and 2,4-D applied by injection into the host tree have given some success (Greenham and Brown, 1957; Kadambi, 1954).

Dodder

Dodder (*Cuscuta*) is a parasitic annual plant with twining, threadlike yellow, white, or orange stems and leaves. The flowers are small, white, and bell-shaped. Because of the parasitic nature of dodder and the organic connection between it and the host plants it attacks, most ordinary control procedures are not applicable to this weed. Shortly after germination, the plant attaches itself to its host and the roots of the dodder die so that it has no direct connection to the soil. It is most serious in alfalfa, clover, and other legumes produced for seed. It also attaches to other plants including flax a⁻d many garden flowers. Most grasses, cereals, etc., are not parasitized by most dodder species and thus may be grown on infested fields to reduce the seed supply. The use of clean seed to prevent infestation of dodder-free land is extremely important. Dodder is listed as a secondary noxious or restricted weed in all seed laws; its occurrence in seed lots will, therefore, be indicated in the tags of all commercial seed. Even a few plants left in the field may spread enough to cause a severe loss in yield; consequently, control must be nearly perfect to be effective. It is probable that under ideal growing conditions a single dodder seedling would develop a mile or more of stem (King, 1966).

If land is badly infested with dodder, the planting of crops other than legumes or flax for several years will reduce the number of seeds in the soil. Such a measure will probably not eliminate the dodder, as the seeds are capable of lying dormant in the soil for a number of years.

CIPC or dinitro-fortified oils are used as a means of controlling dodder in alfalfa (Dawson et al., 1965). The use of CIPC (6 to 8 pounds per acre) is definitely beneficial, assuming that proper application and weather conditions hold, i.e., application immediately prior to germination and adequate moisture and warmth. Germination occurs over several weeks and the CIPC has a short residual life so that timing of application is very critical. The CIPC is selective, but the dinitros and oils are general contact herbicides used for spot treatment. The areas treated with oil may be burned following treatment. Direct flaming is also used to eliminate patches of this weed. Although burning kills the alfalfa foliage, the alfalfa will recover and a crop can be harvested the following year. Dodder is sensitive to a number of chemicals, including 2,4-D, and if the host plant is tolerant, this herbicide may be used. As a rule, however, the difference in susceptibility is not enough to warrant large-scale spraying.

Orobanche

The Orobanchaceae family contains several genera which are troublesome root parasites on many crops such as sugarcane, rice, and maize in the tropics and subtropics. *Aeginetia*, *Christisonia* and *Orobanche* are the most important genera. *Orobanche* is also found in north temperate regions. It is an important pest of solanaceous crops in Europe, including tobacco and tomatoes. It has also been found on tomatoes in California.

Bean plantings have been severely affected in Italy and Egypt. Cattle and goats feed freely on *Orobanche* shoots and the seed is thereby distributed in their excrement. The seeds are minute and survive for many years in the soil. Preemergence treatment with sesone has given good results (King, 1966). The seeds will not germinate unless within close proximity to a host plant.

Various solanaceous crops, including pepper, *Capsicum*, and *Bidens pilosa*, will stimulate the seeds to germinate but no haustoria develop. Thus a rotation with *Capsicum* reduces the infestation in the soil and thereby reduces losses from this parasite.

Witchweed (*Striga*)

Witchweed, a parasitic dicotyledonous weed in corn (maize) and other grasses, is presently limited in this country to sandy soils in North and South Carolina. This parasite is a very serious weed of corn and sorghum in South Africa, causing more loss than all fungus diseases combined, and could become serious in the United States. The plant reproduces by very tiny seeds, as fine as dust, which do not germinate unless in proximity to a grass root. A single plant may produce from 50,000 to 500,000 seeds. Studies are underway to discover an economical method of control and to find ways of preventing the spread of this weed to other corn-growing areas. It appears to be rather susceptible to fenac and TBA at rates which are not injurious to corn. 2,4-D has given good results on a 5-year rotation with corn and other crops. In one study, land heavily infested with witchweed required 3 to 4 years of herbicidal treatments before the competition was reduced sufficiently to give good corn yields (Robinson et al., 1967).

Catch crops or trap crops are used as a means of control. A catch crop is a true host which is plowed under before the witchweed seed matures. A trap crop, like corn, peas, or soybeans, causes the witchweed to germinate but not parasitized. *Striga* parasitizes crabgrass (*Digitaria* sp.) and may survive on this and other wild grass species, such as *Echinochloa*, *Panicum*, and *Dactylis*.

HOME GARDENS

Weeds are as important in home gardens as they are in any other agricultural operation. They reduce yield, affect crop quality, deplete fertility, serve as hosts for insects and diseases, and reduce the attractiveness of the surroundings. The majority of species found in gardens are the same as those found in cultivated fields. Many annuals and perennial weedy grasses and broadleaves grow abundantly. Chemical weed control in home gardens has received less attention than in other phases of agriculture. One reason is that the majority of garden crops are easily injured or killed by 2,4-D and similar common herbicides. Furthermore, the selective application of herbicides requires attention to details which the average homeowner may be unable or unwilling to provide. The hoe and hand weeding are still king in the garden. Mulching with straw, sawdust, wood chips, aluminum foil, or plastic is an effective method of weed control. The amateur gardener should give serious thought to the use of black agricultural plastic. This material should be spread over the garden after the soil is tilled and fertilized. Just before planting, holes should be cut in the plastic with a knife or bulb planter, and the seed or transplant set firmly in the soil. The plastic effectively prevents weed growth and helps to improve temperature and moisture conditions.

The garden should be plowed or spaded in the fall and, if possible, worked again in the spring to stimulate germination of weed seeds. Cultivation (and hand weeding as necessary) should be started as soon as the crop is discernible in the rows, and then continued at regular intervals.

Many gardeners stop weeding when the crop matures and allow the entire garden to go to weeds the latter part of the summer. The abundant seed production amply replenishes the reservoir of weed seeds in the soil for the next year's growth. An effort should be made to prevent weeds from seeding. Little effect may be noticed the first year or two, but a gradual reduction of the weed population will be evident in subsequent seasons.

The ordinary small garden presents a complicated problem since so many varieties of plants are grown within a small space, and in different plots from year to year. There are, however, a number of herbicides which can be used to remove some of the weeds and reduce the back-breaking work of hoeing and weed pulling.

Bedding plants

Certain herbicides may be used before or after transplanting bedding plants. The herbicide should be applied in sufficient water to cover the area and immediately incorporated. Raking in two directions or roto-tilling after application usually gives sufficient mixing. Generally it is desirable to wait a week after application before transplanting. Among the herbicides used as pretransplant weed killers are EPTC, SMDC, trifluralin, and vernolate (see Chapter 8 and the Appendix for more details on these chemicals).

It is usually advisable to wait a few days after setting out transplants before applying herbicides. These herbicides should be applied to the soil, not to the plant. Some herbicides that have been used successfully in garden annuals include amiben, DCPA, dichlobenil, and diphenamid. Read the label carefully before application.

Vegetables

Sweet corn: Atrazine and simazine give good grass and broad-leaf control and are unlikely to injure the corn. Simazine must be applied preemergence, but the atrazine may be applied either preemergence or early postemergence when the weeds are small. When using either atrazine or simazine, be sure to plant corn in the same plot the following year. 2,4-D and DNBP are widely used but have disadvantages; 2,4-D kills the broad-leaf weeds and hardly affects the grasses, and DNBP kills the weeds that have emerged but has little effect on those that emerge later.

Tomatoes: Mulching with plastic is an excellent device for weed control in tomatoes in the small garden. Amiben, CDEC, diphenamid, and trifluralin have been effective herbicides.

Asparagus: Monuron, simazine, sesone, NPA, dalapon and 2,4-D (sodium salt) may be used selectively on asparagus. Any cultivation, even careful hoeing, is likely to damage the asparagus shoots and roots. Timing of application does not appear to be critical except that monuron, NPA, and simazine are preemergence (to the weeds) and dalapon and 2,4-D work better on small emerged weeds. The asparagus is unlikely to be injured by any of these chemicals applied at reasonable rates.

Cucurbits: Squashes, pumpkins, and melons have a trailing habit and their easily injured succulent foliage makes mechanical weed control difficult. Chemicals such as NPA or CDEC may be used at planting time prior to emergence; others such as DCPA, 4 to 6 weeks later. DCPA may also follow the earlier treatments for a longer period of weed control.

General weed control in the garden

SMDC (Metham) should be applied to plowed or spaded soil at least 2 weeks before planting. This fumigant material is applied in a liquid solution to a small area about 10 feet square at a time and then the soil is thoroughly wetted. This process is continued until the entire area has been treated. The ground should be watered freely for the next 10 days to keep it moist. The chemical may injure perennials in the garden so avoid application near strawberries, raspberries, and other shrubs or trees. It kills seeds, seedlings, rhizomes, and roots in the soil although deep-rooted perennials such as bindweed may survive. Other fumigants may be used but have certain disadvantages (Chapter 8).

QUESTIONS

1. What are some of the undesirable effects of aquatic weeds? Some of the desirable effects?

2. How may treatment of aquatic plants with a chemical nontoxic to fish lead to the death of fish?
3. Define submersed, emersed, and floating weeds.
4. What are the limitations of arsenic, 2,4-D, oils, and acrolein for aquatic weed control?
5. Define *temporary* and *permanent* soil sterilization.
6. What are the requirements for successful weed kill with a soil-applied chemical?
7. What factors determine the effectiveness of a nonselective chemical?
8. Define *basal* application.
9. How may herbicides be used in forestry?
10. When is the best time to spray most broad-leaved perennial weeds with 2,4-D? Why?
11. Are seeds more important than rhizomes for dissemination of (1) thistle, (2) rush, or (3) bindweed? Why?
12. If you destroyed a Canada thistle patch and found no seedlings of Canada thistle in the area the following year, what would you suspect?
13. How does cultivation affect the effectiveness of 2,4-D on thistle?
14. How does quackgrass reduce crop yield?
15. What is the effect of horsetail rush on crops?
16. Why is timing so critical in dodder control?
17. Why are parasitic weeds so difficult to kill with herbicides?
18. What is a hyperparasite?
19. What is the host-root parasite relationship in regard to germination of the seed of the root parasite? Does this give you any ideas on possible methods of control?

REFERENCES

Bruns, V. F. 1965. Personal communication.

——, M. M. Hodgson, H. F. Arle, F. L. Timmons. 1955. The Use of Aromatic Solvents for Control of Submersed Aquatic Weeds in Irrigation Channels. *USDA, Circ.* 971, pp. 1–33.

Dawson, J. H., W. O. Lee, and F. L. Timmons. 1965. Controlling Dodder in Alfalfa. *USDA Farmer's Bull.,* 2211.

Gill, L. S. 1935. *Arceuthobium* in the U.S. *Conn. Acad. of Arts and Sci.,* **32**:111-245.

—— and F. E. Hawkesworth. 1961. Mistletoes, a Literature Review. *USDA Tech. Bull.,* 1242.

Greenham, C. G., and A. G. Brown. 1957. The Control of Mistletoes by Trunk Injection. *Austral. Inst. Agr. Sci. J.,* **23**:308–318.

Hiltibran, R. C. 1965. The Effect of Diquat on Aquatic Plants in Illinois. *Weeds,* **13**:71–72.

Hodgson, J. M. 1964. Variations in Ecotypes of Canada Thistle. *Weeds*, **12**:167–170.

Isely, D. 1960. "Weed Identification and Control," Iowa State University Press, Ames.

Kadambi, K. 1954. On Loranthus Control. *Indian For.*, **80**:493–495.

King, L. J. 1966. "Weeds of the World," Interscience Publishers, New York.

Kingsley, J. M. 1964. "Poisonous Plants of the United States and Canada," Prentice-Hall, Inc., Englewood Cliffs, N.J.

Lilly, J. P. 1965. The Sleeping Sod. *Crops and Soils*, **18**:6–7.

Loomis, L. C., and W. E. Wilson. 1953. "Botany," Holt, Rinehart and Winston, New York.

Phillips, W. M., and F. L. Timmons. 1954. Bindweed (*Convolvulus arvensis*)—How To Control It; Results of Bindweed Control Experiments at the Fort Hays Branch Station, Hays, Kansas, 1935 to 1952. *Kans. Agr. Exp. Sta. Bull.*, **366**:1–40.

Quick, C. R. 1964. Experimental Herbicidal Control of Dwarf-Mistletoe on Some California Conifers. USFS Res. Notes PSW 47.

Radke, M. G., L. S. Ritchie, and F. F. Ferguson. 1961. Demonstrated Control of *Australorbi glabratus* by *Marisa cornuarietis* under Field Conditions in Puerto Rico. *Am. J. Trop. Med. Hyg.*, **10**:370–373.

Robinson, E. L., J. E. Dale, and W. C. Shaw. 1967. Herbicide-Crop Rotation for Witchweed Control. *Weeds*, **15**:243–245.

Seaman, D. E., and W. A. Porterfield. 1964. Control of Aquatic Weeds by the Snail *Marisa cornuarietis*. *Weeds*, **12**:87–92.

Shell, E. W. 1962. Herbivorous Fish To Control *Pithophora* sp. and Other Aquatic Weeds in Ponds. *Weeds*, **10**:326–327.

Torrey, J. G. 1958. Endogenous Bud Formation by Isolated Roots of Convolvulus Grown In Vitro. *Plant Physiol.*, **33**:258–263.

Whitworth, J. W. 1964. The Reaction of Strains of Bindweed to 2,4-D. *Weeds*, **12**:57–58.

——— and T. J. Muzik. 1967. Differential Response of Selected Clones of Bindweed to 2,4-D. *Weeds*, **15**:275–280.

Woodford, E. K., and S. A. Evans. 1965. "Weed Control Handbook," Blackwell Scientific Publications, Oxford, 4th ed.

Yeo, R. R. 1965. Life History of Sago Pondweed. *Weeds*, **13**:314–321.

CHAPTER ELEVEN
ABSCISSION, STIMULATION, INHIBITION, AND RELATED ASPECTS

Major emphasis so far has been placed on the importance of species dif-
ferences, age, stage of growth, nutritional condition, formulation, and
concentration of chemical in determining the precise selective herbicidal
effect caused by any chemical. The aim of this chapter is to discuss some
uses of herbicides other than for weed control and to further emphasize the
importance of these factors. The use of herbicides for weed control, while
by far the largest, is only one phase of the general problem of the control
of plant growth.

In this chapter, examples have been selected to demonstrate the remarkable
variety of effects obtained. Many of these effects are undoubtedly due to the
action of the herbicide on the native inhibitors and stimulators of growth
and development, but the exact mechanisms are poorly understood.

Herbicides may be used to induce or prevent abscission of leaves and fruits,
to delay or induce flowering, and to delay or speed up maturity of fruits, as
well as to promote other effects such as decortication, coloring of fruits,
increasing yield of latex, prolongation of storage life of fruits and vegetables,
etc. The same chemical may have a variety of effects ranging from death to
stimulation, depending on amount applied and plant species treated. An
example is 2,4-D which is used to destroy weeds and decorticate bark, to
induce flowering in pineapple, to induce the fall of young fruit or to delay
mature fruit fall in apples, to induce increased production of latex in rubber,

to prolong storage of various fruits, to hasten maturity of unripe fruits, and to cause color changes in potatoes.

ABSCISSION

Defoliation

Defoliation is the removal of foliage from plants. The desired response is for leaves to abscise promptly before much loss of moisture. An excessive amount of defoliant can lead to rapid drying of the leaf blades, thus damaging the abscission zone so that the leaves wither in place. Many contact herbicides have this effect. The desired injury to the leaf blade must occur with little or no injury to the abscission zone. Abscission, the natural shedding of leaves, stems, or fruits from the plant, is a temperature-sensitive process which requires oxygen and is inhibited by respiratory poisons. For satisfactory defoliation with chemicals, warm temperatures (85°F or higher) are desirable, as are moderate to high amounts of moisture in the leaves and a low level of nutrients. No one defoliant works equally well on all species. In fact, some genera such as pepper (*Piper* sp.) are easily defoliated by many chemicals, while others such as tobacco are very resistant to defoliation.

The abscission zone occurs typically (not always) at the base of the leaf stalk, and consists of several layers of closely packed cells. A separation layer develops within the zone and hydrolytic changes in the cell walls eventually permit the leaf to fall. As the cell walls weaken, the leaves fall due to gravity. There is some question about the role of the abscission zone in defoliation. Some plants do not form an abscission zone but defoliate readily, while others such as tobacco form an abscission zone but do not abscise.

Important internal factors are (1) senescent prechanges, and (2) correlative changes concerned with hormonal, nutritional, or moisture relations among the plant parts. The exact nature of these changes is not understood. Young leaves are usually more difficult to defoliate than old leaves. Thus in one experiment in Puerto Rico by the author it was found that *Tabebuia pallida*, a species which produces new leaves immediately following natural leaf fall, would respond to a number of defoliants a few weeks prior to natural defoliation but responded to none of these when the new leaves were fresh and green. Trees treated side by side on the same day gave very different results, depending on the internal condition of the tree. This does not mean that weather conditions are unimportant, but that in this instance the internal condition of the tree was the deciding factor.

Most defoliants work best on a speeding up of natural defoliation and are less successful on plants that do not naturally have leaf fall.

The closer the natural leaf fall period approaches, the more successful they are likely to be. Active cells are necessary to the defoliation process. Any condition such as drought, severe frost, or excessive chemical treatment may severely injure the cells and thus cause desiccation without abscission.

Successful defoliation always involves relatively mild but not serious injury. It is well adapted to preparation of nursery stock prior to shipping or to the harvesting of certain crops. Defoliants have also been used to increase visibility in jungle areas for military purposes.

Chemical thinning of fruits

Chemical thinning or stimulation of fruit drop is accomplished by spraying MH, NAA, IPC, 2,4-D, or 2,4,5-T a few hours before pollination or when the fruits are very small. Damage to the pollen tube or the young embryo causes subsequent drop of the fruits. The specificity of the action is due to the pollen tube and young embryo being more sensitive to damage than are the other tissues (Addicott and Carns, 1964).

Preventing abscission

Prevention of preharvest fruit drop with 2,4-D, 2,4,5-T, and other auxins is widely practiced. For this purpose these chemicals are used at fractions of the amounts used for killing plants, i.e., 10 to 100 ppm. Spraying synthetic auxins on the fruits delays the formation of the abscission layer, thus harvesting is made easier because nearly all the fruits can be picked at the same time.

Prevention of abscission of young fruits is frequently ineffective and it is likely that other factors, such as nutrition, have a major influence on success.

DESICCATION

Desiccation is the chemically accelerated drying of plants and it results in the death of all plant parts covered by the chemical. It facilitates the harvesting of plants that are cultivated for seeds, fruits, or tubers where the survival of leaves and stems after harvest is of no importance.

The critical physiological process of desiccation appears to be injury of cell membranes that permits rapid loss of water. High temperatures and low humidities favor this process. Desiccants are essentially contact herbicides. Most widely used are sodium arsenite, paraquat, pentachlorophenol, and related compounds. Defoliants such as sodium chlorate and magnesium chlorate have been used as desiccants at about twice the rate needed for defoliation. At these higher rates they severely damage the cells, thus effectively preventing abscission.

DECORTICATION

Chemical decortication is the loosening of bark by chemical means. This is accomplished by killing the cambium and the adjacent tissues. It is a valuable practice in preparing pulpwood species for paper manufacture and in the preparation of fence posts. For use as fence posts, many species must be decorticated and treated with preservation to inhibit decay of the wood before being placed in the ground.

Decorticating chemicals are used primarily to increase the flexibility of the operation by lengthening the period during which trees can be easily decorticated. Untreated trees can be decorticated only in the spring, whereas chemically treated trees can be easily decorticated for several weeks longer.

Sodium arsenite is probably the most widely used chemical for decortication. Sodium chlorate, 2,4-D, and 2,4,5-T have also been used for this purpose (Addicott and Carns, 1964).

DWARFING

Synthetic growth inhibitors, like maleic hydrazide (MH), have been used to dwarf ornamental plants and to inhibit lawn and hedge growth and tobacco suckering. High humidity and adequate rainfall appear to be essential for success. Grass species vary in tolerance to MH so that in mixed lawns an uneven appearance is sometimes obtained (Cruzado and Muzik, 1958).

Other chemicals such as amo-1618, phosfon, cycocel, etc., can also be used to retard growth without apparent injury. These chemicals appear to have many possible horticultural applications. The effect of certain of these inhibitors such as maleic hydrazide appears to be due to an interference with cell division. Others (phosfon, cycocel) appear to have an inhibitive effect on vegetative bud growth rather than causing partial retardation of the entire plant.

Some ornamental kinds of plants such as chrysanthemum and azalea may be dwarfed in a way which is beneficial since the plants take up less space, require less pruning, and develop a pleasing foliage (Mitchell, 1961). Kentucky Wonder and other varieties of pole beans may be made to grow as bush beans with the retardant amo-1618. Elongation of wheat plants can be retarded and tillering increased.

It may be desirable to reduce the height of certain plants in order to facilitate breeding programs. Alfalfa height may be reduced by phosfon (2,4-dichlorobenzyl-tributyl phosphonium chloride) but the treatment was found to have the undesirable effect of also reducing the number of racemes per plant (Norwood et al., 1963).

The effect of growth retardants on plants varies greatly, even between varieties of the same species. Some holly (*Ilex* spp.) varieties were induced to flower and fruit by applications of phosfon and cycocel (2-chloroethyl trimethylammonium chloride), or Co 11 (N-dimethylaimino-maleamic acid), whereas others were not affected. One variety was reduced in height about 40 percent, yet another was unaffected (Marth, 1963).

GROWTH STIMULATION

Increase in plant height, early production of flowers, improved quality of flowers, and increased size and quality of certain fruits have been obtained with gibberellic acid. Increased production of amylase by barley seeds subjected to gibberellic acid is of practical importance in malt production (Mitchell, 1961).

Attempts to increase the activity of herbicides by combination with gibberellic acid, thus taking advantage of the increased growth rate, have not shown any advantage to date. This possible interaction merits further testing.

PROLONGING STORAGE

Longer storage of citrus fruit has been reported after treatment with 2,4-D or 2,4,5-T. Sprout formation on stored potatoes is prevented by treatment with CIPC (Hruschka et al., 1965). Maleic hydrazide and 2,4,5-T have been used for this purpose also (Van Overbeek, 1952).

HASTENING MATURITY

When dipped in 2,4-D solutions, detached unripe fruits of certain species, such as bananas, pears, or apples, ripen more quickly than untreated fruits. 2,4,5-T sprayed on developing fruits still attached to the trees hastened maturity of apricots and caused an increase in size (Crane, 1955). Hastened maturity from preharvest sprays with 2,4-D has been reported for apples and pears (Mitchell and Marth, 1944).

COLOR CHANGES

The color of red potatoes is heightened by spraying leaves with very dilute (2 ounces per acre) 2,4-D solution. The color of potato tubers may be changed (with less color in red potatoes) if dalapon is in the soil at the time of tuber formation. Apple color may also be enhanced by appropriate sprays.

CONTROL OF FLOWERING

2,4-D stimulates flowering in certain pineapple varieties. A weak solution of the chemical may be sprayed on the leaves or poured into the center of the leaves (Van Overbeek, 1952). The pineapple is so sensitive to 2,4-D that the application must be very carefully controlled. Abnormally shaped fruits may result, or the production of lateral shoots which are used for propagation may be adversely affected. In any event, 2,4-D is not used at present because other compounds are known which are safer.

Growth and flowering of pineapple can be delayed with maleic hydrazide, but application at the wrong time may cause malformations in the fruit (Figure 11-1; Muzik and Cruzado, 1956).

INCREASING YIELD OF LATEX

Yield of latex from the rubber plant (*Hevea brasiliensis*) has been increased by the application of 2,4-D or 2,4,5-T to the bark (de Jong, 1955). This appears to be a stimulation of the latex-producing cells to greater activity and consequently greater production. Yields have been increased

Figure 11-1 *Effect of late application of maleic hydrazide on pineapple. Fruit from untreated plant at left. Distorted and shrunken fruit at right resulted from an application of maleic hydrazide after floral initiation. Earlier applications delayed flowering without apparent damage to the fruit. (Muzik and Cruzado, 1956.)*

over 25 percent. Bark renewal has been increased by appropriate auxins applied after tapping (Muzik, 1949).

DISCUSSION

These examples demonstrate the multiplicity of effects which may be obtained through the use of appropriate chemicals. Many more applications of herbicides and growth regulators in agriculture will undoubtedly be discovered in the future as their mode of action becomes better understood. The relationship to environment particularly needs further exploration.

Man has only begun to explore the possibilities of chemical control of plant growth. Research to date has been largely empirical, that is, testing materials on particular crops to see if they would achieve a desired purpose. Basic research dedicated to achieving an understanding of these effects is badly needed.

QUESTIONS

1. Define *defoliation*.
2. How does age affect a plant's response to defoliants?
3. What external factors affect the success of defoliants? What internal factors?
4. How is the end result of defoliation different from the end result of desiccation?
5. What environmental factors affect the response of plants to desiccants?
6. Define *decortication*.
7. What is the main value of chemicals in decortication?
8. How is it possible for 2,4-D and 2,4,5-T to both delay and speed up abscission?
9. Define *chemical thinning*.

REFERENCES

Addicott, F. T., and H. R. Carns.   1964.   Abscission Responses to Herbicides, in "Physiology and Biochemistry of Herbicides," L. J. Audus (ed.), Academic Press, Inc., New York, pp. 277–289.

Crane, J. C.   1955.   Preharvest Drop, Size and Maturity of Apricots as Affected by 2,4,5-Trichlorophenoxyacetic Acid. *Proc. Am. Soc. Hort. Sci.*, **65**:75–84.

Cruzado, H. J., and T. J. Muzik.   1958.   Effects of Maleic Hydrazide on Some Tropical Lawn Grasses. *Weeds*, **6**:329–330.

de Jong, F.   1955.   Stimulation of Yield in *Hevea brasiliensis* III. Further Observations on the Effects of Yield Stimulation. *J. Rubber Res. Inst.*, Malaya, **14**:383–400.

Hruschka, H. W., P. C. Marth, and P. H. Heinze.   1965.   External Sprout Inhibition and Internal Sprouts in Potatoes. *Am. Potato J.*, **42**:208–222.

Marth, P. C.   1963.   Effect of Growth Retardants on Flowering, Fruiting, and Vegetative Growth of Holly (*Ilex*). *Proc. Am. Soc. Hort. Sci.*, **83**:777–781.

Mitchell, J. W.   1961.   Fundamental Developments in the Field of Plant Growth Regulators. *Bull. Torrey Bot. Club*, **88**:299–312.

———, and P. C. Marth.   1944.   Effects of 2,4-D on the Ripening of Detached Fruit. *Bot. Gaz.*, **106**:199–207.

Muzik, T. J.   1949.   Effect of Hormone on Bark Removal in *Hevea brasiliensis*. *Mich. Acad. Sci. Publ.*, **35**:33–41.

———, and H. J. Cruzado.   1956.   Effect of Maleic Hydrazide on Pineapple. *Plant Physiol.*, **31**:81.

Norwood, B. L., P. C. Marth, and C. H. Hanson.   1963.   Effect of Phosfon on the Growth of Alfalfa. *Crop Sci.*, **3**:241–242.

Van Overbeek, J.   1952.   Agricultural Application of Growth Regulators and Their Physiological Basis. *Ann. Rev. Plant Physiol.*, **3**:87–108.

CHAPTER TWELVE
TOXICOLOGY

One of the most carefully controlled procedures in the introduction of new agricultural chemicals is the determination of their capacity to cause harm to animals. Since each new compound is potentially different from every other compound, thorough investigation of its properties may require ingenuity, new techniques, and a new point of view. This chapter describes the principal method of determining toxicity and some of the difficulties encountered in arriving at safe levels of application. Certain standard methods are described with the understanding that they may need to be modified or extended for particular chemicals.

The following special terms are defined:

Toxicology: the study of the limits of the harmful biological effects of a chemical or a mixture of chemicals.

Toxicity: the ability of the chemical to alter the biological environment.

Hazard: the probability that toxicity will result following a given exposure. Hazards presented by a compound frequently depend more on how it is used than on how toxic it is.

Risk: the degree of physiological, biochemical, or histological change acceptable in terms of the usefulness of the chemical, and its possible effects on public health.

HAZARDS FROM CHEMICALS

There is no such thing as a completely safe chemical; there are only safe ways of using them. This applies as much to common table salt, pepper, or sugar as it does to the newer and potentially more harmful pesticides. We live in a world where constant care must be exercised to make wise selection of particular alternatives. Excessive or improper use of any chemical may cause severe pain, irritation, or illness. For example, the accidental substitution of salt for sugar has occasionally severely injured infants. Certain individuals exhibit toxic reactions to common foods; thus some people have severe allergic reactions to milk, eggs, rice, or other common elements of the average diet.

Many naturally occurring chemicals are toxic or irritating, as evidenced by allergic responses to poison ivy, ragweed, etc. Deadly nightshade berries contain toxic poisons; and other natural substances such as coffee, tea, cocoa, etc., may have carcinogenic properties (Sax, 1966; Whitten, 1966). Many synthetic materials, on the other hand, such as sucaryl, various medicines, etc., are quite harmless. The point to remember is that any substance in excess, even water, may be harmful.

The main routes of entry for most pesticides are through the skin from drips or splashes, or through the respiratory tract from airborne particles. Skin contamination is the most important route of absorption. Accidental poisoning by mistaking the contents of unlabeled bottles, placing toxic materials where food is prepared, and contact by children at play constitute additional hazards. It is difficult to understand why anyone would store toxic chemicals like DNBP in soft drink bottles and place them in easy reach of children or adults. Yet accidents are caused each year by careless storage of chemicals in unlabeled bottles in the home.

The ideal pesticide is one that is toxic to the pests to be controlled yet harmless to other forms of life. Plant growth regulators and herbicides have generally been found to be relatively harmless to humans, as compared to insecticides. Nevertheless, each new compound must be regarded with suspicion as it undergoes careful toxicological investigation. Among the herbicides toxic to humans or animals are pentachlorophenol, the nitro phenols and cresols, such as DNOC, DNBP, and their salts, endothal, arsenic, acrolein, allyl alcohol, and phenyl mercuric acetate. In addition to the pesticide, most formulations include surfactants, cosolvents, and various additives. These also have varying degrees of toxicity.

In addition to being somewhat toxic when eaten (through treated plants or when eaten directly by salt-hungry cattle), sodium chlorate becomes a fire hazard when applied to vegetation. When mixed with organic materials such as dried leaves or cloth it becomes highly inflammable, much like gunpowder. Other chemicals, such as CDEC, may cause severe irritation without being lethal.

DETERMINING TOXICITY OF A NEW CHEMICAL

Man always attempts to categorize the factors of his environment as *safe* or *harmful*. Unfortunately there is no convenient scale with which to do this. It is the job of the investigator and public health officials to weigh each effect and establish its relationship to the whole picture.

Each chemical must be evaluated separately to elucidate its particular effect on a biological system. Of equal importance is the effect of the environment on the chemical or its action. Also metabolites formed by plants may be only slightly less toxic than the applied chemical, and these may be the agents to which the public is exposed (Alexander, 1963; Fogelman, 1963).

Toxicological studies are designed and conducted to determine the threshold limit of a chemical which an animal or human being may withstand without significant injury. These studies are the responsibility of the manufacturers. They are expensive: on an average about 3 to 4 million dollars is spent per chemical (including screening for effectiveness) before one pound is sold. These tests result in rejection of 90 to 95 percent of potential pesticides before field testing.

Two general principles apply in toxicological research: (1) The degree of alteration in physiological, biochemical, or histological development (changes) is a function of dosage. (2) The animal is capable of taking in, altering or detoxifying, and excreting a chemical. Thus a small amount of hazardous material may not cause any risk.

The research is designed to lead to an understanding of how the chemical produces its toxic effect and how the body protects itself. Answers are sought to the following questions:

1. What is the site of action in the intact animal and what organs are primarily involved?

2. How does dosage influence a particular effect?

3. What is the mechanism by which the effect is produced?

4. What are the conditions which inhibit, modify, or enhance the action of the chemical?

Acute, subacute, chronic, and possible carcinogenic effects must be examined for each compound.

Acute effects

Oral toxicity

The first step in the examination is usually the assessment of the acute toxicity, i.e., the effects of a single dose of the chemical. The determination of the LD_{50} in rats is the usual choice. Groups of test animals are administered varying dosages of the test chemical by stomach tube and closely observed for signs of intoxication or mortality. The compound is administered on a weight per weight basis (milligram or gram of compound per kilogram of body weight of test animal). The mortality data yield a number called LD_{50}, which is the dosage necessary to produce death or a reproducible effect in 50 percent or more of the animals studied. A comprehensive description of the signs of intoxication is as important as the numerical data. An LD_{50} value is a statistic which in itself gives no information on the dosage that will be fatal to a very small proportion of a large group of animals. These values are usually expressed in terms of single dosages only and thus possible cumulative effects are neglected. LD_{50} values for currently used herbicides are listed in the Appendix.

Dermal toxicity

Pesticides may get on the skin of workers and thus gain access to the body. Studies of acute dermal effects afford information on the mode of toxic action not available from the oral studies, since stomach acids may hydrolyze or modify the chemical prior to absorption. Also, bacterial action and digestive enzymes may alter the compound and affect its absorption through the intestine. In the case of a chemical taken into the digestive tract, the liver may detoxify the chemical before it enters the general circulatory system. In skin absorption, the material need only penetrate the epidermis to gain access to the subcutaneous capillaries and other structures.

Eye studies

Eye irritation studies are usually included because of the direct application to industrial and occupational situations. The chemical is applied directly to the eye tissue of test animals, usually rabbits.

Inhalation

Inhalation studies usually are made later in the program because of the higher cost and more elaborate facilities needed. Absorption occurs through the mucous membranes of the nostrils. The absorbed chemical immediately passes into the general arterial circulatory systems, thus reaching more sensitive sites more rapidly than is possible by any other means of administration, except intra-arterial injection.

Subacute effects

Some chemicals are metabolized slowly, others quite rapidly. If the metabolic rate is comparable to or greater than the absorption rate, the rate of excretion is faster than the buildup and there is no toxic reaction. If the metabolic rate is less than the absorption rate, toxicity will result, and the degree of intoxication is a function of the rate of buildup of the toxicant at the site of action. Metabolism continues while absorption is intermittent, thus allowing recovery. For this reason, certain chemicals can be administered repeatedly at lower levels in the diet than can be given in a single dose.

Adaptation, or the development of new metabolic pathways to detoxify and eliminate the foreign chemical, appears to be a factor in the metabolism of such drugs as penicillin in humans or DDT in resistant insects.

The maximum dosage level in the preliminary subacute studies is usually one-fourth the acute oral LD_{50}. These studies, which last from 14 to 16 weeks, evaluate food consumption, body weight, gain, food conversion, gross and microscopical anatomical studies, mortality, and any special parameters suggested by the acute studies.

Chronic studies

After completion of the acute and subacute studies, chronic studies are designed to evaluate more fully the limits wherein the chemical may produce a biological effect, and to test the hypothesis that the chemical can be administered at a nontoxic level in the test animals. They are conducted for the life-span of one species, usually the rat, and for 1 to 3 years or more in a second species, usually dog or monkey. Food consumption, food utilization, body weights, organs, body weight ratios, water consumption, and intoxication may be evaluated. Laboratory studies may include complete blood counts, liver function tests, kidney function tests, and urinalysis.

Carcinogenic potential

Special legislation or hysteria over possible carcinogenic materials appears unwarranted. Carcinogenic activity must be considered in the same light as any other biological lesion in terms of its incidence, type, and location. Conditions under which it occurs are as important as the fact that tumors are produced.

A group of animals is maintained at a dosage level which can be discontinued after 6 months to a year, followed by a holding period equivalent to the life-span of the test animal. This holding period is needed to observe precancerous stages of tumor formation which might occur.

SELECTION OF TEST ANIMALS

Both the proper species and healthy animals within the species must be carefully selected for the studies. Various bacterial and viral diseases are frequently endemic in animal colonies. The variation in these stresses may cause variable results in the same colony at different times. Cleanliness and hygiene are necessary to avoid introducing diseases and thus additional stress to the animals. The use of SPF (specific pathogen-free) rats removes one serious variable.

The health of the second species is of equal importance. Purebred beagles raised in healthful surroundings are commonly used. Mongrels with an unknown background and disease history offer more complications. Dogs are easily handled and readily available. Monkeys, pigs, or goats offer certain advantages. The prime reason for selection should be the degree of sensitivity of the species as compared to the human.

Species are selected primarily to assess biological effects likely to occur in humans, and to evaluate the role of human eating patterns. For example, the rat is a continuous feeder at night but rarely eats in the daytime, whereas humans usually eat three times a day. The dog can be fed at regular intervals. Also, the rat cannot regurgitate, but dogs and humans can. The dog is a carnivore and humans are omnivores, as is the pig. The monkey is closer to man on the evolutionary tree and may provide results more applicable to humans.

INTERPRETATION OF RESULTS

The test results must be assessed in terms of potential hazard to the general public which might result from widespread use. A dosage level must be established which shows effect of the chemical on the biological environment, and one must be established which shows no effect. The highest dosage level of a compound administered to test animals over long periods of time, and which does not result in demonstrable biochemical or biological changes, becomes the maximum safe level for experimental animals. The compound must then be evaluated in terms of significance to the human organism. The amount needed to produce an injury, the type of injury, the significance of the injury in terms of mortality, and the length of time needed for recovery, all play important parts in deciding the degree of potential hazard.

Under present regulations, the human is assumed to be 10 times more sensitive than the most sensitive animal used in the toxicological study. It is further assumed that some members of the population are at least 10 times more sensitive than the average. Thus an arbitrary factor of 100 is used to evaluate the maximum safe dosage to which the population may be exposed. This procedure provides the public with good protection from the release of harmful pesticides.

CLASSES OF PESTICIDES

Pesticides (herbicides, fungicides, insecticides) are divided into several general classes: the chlorinated organic materials, arsenic-containing materials, metallic dithiocarbamates, organic phosphates, etc. When two or more chemicals of the same class are present, the quantity of each residue is determined and divided by its tolerance times 100 to determine the percentage of residue which may be permitted. The percentages are added and must not exceed 100 percent. Thus, to a certain extent the kind of herbicide sprayed may affect the choice of insecticide in order to avoid exceeding the allowable residue for a class of compound.

Table 12-1   Related Pesticides

PESTICIDE	TOLERANCE	RESIDUE	RESIDUE PERCENTAGE OF TOLERANCE
2,4-D	7 ppm	3 ppm	42.8 percent
DDT	7 ppm	5 ppm	71.3 percent
			Illegal—114.1 percent*

*The residues of related pesticides are added together. Although the herbicide 2,4-D and the insecticide DDT are each below acceptable levels, together they exceed 100 percent of the tolerance for chlorinated hydrocarbons.

Spray history of the crop is required by many processors because it is impossible at present to analyze for all possible pesticides, and in many cases the crop must be processed before the analysis can be completed.

Processing must not concentrate the residue, e.g., raw fruits when pitted and dried would be over tolerance due to the loss of moisture and pits. It is illegal to mix products which are above and below tolerance in order to arrive at an acceptable mixture.

TOLERANCE LEVELS

Zero tolerance means, theoretically, that not even one molecule of a forbidden substance can be present in the product. In practice this means a level below the sensitivity of the best available testing method. As new methods are developed, it is becoming possible to analyze at levels of 0.0001 ppm (0.0000001 percent) or less. This means that tolerances above zero may be established as these new analytical methods develop. It has been estimated that if one cup of a certain herbicide were mixed thoroughly with water of all the oceans in the world there would be approximately 300 molecules per cup of the resulting solution. This is a very small amount, but it is not zero. The concept of zero tolerance has therefore been abandoned in favor of "negligible residues" and "permissible residues." This action is desirable because it places reliance on the data available for each chemical and on the judgment of the concerned scientists.

INTERNATIONAL TRADE IN FOODSTUFFS

International trade in foods presents problems to countries with limited local supplies, such as England, that import most of their food.

These countries have little or no control over the use of pesticides on the crops before they reach them, except by setting and maintaining rigid standards for permissible residues. In areas where food stocks are plentiful, there is likely to be more insistence on minimum contamination than in countries where the production of food may be more important than the hypothetical hazard. Hunger is a fact in many parts of the world, and hungry people are likely to be very uncritical about possible contamination of food which is in short supply. International regulation of food shipments is still in its beginning stages but will undoubtedly increase as the use of pesticides increases. Certain industries may be severely affected by such action, which, unfortunately, is more likely to be taken for political or emotional reasons than for scientific ones. For example, the apple industry of Nova Scotia has never recovered from a decision made by England in 1938 not to import apples from Nova Scotia or the United States so long as the fruits were sprayed with arsenate of lead (Horsfall, 1965). Not long before, the British had been through the harrowing experience of discovering that the beer they drank in their pubs was loaded with lead from the lead pipes under the bar and from the spigots on top. The habitués of the pubs had been having painter's colic—that is, lead poisoning. So when the British heard about arsenate of lead, the social pressure was on. Since, at that time, this compound was the only material available to control the worms in the apples, the growers were helpless. There was no other market for the fruit from Nova Scotia, and therefore the apple industry in that country went into an immediate and permanent decline. American apple growers in the New England states continued to spray with no particular outcry from the public since there appeared to be no great hazard to public health and at that time no other chemical was available to control the worms in the apples.

West Germany has recently enacted laws which limit residues of a number of pesticides to considerably lower rates than those presently legal in the United States. This may have serious consequences in reducing trade in certain agricultural items between the two countries.

GENERAL CONSIDERATIONS

Man wishes to avoid weeds, insects, and diseases, but equally he wishes to avoid poisons in his food. It is the interaction between these two strong deep-seated desires that causes the present turmoil.

No one likes to have chemicals added to his food. When, however, the choice becomes maggots or chemicals, or perhaps more limited and more expensive food, then the choice becomes a more difficult matter. As Horsfall (1965) points out, at one time the official tolerance of the U.S. Food and Drug Administration was seven maggots per can of cherries. Since the farmers could not get all the maggots out, the FDA had to set a tolerance if the citizens were to have any canned cherries at all. So long as food continues in short supply and consumers insist on perfect and unblemished fruit, then the use of pesticides will almost certainly continue to increase.

QUESTIONS

1. Name three naturally occurring toxic substances.
2. Can you name a completely safe chemical?
3. What are toxicological studies designed to do?
4. Define (1) *toxicology*, (2) *toxicity*, (3) *hazard*, (4) *risk*.
5. Although 2,4-D is known to be harmless, certain individuals have reported illness after prolonged contact. To what might this be due?
6. What are the main routes of ingestion of most chemicals?
7. How is dosage important?
8. What is meant by LD_{50}?
9. Does the LD_{50} give any information on the cumulative effects of several successive light exposures to a chemical?
10. How does entry through skin differ in its possible effects on the chemical as compared to entry through the mouth?
11. How does the rate of metabolic breakdown affect toxicity?
12. What are the chronic studies designed to do?
13. What criteria are used in selecting test animals?
14. Suppose you wish to control insects, fungi, and weeds on a crop such as grain or beans. What role would tolerance levels play on your choice of the various pesticides?
15. What questions should one ask about a new pesticide in addition to knowing its ability to achieve the desired control of a pest?
16. How could a hazardous chemical be consumed without risk?

REFERENCES

Alexander, M. 1963. Microbiology of Pesticides and Related Hydrocarbons. *Rudolfs Res. Conf. Proc.*

Fogelman, R. W. 1963. Principles of Toxicological Testing Methods. *Rudolfs Res. Conf. Proc.*

Horsfall, J. G. 1965. A Socio-Economic Evaluation, in "Research in Pesticides," C. O. Chichester (ed.), p. 3–29, Academic Press, Inc., New York.

Sax, Karl. 1966. Biological Problems of the Age of Science. *Wash. State Rev.*, **10**:5–9.

Whitten, J. 1966. "That We May Live," D. Van Nostrand Co., New York.

CHAPTER THIRTEEN
BIOLOGICAL CONTROL

The principles of biological control and the precautions to be observed in the introduction of predators are presented in this final chapter. The role of grazing animals and the interaction between chemicals and biological control are also discussed.

GENERAL PRINCIPLES

Biological control is the "action of parasites, predators or pathogens in maintaining another organism's population density at a lower average than would occur in their absence" (Huffaker, 1964). The progeny of any organism, if left to grow unchecked, would soon cover the earth. The natural balance of plant and animal life reflects in part the natural processes of biological control.

Regulation of an organism's abundance below the level of economic injury is the target of applied biological control. The population control of plants by insects and disease is a process that has been going on for countless centuries, but only recently has man deliberately sought to use this method for the control of weeds. The emphasis on biological control has been much less than the emphasis on chemical control. However, there is more awareness of biological control efforts today because of the pesticide residue problem.

Examples of undesirable biological control of one organism by another are common, as for example, the eating of undesirable shrubs by livestock, preferential grazing by cattle, disease or insect attacks on garden plants, trees, and shrubs. Man has attempted to control certain weeds (and other pests) by introducing predators which will attack these pests and reduce their numbers below an economically important level. This is a slow and difficult process.

The imported predator or parasite must (1) ideally feed only on the weed species even if it starves to death when this species is unavailable, (2) be free of its own predators and parasites and be resistant to those found in the new area, (3) be adapted to the climate, (4) have the capacity to seek out the host environment.

One weakness of the biological control method, as well as chemical methods, is that unless the imbalance encouraging the weed growth —as in the overgrazing of ranges—is corrected, the weed may be replaced not by a desirable plant, but by some other weed. This replacement process is already occurring in certain Western ranges. Biological control has the advantage over chemicals in that it is essentially permanent, cheap, safe, and effective in inaccessible areas.

Work in biological control of weeds has usually involved grazing lands. Management practices frequently determine whether specific weeds become serious pests. Some weeds become serious because of severe over-grazing or poorly timed grazing.

In general, the more simplified the human economy and ecology of a region the better are the chances of attempting biological control without operating at cross-purposes with self-interests. Certain plants may be regarded as weedy in one situation and may be quite valuable in another. Downy brome or cheatgrass (*Bromus tectorum*), for example, is a serious pest in winter wheat in the Northwest, but forms a valuable source of food on many low-rainfall cattle ranges in the spring. Certain species of the prickly pear cactus are favored by some cattlemen as a source of food and water for their stock. Yellow starthistle infests ranges and grain and seed crops. It is also a key plant in maintaining the bee industry at a level needed for the pollination of fruit and seed crops. Introduction of predators for these pests becomes a matter of balancing all interests, both long and short range.

WEED CONTROL BY INSECTS

The outstanding examples of biological weed control by introduced predators have all concerned insects: the goatweed beetle in Australia and the United States, the cactus moth in Australia, and several kinds of moths which have given partial control of *Lantana* in Hawaii (Holloway, 1957).

Complete eradication is not achieved through biological control. Rather, the insect attacks the established pest and rapidly multiplies until much of the plant growth is destroyed and the food supply becomes limiting

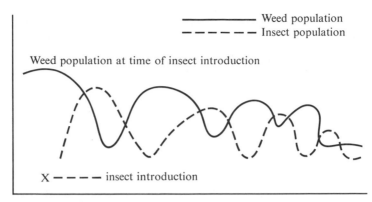

————— Weed population
— — — — — Insect population

Weed population at time of insect introduction

X — — — — insect introduction

Figure 13-1 *Weed control by insects. Fluctuation in numbers of weeds and insects leads to a series of ups and downs in populations until an equilibrium of low numbers of both weed and insect is reached.*

to the insect, which thereupon decreases in numbers. With the insect numbers depleted, the weed growth resumes, followed by a corresponding increase in the insect population and a resultant decrease in weed numbers. Several of these "waves" may occur with steadily decreasing "peaks" of weed population until a stable equilibrium is reached (Figure 13–1).

Goatweed beetle

The goatweed beetle is a good example of the relationships necessary between predator and pest for successful biological control. This insect controls a rangeweed (*Hypericum perforatum*) which has several common names: Klamath weed, St. Johnswort, or goatweed. It was at one time a very serious rangeweed in many parts of California and the Pacific Northwest.

Goatweed beetles (*Chrysolina hyperici* and *C. quadrigemina*) were imported from Australia into California and released in the fields in 1945. The adults emerge from the pupa in the spring and feed on the foliage. In June and July, when the plant is dormant, the beetles have a resting stage in the soil. With the fall rains, the weeds and beetles become active. The beetles mate and lay eggs, and some of the eggs hatch into larvae. All three forms can live throughout the winter. In the spring, the eggs complete hatching and the larvae feed on the trailing growth until the plants develop upright shoots. At that time the larvae pupate in the soil, thus completing the cycle. The specificity of the insect stages to plant growth is remarkable, as demonstrated in experiments where the larvae were shown to feed only on the trailing foliage and the mature beetles only on the foliage of the upright shoots (Seeley, 1965).

The beetles can fly to new infestations or be spread by man. Man helps to disperse them by collecting the beetles and placing them in new areas. Experiments show that approximately 3500 to 5000 beetles are needed to make an effective infestation in a new area within a reasonable time.

The beetles aid in control not only by killing the plant but by reducing its ability to compete and its ability to survive adverse conditions, such as dry summers (Holloway, 1957). Goatweed has been reduced to less than 1 percent of its former abundance in California. Introductions of the beetle into Washington, Oregon, and Idaho have also been successful. Where the poor grazing practices that led to the infestation of goatweed have not been corrected, other weeds such as knapweed (*Centaurea* sp.), dalmatian toadflax (*Linaria dalmatica*), medusa head rye (*Elymus caput-medusae*), etc., have taken over.

Cactus moth

Various species of *Opuntia*, the prickly pear cactus, which originated in the Western Hemisphere, have been transported by man around the world. It has been used as food for humans or cattle, for dye-producing insects, and as a water source in deserts. In many places it has escaped from cultivation and become an extremely aggressive weed, occupying millions of otherwise productive acres.

About six species were established in Australia and over 60 million acres had become infested by 1925; half of this area was so dense that it was practically impenetrable by man and large animals. Explorers were sent to the United States, Mexico, and Argentina seeking specific insects which might bring about control. Some 50 species were studied and 12 were introduced. Of these, *Cactoblastis cactorum*, the cactus moth, was the most successful.

The larvae of this moth feed on the plant, tunneling through and destroying all plant parts above the ground. Their attacks allow entry of bacteria and fungi which complete the destruction.

Within 5 years the moth population had increased to such great numbers that huge areas of *Opuntia* were being killed off at one time. This great depletion of food source led to a drastic drop in the insect population. This reduction in numbers of moths permitted a resurgence of the weed, but the *Cactoblastis* was able to increase with sufficient rapidity to lower the plant population again before it reached alarming proportions. Over the years the prickly pear has receded and now only an occasional plant or a few patches can be found. Millions of acres have been returned to productive use.

The importation of this moth into Hawaii was delayed for several years due to the objection of cattlemen because the tree cactus *Opuntia megachantha* is a valuable source of feed and water for stock on some dry ranges.

There has been opposition to the introduction of the cactus moth into the Southwestern United States and Mexico for similar reasons and because of the value placed on the *Opuntia* species for soil and wildlife conservation.

Other insects and hosts

Tansy ragwort (*Senecio Jacobaea*), a biennial yellow-flowered composite, is a serious rangeweed in the wetter areas of California and the Northwest. It has spread over thousands of acres of good rangeland. To control it, the cinnabar moth (*Tyrea Jacobaea*) was introduced into California and the Northwest. Only moderate success has been obtained because indigenous parasites appear to have moved over from near relatives of this moth and reduced its numbers. A seed fly (*Pegohylemyia seneciella*) has proven effective on the tansy ragwort in Australia.

The flea beetle (*Haltica carduorum*) was recently introduced into Canada and the Pacific Northwest for control of Canada thistle but no data are available on its effectiveness. It looks promising in California but may be less effective in colder climates.

Gorse (*Ulex europeus* L.) is an attractive yellow-flowered perennial which was introduced as an ornamental and which has the peculiarity of burning well when green. It spreads rapidly over burned-over timber or brush acres, keeping out the native forage species as well as the conifers and thus interfering greatly with reforestation. To cope with this problem, its natural enemy, the gorse seed weevil (*Apion ulicis*), has been introduced from England into Australia, New Zealand, Hawaii, and California. As a result, seed production in New Zealand has been reduced by more than 98 percent.

While insects which feed only on seeds are not useful for killing established plants, they could be very valuable in preventing reinfestation of cleared land and in reducing spread of the weed to new areas.

Harvester ants

The work of insects may be more subtle than the dramatic spectacle provided by the cactus moth. For example, the harvester ants (*Veromesser pergandei*) are selective foragers, avoiding the seeds of plantain, even though these may form as much as 86 percent of the available seed supply (Huffaker, 1964). Such selection of seed over a period of years would favor the plantain over other plants—a kind of "reverse" biological control.

OTHER ORGANISMS

Spider mite is useful against *Opuntia* sp., although not as spectacular as the cactus moth (Huffaker, 1964).

Snails (Seaman and Porterfield, 1964; Radke et al., 1961), carp and other fish (Shell, 1962), and manatees, all of which feed on aquatic weeds, have shown good results under certain conditions in ponds and waterways.

Geese are frequently used for weed control in cotton, strawberries, mint, and other crops. The geese prefer the young grass weeds.

Fungi have been tested without success, although some of the bacterial rots and wilts are known to attack *Opuntia* following invasion by *Cactoblastis*, thereby aiding in the destruction of the cactus. Accidental and undesirable introductions, the chestnut blight and the Dutch elm disease, have wiped out native chestnuts and American elms in the Eastern United States, pointing up the possibility of finding fungi specific to certain weed species.

Viruses are known to be very specific in their hosts. The danger in working with these organisms lies in their ability to mutate and attack new hosts.

Grazing animals

Preferential grazing will favor the less palatable weeds over the more palatable grass and legumes (Gangstad, 1964). This is a function of overgrazing and will, of course, lead to progressive deterioration of a pasture, particularly if carried to excess.

Care must be exercised in moving livestock from areas treated with certain herbicides to new areas where the crop plant may be sensitive. For example, the use of manure from cattle that are fed herbage sprayed with TBA has led to injury to certain crops. However, this may well apply to other chemicals and crops as well. Picloram appears to cause damage to sensitive crops such as potatoes when excreted from deer, cows, horses, or sheep that have recently fed on plants treated with this chemical.

Biological control by plants

The production of selective phytotoxins by plants has been used with some success as a means of controlling undesirable vegetation. Black mustard (*Brassica nigra*) was planted on California ranges because it inhibited germination of chaparral but did not inhibit the growth of some desirable range plants (Went et al., 1952).

INTERACTION OF CHEMICALS AND BIOLOGICAL CONTROL

In any plant and animal complex, many potential pests will be under good biological control. Haphazard application of chemicals may so seriously disrupt host-natural enemy interactions that "biological explosions" or "upsets" result from the differential toxic effect of the chemicals on the host and its enemies. Biological control may lead to a similar result. Frequently, a new pest may emerge which is worse than the original. Control of any weed by chemical or biological means will have little value if the mismanagement leading to the infestation is not corrected. Something will grow on the land sooner or later. Planning on this eventuality is critical in a weed control program else we are likely to find ourselves in a biological variation of Russian roulette, i.e., killing off relatively innocuous plants until we finally help to establish a weed which we cannot control but which then becomes a far more serious pest than the original plant species.

Various examples may be given of the relationships between the organic herbicides and animals or insects. The influence of the chemical on changing normal metabolic patterns is apparently critical. Thus, aphids reproduce more rapidly on broad beans treated with 2,4-D, presumably because of the changes in amino acids induced by the chemical (Maxwell and Harwood, 1960). Other examples have been reported: (1) Cattle will eat toxic plants they normally reject if the plants are sprayed with 2,4-D. Nitrate levels may be raised to toxic levels by 2,4-D sprays (Stahler and Whitehead, 1950). (2) Corn treated with 2,4-D is more attractive to rodents (Raleigh and Patterson, 1948). (3) Tobacco plants infested with tobacco mosaic virus are more sensitive to simazine than are healthy plants (Ulrychová and Blattný, 1961). Chemicals which make the corn plant more resistant to stalk rot and corn borer also make the plants resistant to atrazine and simazine (Anderson, 1964).

The use of 2,4-D, 2,4,5-T mixtures to kill brush and trees along rivers in an effort to eliminate breeding sites for the tsetse fly (the bearer of sleeping sickness) has had considerable success in Africa. In the United States, large-scale attempts are made to reduce or eliminate the stands of wild barberry in order to reduce rust infection on wheat.

The use of 2,4-D or 2,4,5-T to remove brush may also be effective in reducing rodent population by reducing the cover and food supply. Rodent damage in orchards may be reduced by keeping the ground bare around the trees with appropriate herbicides.

COMPARISON OF BIOLOGICAL AND CHEMICAL WEED CONTROL

There are two definite advantages of chemical weed control as compared to biological control: (1) herbicides may be applied to specific, restricted areas; (2) they are quick-acting. Application to specific areas is important when a weed in one crop may be a neighbor's valuable forage plant, and quick action is necessary since the main competition from weeds comes in the first 6 to 8 weeks of crop growth.

The disadvantages of chemicals are (1) they must be applied each season; (2) they may leave harmful residues in soil which may be absorbed by succeeding crops; (3) their cost is high, in both initial investment and subsequent application.

The advantages of biological control are (1) low cost; (2) no residue in soil; (3) simplicity of control, i.e., once the insect has been introduced it will propagate itself and spread naturally or it may be spread by man rather simply.

The disadvantage of biological control is mainly slowness of action. Seldom will an organism multiply rapidly enough to be effective on weeds in crops, that is, to kill the weeds in the first 6 to 8 weeks of growth when competition is most critical. Although one might argue that over a period of time, a weed such as mustard, for example, might be controlled to the point where it would not be an important factor, the large numbers of weed seeds in the soil must be considered. These seeds will serve to repopulate infested areas for many years.

Considering that there are about 1200 important weed species (Fogg, 1966), many of which are closely related to crop plants, it is unlikely that a biological control will be discovered for each one in the foreseeable future. As pointed out in Chapter 1, modern methods of crop management, such as growing a single species in pure stands in rows, leave many spaces and resources unexploited. Some weed is certain to take advantage of the unused water, nutrients, space, and light.

The key to weed control is wise management of all available weapons, including cultivation, fertilization, burning, flooding, mulching, crop rotation, biological control, and the intelligent use of agricultural chemicals.

QUESTIONS

1. Define *biological control*.
2. Give some examples of biological control other than those discussed in this chapter.
3. What are the requirements for successful introduction of a predator?

4. What are the advantages and disadvantages of biological control compared to chemicals?
5. How does the goatweed beetle kill goatweed?
6. What is the relationship of the goatweed plant life cycle and goatweed beetle life cycle?
7. How do fungi contribute to the effect of the cactus moth on the cactus plant?
8. How do the cactus moth and the goatweed beetle differ in their action?
9. Why hasn't the cactus moth been introduced into the Southwestern United States?
10. What is the selective action of the harvester ant?
11. Why hasn't the cinnabar moth been effective in the Northwest?
12. What animals have been used for aquatic weed control?
13. Give some examples of herbicide influences on plant-parasite interaction.
14. Is grazing a kind of biological control?
15. How may the application of 2,4-D affect animal population?

REFERENCES

Anderson, R. N. 1964. Differential Response of Corn Inbreds to Simazine and Atrazine. *Weeds*, **12**:60–61.

Fogg, J. M. 1966. The Silent Travelers, Handbook on Weed Control. *Brooklyn Botanical Gardens Record*, **22**:4-7.

Gangstad, E. O. 1964. Physical and Chemical Composition of Grass and Sorghum as Related to Palatability. *Crop Sci.*, **4**:269–270.

Holloway, J. K. 1957. Weed Control by Insect. *Sci. Am.*, **197**:56–62.

Huffaker, C. B. 1964. Fundamentals of Biological Weed Control, in "Biological Control of Insect Pests and Weeds," P. Debach (ed.), Section VII, Chapter 22, pp. 631–649, Reinhold Publishing Corporation.

Maxwell, R. C., and R. F. Harwood. 1960. Increased Reproduction of Pea Aphids on Broad Beans Treated with 2,4-D. *Ann. Entom. Soc. Am.*, **53**:199–205.

Radke, M. G., L. S. Ritchie, and F. F. Ferguson. 1961. Demonstrated Control of *Australorbis glabratus* by *Marisa cornuarietis* under Field Conditions in Puerto Rico. *Am. J. Trop. Med. Hyg.*, **10**:370–373.

Raleigh, S. M., and R. E. Patterson. 1948. Rodent Injury on 2,4-D Pre-emergence Treated Corn. *J. Am. Soc. Agron.*, **40**:472–473.

Seaman, D. E., and W. A. Porterfield. 1964. Control of Aquatic Weeds by the Snail *Marisa cornuarietis*. *Weeds*, **12**:87–92.

Seeley, C. 1965. Private communication.

Shell, E. W.   1962.   Herbivorous Fish to Control *Pithophora* sp. and Other Aquatic Weeds in Ponds. *Weeds,* **10**:326–327.

Stahler, L. M., and E. I. Whitehead.   1950.   The Effect of 2,4-D on Potassium Nitrate Levels in Leaves of Sugar Beets. *Science,* **112**:749–751.

Ulrychová, M., and C. Blattný.   1961.   Synergistic Action of Simazine and of Plant Viruses as a Method for the Possible Detection of Viral Diseases. *Biologia Plantarum (Prague),* **3**:122–125.

Went, F. W., G. Juhren, and M. C. Juhren.   1952.   Fire and Biotic Factors Affecting Germination. *Ecology,* **33**:351–354.

GLOSSARY

ABSCISSION	The shedding of fruits, leaves, or stems from the parent plant.
ABSORPTION	Movement of a pesticide from the surface into a body.
ACID EQUIVALENT (ae)	The theoretical yield of parent acid from an active ingredient.
ACTIVE INGREDIENT (ai)	The chemical in a product that is responsible for the effects.
ACUTE EFFECT	Rapid and severe (opposed to chronic effect).
ADSORB	To gather on a surface (opposed to absorb).
Aihg	Active ingredient per hundred gallons.
AMINE	A class of compound derived from ammonia by replacing the hydrogens with organic radicals.
ANGIOSPERM	A plant having its seeds enclosed in an ovary.
ANNUAL	A plant that completes its life cycle from seed in 1 year.
APOPLAST	Nonliving cell walls forming a continuous translocation system in the plant body.
AQUATIC PLANTS	A plant that grows in water. There are three kinds: submersed, which grows beneath the surface; emersed, which root below but extend above the water, such as cattails and water lilies; and floaters, such as water hyacinths.
AREOLE (islet)	A small area of mesophyll delimited by intersecting veins.

217

AROMATICS — Compounds derived from the hydrocarbon benzene (C_6H_6).

BAND APPLICATION — An application to a continuous restricted area such as in or along a crop row rather than over the entire field area.

BASAL TREATMENT — An application to the stems of plants at and just above the ground line.

BED — (1) A narrow flat-topped ridge on which crops are grown with a furrow on each side for drainage of water. (2) An area in which seedlings or sprouts are grown before transplanting.

BIENNIAL — A plant that completes its growth in 2 years. The first year it produces leaves and stores food. The second year it produces fruit and seeds.

BIOASSAY — A test method using living organisms to determine the presence of a chemical.

BLANKET APPLICATION — An application of spray or granules over an entire area rather than only in rows, beds, or middles.

BLIND CULTIVATION — Cultivation before a crop emerges.

BOILING POINT — The temperature at which a liquid boils.

BOILING RANGE — The range of temperatures over which a mixture or an impure compound boils.

BOOT STAGE — See *growth stages of grain crops*.

BROADCAST APPLICATION — See *blanket application*.

BROAD-LEAVED PLANTS — In general, opposed to mosses or grasslike plants.

BRUSH CONTROL — Control of woody plants.

CAMBIUM — A meristem with products of divisions arranged in orderly fashion in parallel files. Consists of one layer of initial cells and their derivatives.

CARRIER — The liquid or solid material added to a chemical compound to facilitate its application.

CHLOROSIS — A yellowing of plant foliage which results from the halting of the development of the green coloring matter.

CHRONIC EFFECT — Slow and long continued effect.

COMPATIBLE — Two compounds are compatible when they can be mixed without undesirably affecting each other's properties.

CONCENTRATION — The amount of active material in a given volume of diluent or given weight of dry material. Recommendations and specifications for concentration of herbicides should be on the basis of *pounds per unit volume of diluent.*

CONTACT HERBICIDE

An herbicide that kills primarily by contact with plant tissue rather than as a result of translocation.

CONTAMINATE

To alter or to render a material unfit for a specified use, as by the introduction of a chemical.

CONTROL

The process of limiting an infestation.

CORTEX

The tissue region between the vascular system and the epidermis.

COTYLEDON LEAVES

The first leaf, or pair of leaves—depending on whether the plant is monocotyledonous or dicotyledonous—developed by the embryo of seed plants.

CROOK STAGE

The stage after bean seedlings have broken through the soil but before the stem has become erect.

CROP

Useful plants growing where desired.

CROWN

The point where stem and root join in a seed plant.

CULM

The jointed stem of a grass which is usually hollow except at the nodes or joints.

CUTICLE

A varnishlike layer covering the entire shoot, formed by oxidation of plant oils.

CUTIN

A waxy, fatty material that with the cuticle forms the cuticularized layers covering the shoot of a plant.

DECIDUOUS PLANTS

Plants which lose their leaves during the winter (leaf loss may also be induced by drought, etc.).

DEFOLIATOR OR DEFOLIANT

A compound which causes the leaves or foliage to drop from the plant.

DELAYED ACTION

As opposed to immediate effect. Some herbicide chemicals (2,4-D; 2,4,5-T; MCP; dalapon) provide a delayed response. Considerable time may elapse before maximum effect can be observed. Usually treated plants stop developing soon after treatment, then gradually die.

DESICCANT

A crop drying agent. For example, when seed alfalfa or red clover preharvest are sprayed with dinitro and oils, usually the foliage is killed by contact action, and often seed moisture is reduced, which aids harvest.

DICOTYLEDON (dicot)

Any seed plant having two cotyledons.

DILUENT

Any liquid or solid material serving to dilute or carry an active ingredient.

DINITRO	A common designation for dinitro-phenols. These materials are used as contact chemicals, as crop defoliants, or as a control for succulent annuals.
DIOECIOUS	Plants with separate male and female individuals.
DIRECTED APPLICATION	An application of spray or dust to a restricted area, such as a row or a bed, at base of plants.
DISPERSAL UNIT	Seed plus associated tissues of flower, fruit, or specialized leaves.
DORMANT	Stage of inhibited growth of seeds or other plant organs due to internal causes; temporary suspension of visible growth.
EDIBLE	Not toxic; nutritious, as a worm to a chicken, a chicken to a man, and a man to a worm.
EMERGENCE	The time when the first leaves of the crop plant come through the ground.
ENDOGENOUS	Originating within an organism.
ENZYME	An organic substance which regulates the rate of a reaction but which remains chemically unchanged.
EPINASTY	The twisting or curling of leaves and stems caused by uneven growth of cells, especially in leaves, in which the upper surface grows faster than the lower surface and thus causes the leaf edges to bend down.
EXOGENOUS	Originating externally, outside the organism.
FACULTATIVE WEED	A weed found growing both wild and in association with man.
FIBROUS ROOT SYSTEM	Composed of profusely branched roots with many lateral rootlets but with no main or tap root development.
FLAG STAGE	(Also knee stage in onions) The early postemergence stage of onion seedlings between the crook stage and the emergence of the first true leaf. The bent tip of the seed leaf resembles a flag attached to a staff. Also used to designate the stage of development in cereals and other grasses at which the sheath and leaf have been produced.
FORMULATION	A mixture of an active pesticide chemical with carriers, diluents, or other materials; usually to facilitate handling.
FUNGICIDE	A chemical used for killing or controlling the growth of fungi.
GERMINATION	The period during which physiological processes are initiated in the seed leading to the elongation of cells

and the formation of new cells, tissues, and organs, i.e., the period between hydration and the onset of meristematic activity.

GROWTH REGULATOR — An organic substance effective in minute amounts for controlling or modifying plant processes.

GROWTH STAGES OF GRAIN CROPS —
1. Tillering stage: when a plant produces additional shoots from a single crown, as in wheat.
2. Jointing stage: when the internodes of the stems are elongating.
3. Boot stage: when the leaf sheath swells up due to the growth of developing spike or panicle.
4. Heading stage: when the seed head of a plant begins to emerge from the sheath.

HARD WATER — Water which contains certain minerals, usually calcium and magnesium sulfate, chlorides, or carbonates in solution to the extent that a curd or precipitate rather than a lather occurs when soap is added. Very hard water may cause objectionable precipitates in some herbicidal sprays.

HECTARE — Land measure in metric system approximately equal to 2.2 acres.

HERB — A vascular plant that does not develop woody tissues.

HERBICIDE — A chemical used for killing or inhibiting the growth of plants.

HERMAPHRODITIC — Having male and female parts in the same flower.

HORMONE — A growth-regulating substance occurring naturally in plants or animals.

HUMIDITY — Moisture or dampness in the air. Weed killers are often comparatively more effective under moderately humid conditions. In areas or at times when humidity is very low, high herbicidal rates or high volumes of carrier may be required because sprays dry more quickly and absorption is poor.

INERT INGREDIENT — Any ingredient in a formulation which has no pesticidal action.

INHIBIT — To hold in check or stop, as to inhibit or check seed germination or plant growth with chemicals.

INTERCALARY MERISTEM — Meristematic tissue derived from the apical meristem and interposed between tissues that are more mature. Often found above the nodes in immature grass stems.

INVERT EMULSION

One in which the water is dispersed in oil rather than oil in water. Oil forms the continuous phase with the water dispersed therein; usually a thick, mayonnaiselike mixture results.

JOINTING STAGE

The stage when grass stems begin elongating.

KILOGRAM (kilo)

Weight measure in metric system; 1000 grams or about 2.2 pounds.

LAY-BY APPLICATION

Application of herbicides after the last cultivation.

LEAF BLADE

The expanded flat portion of a leaf.

LOGARITHMIC SPRAYER

A device for spraying a pesticide at a steadily decreasing rate of application.

MATURE

A term applied to cells or tissues which have completed their differentiation.

MERISTEM

A tissue primarily concerned with protoplasmic synthesis and formation of new cells by division.

MISCIBLE

Two or more liquids which, when combined together, form a uniform stable mixture.

MONOCOTYLEDON (monocot)

Any seed plant having a single cotyledon or seed leaf. Includes corn and grass-type plants. Leaves are mostly parallel veined.

MONOECIOUS

Plants with separate male and female flowers on same individual.

NECROSIS

The death of all or a part of the plant.

NODE

The joint in a stem; point of divergence of a leaf.

NONSELECTIVE HERBICIDE

An herbicide that can be used to kill plants generally without regard to species.

NOXIOUS WEED

A weed arbitrarily defined by laws as being especially undesirable, troublesome, and difficult to control. Definition will vary according to legal interpretations.

OBLIGATE WEED

A weed never found in the wild stage, but growing only in association with man.

PALATABLE

Good to the taste, not necessarily healthful. Some poisonous plants that livestock usually avoid are made more palatable by treatment with certain chemicals and may cause injury to the animal.

PANICLE

A group of flowers borne at unequal distances from the central stem, as in orchard grass.

PARENCHYMA CELL

A living cell concerned with one or more of the physiologic activities in plants.

PETIOLE

The slender stem that supports the blade of a foliage leaf.

PHLOEM

The principal food-conducting tissue of the vascular plant, basically composed of sieve tube, companion cells, fibers, and sclereids.

pH VALUE

An expression of the degree of acidity or alkalinity. pH values below 7.0 indicate acidity with its intensity increasing as the numbers decrease. Conversely, pH values above 7.0 indicate alkalinity with its intensity increasing as the numbers increase.

PHYTOTOXIN

A substance poisonous to plants.

POSTEMERGENCE TREATMENT

Any treatment made after the specified weed or crop plants emerge.

PREEMERGENCE TREATMENT

Any treatment made after a crop is planted but before a specified weed emerges.
1. Contact preemergence: an application made after weed emergence.
2. Residual preemergence: an application which kills weeds as the seed germinates or as they emerge either before or after the crop has emerged.

PREPLANTING TREATMENT

Any treatment made before the crop is planted.

PRIMARY NOXIOUS WEEDS

Perennial weeds that are difficult to control and that have been designated by the state as *primary noxious*.

PUBESCENT

Hairy stems or leaves. May affect wetting of foliage and retention of spray.

QUICK-BREAKING EMULSION

An emulsion in which the components separate rapidly.

RATE AND DOSAGE

These terms are synonymous. *Rate* is the preferred term. Rate refers to the amount of active ingredient material (such as 2,4-D acid equivalent) applied to a unit area.

REGISTERED

Chemicals that have been approved for use in agriculture by the U.S. Department of Agriculture.

REPLACEMENT TISSUE

Thick-walled parenchymatous cells replacing the mesophyll of leaves injured by 2,4-D.

RESIDUAL

To continue over a period of time to have a killing effect on all or specific life forms.

RESIDUE TOLERANCE

The amount of chemical pesticide residue which may legally remain in or on a food crop.

RESISTANCE

Same meaning as *tolerance*. Resistance of weed determines the rate of the weed-killer application required for control or eradication.

RHIZOME

Horizontal, slender, underground rootlike stem that sends out roots and leafy shoots.

ROOTSTOCK

Same as *rhizome*.

ROSETTE

A circular cluster of leaves.

SECONDARY GROWTH

Growth resulting from the formation of new cells by the cambium.

SECONDARY NOXIOUS WEEDS

Annual and biennial weeds that are difficult to control and which have been designated by the state as *secondary noxious*.

SEEDLING STAGE

Usually refers to the early stages of growth of crop plants or weeds; technically a plant prior to the development of a root system other than the seed or seminal root.

SELECTIVE HERBICIDE

An herbicide that will kill some plant species when applied to a mixed population, but without serious damage to other species.

SENSITIVITY

Not capable of withstanding effects. Many broad-leaved plants are sensitive to 2,4-D.

SOFT WATER

Water which does not contain those minerals that prevent free lathering when soap is added.

SOIL PERSISTENCE

Refers to the length of time that an herbicide applied to or in the soil remains effective; to some degree phytotoxic to some species.

SOIL STERILANT

A material which renders the soil incapable of supporting plant growth. Sterilization may be temporary or relatively permanent.

SOLUBILITY

A measure of the amount of substance that will dissolve in a given amount of another substance.

SOLVENT

A substance (usually water) used to alter the form of a compound; i.e., cause it to flow freely.

SPIKE STAGE

The early emergence stage of corn in which the leaves are still tightly rolled to form a "spike," usually before the corn is more than 2 inches tall.

SPOT TREATMENT

An application of spray to a localized or restricted area as differentiated from an overall (broadcast) or complete coverage.

SPRAY DRIFT	The movement of airborne spray particles outside the intended area of application.
SPREADING AGENT	A substance used to improve the wetting, spreading, or possibly the adhesive properties of an herbicide spray solution.
STEM	The part of the plant above ground which supports leaves, flowers, and fruit.
STOLONS	Runners or slender stems that develop roots and shoots at the tip or nodes as in the strawberry plant.
STOOL	To send out shoots, to tiller.
SUBLETHAL	A dosage which injures but does not kill.
SURFACE TENSION	A physical property of liquids, due to molecular forces, that causes them to form drops, rather than spread as a film.
SURFACTANT	A material which, when used in pesticide formulations, imparts emulsifiability, spreading, wetting, dispersability, or other surface-modifying properties.
SUSPENSION	A system in which very fine solid particles are dispersed but not dissolved in a solid, liquid, or gas.
SYNERGISM	Cooperative action of different agencies such that the total effect is greater than the sum of the two effects working independently.
SYSTEMIC HERBICIDE	A compound which is translocated readily within the plant and has an effect throughout the entire plant system.
TILLERING STAGE	See *growth stages of grain crops.*
TOLERANCE (pesticides)	The amount of pesticide chemically allowed by law to be in or on the plant or animal product sold for human consumption.
TOLERANT	Capable of withstanding effects. For example, grasses are tolerant of 2,4-D to the extent that it can be used selectively to control broad-leaved weeds in cereals, pastures, and turf.
TOXIC	Poisonous; injurious to animals and plants through contact or systemic action.
TRANSLOCATION	Transfer of food or other materials from one part to another in plants.
TRANSPORT	See *translocation.*

VAPOR DRIFT — The movement of herbicidal vapors from the area of application.

VAPOR PRESSURE — That property which causes a chemical compound to evaporate.

VASCULAR TISSUE — A general term referring to either or both xylem and phloem.

VEIN — A strand of vascular tissue in a flat organ, as a leaf.

VOLATILE — A compound is said to be volatile when it evaporates or vaporizes (changes from a liquid to a gas) at ordinary temperatures on exposure to the air.

WEED — A plant with a negative value; a nuisance; an organism which causes a diversion of energy from a direction desired by man.

WEED CONTROL — The process of limiting weed infestations so that crops can be grown profitably or other operations can be conducted efficiently.

WEED ERADICATION — The complete elimination from an area of all live plants, plant parts, and seeds of a weed infestation.

WETTABLE POWDER — A powder that will readily form a suspension in water.

WETTING AGENT — A compound which when added to a spray solution causes it to spread over and wet plant surfaces more thoroughly.

WOODY PLANTS — Plants that develop woody tissues.

XYLEM — The principal water-conducting tissue in vascular plants characterized by the presence of tracheids. May also contain vessels, parenchyma cells, fibers, and sclereids.

CONVERSION FACTORS

LIQUID MEASURE

1 gallon (U.S.) = 3785.4 milliliters; 256 tablespoons; 231 cubic inches; 128 fluid ounces; 16 cups; 8 pints; 4 quarts; 0.8333 imperial gallon; 0.1337 cubic foot

1 liter = 1000 milliliters; 1.0567 liquid quarts (U.S.)

1 gill = 118.29 milliliters

1 fluid ounce = 29.57 milliliters; 2 tablespoons

3 teaspoons = 1 tablespoon; 14.79 milliliters

1 gallon of water = 8.355 pounds

1 cubic foot of water − 62.43 pounds; 7.48 gallons

1 pint = 1.043 pounds

1 quart = 2.086 pounds

WEIGHT

1 gamma = 0.001 milligram

1 grain = 64.799 milligrams

1 gram = 1000 milligrams; 15.432 grains; 0.0353 ounce

1 pound = 16 ounces; 7000 grains; 453.59 grams

1 ounce = 28.35 grams

1 short ton = 2000 pounds; 907.2 kilograms

1 long ton = 2240 pounds

1 kilogram = 2.2 pounds

LINEAR MEASURE

12 inches = 1 foot

36 inches = 3 feet; 1 yard

1 rod = 16.5 feet

1 mile = 5280 feet; 1760 yards; 160 rods; 80 chains; 1.6094 kilometers

1 chain = 66 feet; 22 yards; 4 rods; 100 links

1 inch = 2.54 centimeters

1 millimeter = 0.394 inch or $\frac{1}{25}$ inch

1 meter = 39.37 inches; 10 decimeters; 3.28 feet

1 micron (μ) = 1/1000 millimeter

1 kilometer = 1000 meters; 3280 feet; 0.62 mile

1 mile per hour = 1.47 feet per second; 88 feet per minute

AREA

1 township = 36 sections; 23,040 acres

1 square mile = 1 section; 640 acres; 259 hectares

1 acre = 43,560 square feet; 160 square rods; 4840 square yards; 208.7 feet squared; an area one rod wide and $\frac{1}{2}$ mile long; 0.4 hectare

1 hectare = 2.471 acres; 10,000 square meters

CAPACITY (DRY MEASURE)

1 bushel (U.S.) = 4 pecks; 32 quarts; 35.24 liters; 1.244 cubic feet; 2150.42 cubic inches

PRESSURE

1 foot lift of water = 0.433 pound pressure per square inch (psi)

1 pound pressure per square inch will lift water 2.31 feet

1 atmosphere = 760 millimeters of mercury; 14.7 pounds; 33.9 feet of water

GEOMETRIC FACTORS (π = 3.1416; r = radius; d = diameter; h = height)

Circumference of a circle = $2\pi r$ or πd

Diameter of a circle = $2r$

Area of a circle = πr^2 or $\frac{1}{4}\pi d^2$ or $0.7854d^2$

Volume of a cylinder = $\pi r^2 h$

TEMPERATURE (degrees)

$$°F = °C + 17.78 \times 1.8 \qquad 1°C = 1.8°F$$
$$°C = °F - 32.00 \times \frac{5}{9} \qquad 1°F = \frac{5}{9}°C$$

°C	°F	°C	°F
100	212	30	86
90	194	20	68
80	176	10	50
70	158	0	32
60	140	− 10	14
50	122	− 20	− 4
40	104	− 30	− 22

APPLICATION RATES BASED ON AREA

1 ounce per square foot = 9 ounces per square yard = approximately 17 pounds per square rod or 2722.5 pounds per acre

1 ounce per square yard = approximately 2 pounds per square rod or 302.5 pounds per acre

1 pound per square rod = approximately ½ ounce per square yard or 160 pounds per acre

1 pound per 100 square feet = 2.72 pounds per square rod or 435.6 pounds per acre

1 pint per square yard = approximately 3¾ gallons per square rod

1 cup per square rod = 5 gallons per acre

1 pint per square rod = 20 gallons per acre

1 quart per square rod = 40 gallons per acre

1 gallon per square rod = 160 gallons per acre

APPENDIX

PROPERTIES AND USES OF HERBICIDES*

COMPOUND	COMMON OR ABBREVIATED NAME	STRUCTURE	LD$_{50}$ (rats, mg/kg)	USES
		PHENOXY COMPOUNDS (-ACETIC, -PROPIONIC, -BUTYRIC, ETC.)		
2,4-dichlorophenoxy-acetic acid	2,4-D	OCH$_2$COOH (phenyl ring with Cl, Cl)	400–500 666 300–1000	Control of broad-leaved weeds in cereals, asparagus, corn (maize), rice, in turf areas and orchards for broad-leaved weeds, or combined with 2,4,5-T for woody plant control; growth regulation for preharvest drop of apples.
4-chloro-2-methyl-phenoxy-acetic acid	MCPA MCP	OCH$_2$COOH (phenyl ring with CH$_3$, Cl)	700 800	Postemergence control of broad-leaved weeds. Selective in cereals, some leguminous plants, and flax; growth regulation for preharvest drop of apples.

*For a more complete listing, see "Herbicide Handbook of the Weed Society of America," 1967; "British Weed Control Handbook," 1967; or current issues of *Weed Science*.

		Structure		Uses
2,4,5-trichlorophenoxy-acetic acid	2,4,5-T	OCH₂COOH on trichlorophenyl ring: OCH_2COOH	300 375 500	Control of woody plants in pastures, roadsides, and forests, often combined with 2,4-D. Also used as growth regulator to delay coloration of lemons, increase size of citrus fruits, reduce drop of deciduous fruit.
2-(2,4,5-trichloro-phenoxy)-propionic acid	2,4,5-TP Silvex fenoprop	CH_3 / $OCHCOOH$ on trichlorophenyl ring	500 650	Postemergence control of broad-leaved weeds in turf and rice, woody plants; submerged and emergent aquatic weeds.
4-(2,4-dichloro-phenoxy)-butyric acid	2,4-DB	$OCH_2CH_2CH_2COOH$ on dichlorophenyl ring	500 700	Selective postemergence control of broad-leaved weeds in many legumes. Principal use in cocklebur control in soybeans.
2-(2-methyl-4-chloro-phenoxy) propionic acid	MCPP mecoprop	CH_3 / $OCHCOOH$ on methyl-chlorophenyl ring, CH_3	650	Selective postemergence for selective control of annual broad-leaved weeds in cereals, grasses.

COMPOUND	COMMON OR ABBREVIATED NAME	STRUCTURE	LD$_{50}$ (rats, mg/kg)	USES
		PHENOXYETHYL SULPHATES AND RELATED COMPOUNDS		
Sodium 2(2,4-dichloro-phenoxy)ethyl sulphate	2,4-DES Sesone disul-sodium	$OCH_2CH_2OSO_3Na$ (2,4-dichlorophenyl)	730 1400 1230	Preemergence broad-leaved weed control in straw-berries, peanuts, maize, potatoes, asparagus, nursery stock. Safe on foliage. Soil microorganisms convert to 2,4-D.
Tris-(2,4-dichloro-phenoxy-ethyl) phosphite	2,4-DEP	$(Cl{-}\quad{-}OCH_2CH_2O)_3P$ (2-Cl)	850	Selective preemergence broad-leaved weed control in peanuts, maize, strawberries, asparagus, pota-toes, alfalfa, and some ornamentals. Controls a wide range of annual grasses.
2-(2,4,5-trichloro-phenoxy)ethyl 2,2-dichloropropionate	Erbon	$OCH_2CH_2OCCCl_2CH_3$ (with C=O, 2,4,5-trichlorophenyl)	1120	Contact herbicide or temporary soil sterilant for nonselective weed control. Requires moisture to activate it.

234

2,6-dichlorobenzon-itrile	Dichlobenil		2710 3160	Nonselective for control of germinating weed seeds; well tolerated by established plants, thus useful in transplanted crops, orchard, and berry-fruit areas; around ornamental shrubs and in nurseries; in aquatic weeds; in established pastures to control seedling weeds; and for general weed control.
4-hydroxy-3,5-diiodo-benzonitrile	Ioxynil		110	Selective postemergence for broad-leaved weeds in cereals; contact action, most effective when weeds are small.
3,5-dibromo-4-hydroxybenzonitrile	Bromoxynil		190 260	Selective postemergence for broad-leaved weeds in cereals; contact action, most effective when weeds are very small.

COMPOUND	COMMON OR ABBREVIATED NAME	STRUCTURE	LD_{50} (rats, mg/kg)	USES
BENZOIC AND PHENYLACETIC ACIDS				
2,3,6-trichlorobenzoic acid	TBA		750 1500 1644	Pre- and post-emergence; both foliage and root absorption. For nonselective control of noxious perennial broad-leaved weeds.
3-amino-2,5-dichloro-benzoic acid	Amiben Chloramben		3500 5620	Selective preemergence control of grasses in soybeans, tomatoes, some cucurbits, asparagus, dry beans, and lima beans.
3,6-dichloro-2-methoxybenzoic acid	Dicamba		1040 1100 2900	Selective control of broad-leaved weeds in cereals; also control of broad-leaved perennial weeds at higher rates; relatively short residual life in soil.

CARBAMATES

Chemical name	Common name	Structure	Values	Uses
2,3,6-trichlorophenyl-acetic acid	Fenac Chlorfenac	CH$_2$COOH (2,3,6-trichlorophenyl ring)	1780 3000	Preemergence selective; temporary soil sterilant; effective on perennial weeds, also preemergence use in sugarcane and asparagus; used in corn for witchweed (*Striga*). Postemergence for perennial weed control in noncrop areas.
Isopropyl *N*-phenylcarbamate	IPC Propham	NH · C · O · CH (with =O and CH$_3$, CH$_3$; phenyl ring)	1000 4500 5000	Preplant or preemergence, incorporated for control of annual grasses in legumes, wild oats in peas. Postemergence for downy brome control in grasses grown for seed.
Isopropyl *N*-(3-chlorophenyl)-carbamate	CIPC Chlorpropham	NHCOCH (with =O and CH$_3$, CH$_3$; chlorophenyl ring)	3800 5000 7500	Preplant; incorporated preemergence or post-emergence. Selective in peas, spinach, onions, cole crops, established stands of alfalfa and clover.
4-chloro-2-butynyl *N*-(3-chlorophenyl) carbamate	Barban	NHCOCH$_2$C $\equiv$ CCH$_2$Cl (with =O; chlorophenyl ring)	600 1350	Postemergence control of wild oats in wheat, barley, peas, rapeseed, flax, sugar beets, lentils, and soybeans.

CARBAMATES (*continued*)

COMPOUND	COMMON OR ABBREVIATED NAME	STRUCTURE	LD$_{50}$ (rats, mg/kg)	USES
S-2,3-dichloroallyl N,N-diisopropyl thiol-carbamate	Diallate DATC	(CH$_3$)$_2$CH, (CH$_3$)$_2$CH–N–C(=O)–SCH$_2$C=CHCl, Cl	395	Preplant or postplant; incorporated treatment for control of wild oats in peas, wheat, barley, lentils, potatoes, corn, flax, rapeseed, sugarbeets and safflower.
S-2,3,3-trichloroallyl N,N-diisopropylthiol-carbamate	Triallate	(CH$_3$)$_2$CH, (CH$_3$)$_2$CH–N–C(=O)–SCH$_2$CCl=CCl$_2$	1675–2165 1340–1810 1400	Incorporated preplant or postplant treatment for wild oat control in wheat, barley, peas, and lentils.
2-chloroallyl diethyl-dithiocarbamate	CDEC SULFALLATE	CH$_3$CH$_2$, CH$_2$CH$_3$–N–C(=S)–SCH$_2$CCl=CH$_2$	850	Preemergence control of annual weeds in maize, beans, celery, cole crops, soybeans, salad crops, many vegetables, and nursery stock.
Ethyl N,N-di-propyl-thiolcarbamate	EPTC	CH$_3$CH$_2$CH$_2$, CH$_3$CH$_2$CH$_2$–N–C(=O)–SCH$_2$CH$_3$	1630	Preemergence and preplanting in alfalfa, potatoes, beans, pineapple, citrus and tomatoes; incorporate immediately after application. Controls many annual weeds.

			Structure	
Sodium N-methyl (dithiocarbamate)	Metham SMDC	820	CH_3NHCSN_2 with $C=O$	Soil fumigant in seed beds prior to sowing. Also toxic to fungi, bacteria and insects.
S-ethyl-hexahydro-1 H-azepine-1-carbothioate	Molinate	720	$C_2H_5S-\overset{O}{\overset{\|}{C}}-N$ (ring)	Preemergence control of crabgrass, wild oats, barnyardgrass, nutsedge, sprangletop in rice, barley, and wheat; incorporated into soil mechanically or by flooding.
S-propyl-butyl-ethylthiocarbamate	Pebulate	921–1120	$\begin{array}{c}CH_3CH_2CH_2CH_2\\ CH_3CH_2\end{array}\!\!> N\overset{O}{\overset{\|}{C}}SCH_2CH_2CH_3$	Annual weed control in tomatoes, sugar beets, and tobacco. Must be incorporated immediately after application.
S-propyl-di-propyl-thiocarbamate	Vernolate	1780	$\begin{array}{c}CH_3CH_2CH_2\\ CH_3CH_2CH_2\end{array}\!\!> N\overset{O}{\overset{\|}{C}}-S-CH_2CH_2CH_3$	Annual weeds in cotton, soybeans, peanuts, tobacco, and sweet potatoes.

COMPOUND	COMMON OR ABBREVIATED NAME	STRUCTURE	LD_{50} (rats, mg/kg)	USES
		SUBSTITUTED PHENOLS		
Pentachlorophenol	PCP	(pentachlorophenol structure)	27–80 78 210 280	Preemergence and postemergence. Rapid topkill of many weed species. Also useful as fungicide and insecticide. Contact weed killer for general vegetation control.
2,4-dinitro-6-sec butylphenol	Dinoseb DNBP "Dinitro"	(2,4-dinitro-6-sec-butylphenol structure)	15 35 40 50 60	Oil-soluble, also water-soluble salts, preemergence for annual weeds in peas, beans, maize, potatoes, strawberries. Contact weed killer for general vegetation control.
		SUBSTITUTED UREAS		
1,3-bis (2.2.2-trichloro-1-hydroxy-ethyl)urea	Dichloral urea	$CCl_3CHOHNHCNHCHOHCCl_3$ with O on C	31600	Control of grass weeds in sugar beets; tassel inhibition in sugarcane.

		Structure		
3 (p-chlorophenyl)-1,1-dimethylurea	Monuron	$\begin{array}{c} O \\ \parallel \\ \text{NHCN} \end{array}\begin{array}{c} CH_3 \\ CH_3 \end{array}$, phenyl ring with Cl	3600	Preemergence or shortly after germination of weeds in well-established crops of sugarcane, pineapple, cotton, asparagus, orchard fruits. Soil sterilant at high rates.
3-phenyl-1,1-dimethylurea	Fenuron	$\begin{array}{c} O \\ \parallel \\ \text{NHCN} \end{array}\begin{array}{c} CH_3 \\ CH_3 \end{array}$, phenyl ring	6400	For control of woody plants and bindweed in noncultivated areas; soil sterilant.
3-(3,4-dichlcrophenyl)-1,1-dimethylurea	Diuron	$\begin{array}{c} O \\ \parallel \\ \text{NHCN} \end{array}\begin{array}{c} CH_3 \\ CH_3 \end{array}$, phenyl ring with Cl, Cl	3400	Preemergence or postemergence for control of weed seedlings in well-established crops of sugarcane, pineapple, peppermint (lay-by), irrigated cotton (lay-by), alfalfa (dormant), perennial grass crops, certain small berry crops, and wheat. Soil sterilant at high rates.

COMPOUND	COMMON OR ABBREVIATED NAME	STRUCTURE	LD$_{50}$ (rats, mg/kg)	USES
		SUBSTITUTED UREAS (*continued*)		
1-*n*-butyl-3-(3,4-dichlorophenyl)-1-methylurea	Neburon		11000	Preemergence in nursery plantings of woody ornamentals for control of annual weeds and grasses.
N'-(3,4-dichloro-phenyl)-N-methoxy-N-methylurea	Linuron		1500 3500	Preemergence and postemergence for annual weeds in maize, tomatoes, peppers, potatoes, carrots, cereals, strawberries, soybeans.

3-phenyl-1,1-dimethyl-urea trichloroacetate	FenuronTCA	4000–5700	General vegetation control in noncrop areas, brush control.
3-(p-chlorophenyl)-1,1-dimethylurea trichloroacetate	MonuronTCA	2300–3700	General vegetation control in noncrop areas.
N'-4-(4-chlorophenoxy)-phenyl-N,N-dimethylurea (3-(p-(p'-chlorophenoxy)-phenyl)-1,1-dimethylurea)	Chloroxuron	3700	Preemergence or postemergence to soybeans, peas, beans, strawberries, carrots, onions, rice, grain sorghum, peanuts, potatoes, squash, okra, lima beans, snap beans, and ornamentals for control of annual grasses and broad-leaved weeds.

FenuronTCA structure:

$$O = \overset{CH_3}{\underset{CH_3}{NHCNH}} \quad CCl_3COOH$$

MonuronTCA structure:

$$O = \overset{CH_3}{\underset{CH_3}{NHCN}} \quad CCl_3COOH$$

Chloroxuron structure:

$$\underset{CH_3}{\overset{CH_3}{N}} - \overset{O}{\overset{\|}{C}} - \overset{H}{N} - - O - - Cl$$

243

COMPOUND	COMMON OR ABBREVIATED NAME	STRUCTURE	LD$_{50}$ (rats, mg/kg)	USES
		SUBSTITUTED UREAS (*continued*)		
3-(hexahydro-4, 7-methanoindan-5-yl)-1, 1-dimethylurea	Norea		1476 6830	Preemergence control of grasses and broadleaves in cotton, sorghum, sugarcane, lima beans, sweet potatoes, spinach, and peas. Early postemergence spray on cotton either alone or mixed with DSMA and MSMA. Soil applications of Norea are tolerated by many woody and herbaceous ornamentals.
3-(*m*-trifluoromethyl-phenyl)-1,1 dimethylurea	Cotoran		7900 8900	Pre- or postemergence application to annual grass and broad-leaved weeds in cotton, corn, potatoes, peas, onions, asparagus, bulb crops, and ornamentals.
1-(2-methylcyclohexyl)- 3-phenylurea	Siduron		5000	Preemergence for annual grasses such as crabgrass, foxtail, and barnyardgrass in newly seeded or established plantings of bluegrass, bentgrass, fescue, redtop, smooth brome, perennial ryegrass, and orchardgrass.

TRIAZINES				
2-chloro-4, 6-*bis* (ethyl-amino)-1,3,5-triazine	Simazine	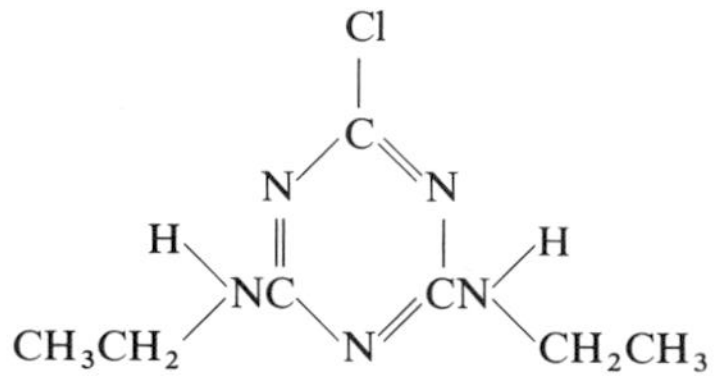	5000	Preemergence for annual weeds in maize; conifers, orchards; strawberries; for quackgrass control; for general vegetation control; requires moisture to activate it in soil. At high rates for general vegetation control.
2-methoxy-4, 6-bis (isopropyl-amino)-1,3,5-triazine	Prometon Prometone	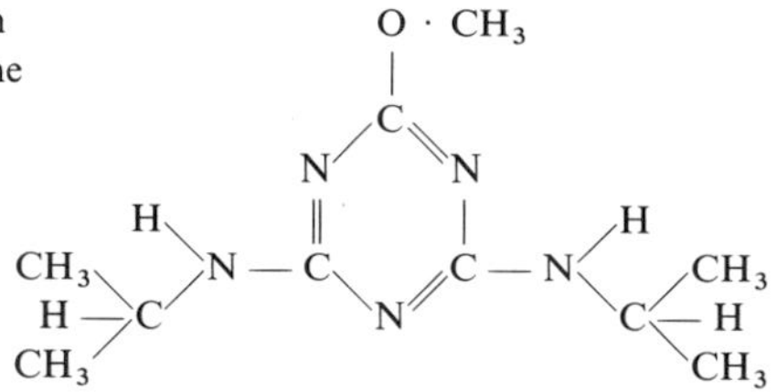	2980	Contact herbicide; nonselective; for most annual and many perennial broad-leaved weeds and grasses; at high rates for total weed control.
6 methylmercapto-2,4 bis (isopropylamino)-*s*-triazine	Prometryne	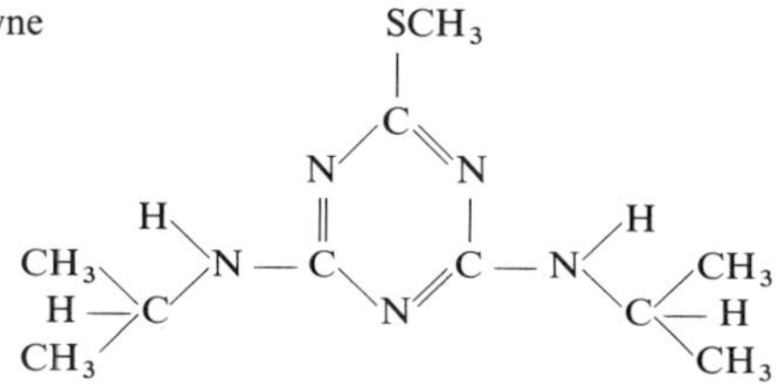	3750	Selective preemergence and postemergence control of seedling weeds in certain vegetables, cotton and grasses grown for seed.

COMPOUND	COMMON OR ABBREVIATED NAME	STRUCTURE	LD$_{50}$ (rats, mg/kg)	USES
		TRIAZINES (*continued*)		
2-chloro-4-ethylamino-6-isopropylamino-1,3,5-triazine	Atrazine	(chemical structure)	2000 2000–3000 3080	Pre- and postemergence for annual weeds in maize, sugar cane and conifers; for quackgrass and nutgrass control; for general vegetation control, chemical fallow.
2-chloro-4,6-bis (isopropylamino)-1,3,5-triazine	Propazine	(chemical structure)	5000	Preemergence for annual broad-leaved weeds and grasses in sorghum.

5-bromo-3-sec-butyl-6-methyl-uracil	Bromacil	5200	Nonselective for control of grasses and broad-leaved annual and perennial weeds on industrial sites, noncropland. Selective in certain deep-rooted crops such as pineapple, citrus and alfalfa.
5-amino-4-chloro-2-phenyl-3(2H)-pyridazinore	Pyrazon; PCA	3000	Pre- and early postemergence, and preplant soil incorporation; control of annual broad-leaved weeds in sugar beets, table beets, spinach.
3-tert-butyl-5-chloro-6-methyluracil	Terbacil	5000	Preemergence and postemergence; annual weeds in sugarcane and orchards, soil sterilant at high rates.

Bromacil structure:

$$CH_3-C, Br-C, N-H, C=O, N-CHCH_2CH_3 \; (CH_3), C=O$$

Pyrazon structure:

$$NH_2-C, Cl-C, C=CH, O=C, N=N-\text{(phenyl)}$$

Terbacil structure:

$$CH_3-C, Cl-C, N-C, N-CHCH_2CH_3 \; (CH_3), C$$

COMPOUND	COMMON OR ABBREVIATED NAME	STRUCTURE	LD_{50} (rats, mg/kg)	USES
DIAZINES (continued)				
(1,2 dihydropyridazine-3, 6-dione)	MH, Maleic hydrazide		2340 (diethanolamine salt) 3800–6800 4000 5800 6950 (Na salt)	Retarding growth of perennial grasses along roadsides; suppresses regrowth of pruned trees and hedges and tobacco suckering; quackgrass control in maize, certain vegetables and sugarbeets.
CHLORINATED ALIPHATIC ACIDS				
Trichloroacetic acid	TCA	CCl_3COOH	3200 3320 5000	Preemergence and postemergence; controls many annual and perennial grasses, bamboo; mainly root absorbed.
2,2-dichloropropionic acid	Dalapon	CH_3CCl_2COOH	3860 6950–8120 7570–9330	Preemergence and postemergence for control of bamboo, many annual and perennial grasses in industrial areas, drainage ditches, sugarcane, potatoes, citrus and deciduous fruit.

Name	Common name	Structure	Values	Use
3,4-dichloro-2-methacrylamide	Dicryl chloranocryl	(3,4-dichlorophenyl)—NH—C(=O)—C(CH$_3$)=CH$_2$	3160	Postemergence for weeds in cotton and Bermuda grass.
2-chloro-N,N-diallyl-acetamide	CDAA allidochlor	(CH$_2$=CHCH$_2$)(CH$_2$=CHCH$_2$)N—C(=O)—CH$_2$Cl	700 750	Preemergence control of annual weeds in beans, tomatoes, maize, sorghum, soybeans. Postemergence on onions and sugar cane.
3,4-dichloropropion-anilide	Propanil	(3,4-dichlorophenyl)—NH·C(=O)·CH$_2$CH$_3$	1384	Selective postemergence for certain grass and broadleaf weeds in rice and tomatoes.
N,N-dimethyl-2,2-diphenylacetamide	Diphenamid	(CH$_3$)(CH$_3$)N—C(=O)—CH(C$_6$H$_5$)$_2$	1050 970	Preemergence control of annual weeds in direct-seeded and transplant tomatoes, peppers, tobacco, Irish potatoes, sweet potatoes, cotton, grapes, ornamentals and strawberries.

COMPOUND	COMMON OR ABBREVIATED NAME	STRUCTURE	LD_{50} (rats, mg/kg)	USES
		AMIDES (*continued*)		
N-(3-chloro-4-methylphenyl)-2-methylpentanamide	Solan pentanochlor		10,000	Postemergence control of both broad-leaved and grass weeds in tomatoes, also in carrots and celery; useful for control of annual bluegrass (*Poa annua*) and chickweed (*Stellaria media*) in evergreen tree nurseries.
N-(beta-O-O-diisopropyldiphosphorylethyl)-benzene sulfonamide	Bensulide		1910	Preemergence selective in grass and dichondra. For control of many annual weeds.
2-chloro-N-isopropylacetanilide	Propachlor		1580 1200	Preemergence selective control of grasses and *Chenopodium* and *Polygonum* in potatoes, maize, and certain vegetables.

Name	Common name	Value	Structure	Use
1,1'-ethylene-2,2'-bipyridylium dibromide	Diquat	400–440	(bipyridylium dibromide structure) $2+$ $2\ Br^-$	Postemergence weed control in some fresh fruits; also submerged, floating, and emerged aquatic weeds; desiccant.
1,1'-dimethyl-4,4'-bipyridylium dichloride	Paraquat	157	(bipyridylium dichloride structure) $2+$ $2\ Cl^-$	Postemergence use on dormant raspberries, black currants, and around trees; effective on grasses, sedges, reeds; promising for control of submerged, floating, and emerged aquatic weeds; desiccant.

TOLUIDINES

Name	Common name	Value	Structure	Use
N,N-di-(n-propyl)-2,6-dinitro-4-trifluoro-p-toluidine	Trifluralin	10,000 3700	$CH_3CH_2CH_2 - N - CH_2CH_2CH_3$, with NO_2, NO_2, CF_3 substituents on ring	For preemergence weed control in cotton, soybeans, beans, safflower, fruit and nut crops, ornamentals, and many vegetables.
N,N-di-(n-propyl)-2,6-dinitro-p-toluidine	Dipropalin		$CH_3CH_2CH_2 - N - CH_2CH_2CH_3$, with NO_2, NO_2, CH_3 substituents on ring	Preemergence use, or against seedling grass weeds established in turf.

COMPOUND	COMMON OR ABBREVIATED NAME	STRUCTURE	LD_{50} (rats, mg/kg)	USES
		TOLUIDINES (*continued*)		
N-butyl-N-ethyl trifluoro-2,6-dinitro-p-toluidine	Benefin	$CH_3CH_2CH_2CH_2 - N - CH_2CH_3$ with NO_2, NO_2, CF_3 on ring	10,000	Preplant or postplant soil incorporated selective for annual grass control in lettuce, peanuts, alfalfa and turf.
		PHTHALIC COMPOUNDS		
Disodium 3,6-endoxohexahydro-phthalate	Endothal Endothall	bicyclic structure with $O=C-O-Na$, $H-C-O-Na=O$, H_2, O, H_2	35 51 80 182 (Na salt) 206 (amine salt)	Defoliant and desiccant; aquatic weeds.
N-1-naphthyl phthalamic acid	NPA naptalam	benzene ring with $-COOH$, $-CONH-$ naphthalene	8200 1770 (Na salt)	Preemergence in asparagus, cucurbit crops.

Name	Abbreviation	Structure	Values	Uses
Dimethyl 2,3,5,6-tetrachloroterephthalate	DCPA chlorthal	O = C — OCH₃, ring with Cl, Cl, Cl, Cl substituents, O = COCH₃	1476 3000 3160 6830	Selective long residual preemergence control of crabgrass and other weeds in turf, certain vegetables.

METAL ORGANIC COMPOUNDS

Name	Abbreviation	Structure	Values	Uses
Phenyl mercuric acetate	PMA	CH₃—C(=O)—O—Hg—(phenyl)	40	Controls crabgrass in turf; has fungicide value.
Disodium methane arsonate	DSMA	CH₃—As(=O)(O—Na)(O—Na)	600 1800	Selective contact postemergence in cotton for grass control, turf for crabgrass control and noncrop areas.
Dimethylarsinic acid	Cacodylic acid	(CH₃)(CH₃)As(=O)(OH)	830	Defoliant in cotton, potatoes; dodder control in alfalfa; turf and nonbearing orchards, general vegetation control; thinning of conifers.
Monosodium acid methanearsonate	MSMA	CH₃—As(=O)(OH)(O—Na)	700	Selective in cotton for control of grasses, also in noncrop areas and turf.

253

COMPOUND	COMMON OR ABBREVIATED NAME	STRUCTURE	LD_{50} (rats, mg/kg)	USES
MISCELLANEOUS (ORGANIC)				
4-amino-3,5,6-trichloropicolinic acid	Picloram	(structure: trichloropicolinic acid, COOH, NH_2, Cl)	8200	Readily absorbed by plant foliage and roots, and translocated through the plant; for control of woody species, deep-rooted perennial weeds; for broad-leaved weeds in turf; most grasses tolerant.
3-amino-1,2,4-triazole	Amitrole ATA aminotriazole	(structure: triazole ring, NH_2)	1100 5000 14700 15000 25000	Perennial weeds in noncrop areas, quackgrass control before planting corn, aquatic weeds, chemical fallow.
Amitrole plus ammonium thiocyanate	Amitrole-T		5000	Same as amitrole but generally more effective.

Oils	Petroleum compounds	Not Toxic	Weed killing oils are both selective and nonselective applied postemergence or preemergence to carrots, cotton, onions, soybeans, flax.
Aromatic solvents	Petroleum derivatives		Aquatic weed control especially for submerged aquatics; may injure fish and mosquito larvae.
Acrylaldehyde	Acrolein $$CH_2 = CHCH \overset{O}{\parallel}$$	42 46	Injected into irrigation channels for control of aquatic weeds; potent irritant and lachrymator.

INORGANIC COMPOUNDS

Ammonium sulphamate	AMS $(NH_4)SO_3NH_2$	3900 4000	Nonselective postemergence for control of all vegetation around buildings, fence rows; both contact and translocated; particularly useful for control of poison ivy; short residual activity; controls sprouting in cut-over brush.
Calcium cyanamide	Cyanamide $Ca = N - C \equiv N$ $CaCN_2$	1400	Selective in asparagus before spear emergence for control of germinating annual weeds; tobacco and turf seedbeds; has fertilizer value; defoliant on cotton.

255

COMPOUND	COMMON OR ABBREVIATED NAME	STRUCTURE	LD$_{50}$ (rats, mg/kg)	USES
		INORGANIC COMPOUNDS (*continued*)		
Potassium Cyanate		KOCN	841	Postemergence weed control in onions; also controls crabgrass in turf; defoliant in cotton and soybeans.
Sodium arsenite		NaAsO$_2$	10–50	Control of submerged vegetation in static water; soil sterilization; long residual action.
Sodium tetraborate	Borax	Na$_2$B$_4$O$_7$ · 10H$_2$O	2000–5560	Soil sterilization; long residual action.
Sodium chlorate		NaClO$_3$	1200 7000 6810 5000	Nonselective for control of all vegetation; soil sterilization; because of fire hazard, often combined with borates or calcium chloride; long residual action. From 15 to 30 grams may be fatal to humans.

DECONTAMINATION PROCEDURE

DECONTAMINATION PROCEDURE

The best safety precaution is to use a separate sprayer for different pesticides. This will reduce the possibility of damage to a sensitive crop from herbicides left in the spray equipment. Even when a separate sprayer is used solely for herbicides and the applicator changes from one herbicide to another, one should give the sprayer a thorough cleaning. A number of procedures are given below:

1. The sprayer should be emptied, then filled with water and sprayed out on an area of waste ground where there is no danger from residues. The machine should then be refilled and left overnight if no more spraying is to be done that day. This will prevent the chemical from drying and caking inside and eventually flaking off to block the nozzles. If the same chemical is to be sprayed on the following day, the water left overnight in the tank may be used to prepare the required concentration of herbicide.

2. With dinitro, ureas, carbamates, or triazine compounds, simply wash with water until the washings are colorless. The addition of a synthetic detergent will often speed up the process.

3. When the salts of growth-regulating herbicides such as 2,4-D, dicamba, or picloram have been used, one of the following procedures should be carried out:

(a) Wash the equipment thoroughly by filling with a strong solution of synthetic detergent. The inside of the tank including its ceiling and lid, should be scrubbed, and the solution circulated through the pump and back into the tank. Follow this treatment with two further washings with water. If possible, the machine (and particularly the rubber hose lines) should stand overnight completely full of water containing detergent.

(b) Thoroughly flush the equipment with plenty of water. Then fill the tank with water and add two pounds of washing soda or soda ash per 100 gallons of water. Wash the inside of the tank thoroughly with this solution, running some through the pump and making sure that the solution goes through all the systems.

257

All lines must be thoroughly washed out. Leave this mixture in the tank for about 12 hours. Wash out the tank, pump, hose, and nozzles again with the soda ash mixture, then run fresh water through the pumps, all hoses, and nozzles. Finally, rinse out thoroughly with additional fresh water.

(c)   A faster but more expensive method utilizes activated charcoal. For example, 2,4-D-amine can usually be removed by rinsing the sprayer for about 2 minutes with a 1 percent solution of activated charcoal. Always follow this with a thorough rinse in clean water.

(d)   Decontamination of machines following the use of the ester formulations of growth-regulator weed killers is more difficult, but the following procedure has given satisfactory results. Put enough light-weight oil into the tank to enable the pump to circulate it adequately through the pipework. Use either a mop or a scrubbing brush to wash down the sides of the tank, and also its ceiling, and then spray through the pipelines. The procedure thereafter is the same as is described above (a) for cleaning the tank after using either the sodium or amine salts of weed killers, i.e. use a detergent or similar preparation and plenty of water. The tank should be cleaned immediately after using ester formulations. As this method will also remove grease, it is advisable to regrease the pump after treatment.

(e)   For hand spray equipment such as a 3-gallon garden sprayer, where the cost factor is not so important, household ammonia is convenient to use, provided no part of the sprayer is made of brass. Thoroughly rinse the equipment out with fresh water after spraying 2,4-D. Fill the spray equipment with the ammonia solution, using one-half cup of ammonia to 3 gallons of water. Let the equipment soak for 18 to 24 hours. Always spray some of this mixture through the pump, hose, and nozzles, at both the beginning and the end of the soaking period.

(f)   As a safety check, when the time permits, it is possible to be reasonably sure that all of the 2,4-D is out of the sprayer if the tank is filled with water and a few seedlings of very sensitive plants such as beans or tomatoes are then sprayed. If the plants are not affected within a day or two, the equipment is probably safe for further use. It is more difficult to clean herbicides from old hoses than from most other parts of the sprayer.

4.   Where a detergent has been used, the final wash should always be with plain water in order to remove any detergent which might reduce the selectivity of the next herbicide to be used.

5.   Machines with wooden tanks or other parts made of absorbent materials should not be used for spraying insecticides or fungicides if they are also being used with herbicides.

6.   Chemicals other than ammonia, charcoal, wetting agents, or oils are not recommended for cleaning tanks. Some, e.g. permanganate, may remove the odor of the weed killers without affecting the active ingredients, thus giving a misleading impression of cleanliness. Many of the herbicide preparations, such as 2,4-D, now on the market have been specially prepared to reduce the volatile impurities that were previously responsible for their smell and for causing the tainting in tomatoes, etc.; the absence of odor cannot now be taken as an indication of cleanliness. (Source: Woodford, E. K. and Evans, S. A. 1965. "Weed Control Handbook," Blackwell Scientific Publications, 4th ed, Oxford.)

AUTHOR INDEX

Aberg, E., 83 *93*
Adams, D. F., 111, *121*
Addicott, F. T., 192, 193, *196*
Alexander, M., 200, *206*
Alley, H. P., 162, *168*
Anderson, R. N., 137, *147*, 213, *215*
Ard, J. S., 90 *94*
Arle, H. F., 171, *188*
Arnold, L. E., 126, *147*
Ball, W. S., 71, *77*
Bamesburger, W. L., 111, *121*
Barnes, J., 41, *45*
Barton, L. V., 33, 37, *45*
Behrens, R. W., 98, *121*
Bell, E. G., 92, *94*, 143, *148*
Bellue, M. K., 71, *77*
Beyer, H., 5, *13*
Bissey, R., 126, *147*
Blackman, G. E., 81, 85, *93*, *94*
Blattný, C., 83, *95*, 213, *216*
Boswell, L. V., 30, *45*
Boyd, F. T., 81, *95*
Brian, R. C., 88, 89, *93*
Brooks, F. A., 111, *121*
Brown, A. G., 183, *188*
Bruns, V. F., 43, *45*, 61, 71, *77*, 171, *188*
Burnside, O. C., 72, *77*
Carns, H. R., 192, 193, *196*
Carter, A. S., 62, *66*
Claasen, M. M., 3, *13*
Clark, L. E., 61, *67*
Clerx, W. A., 86, *94*, 137, 140, *147*
Coggins, C. W., 140, *147*
Colby, S. R., 100, *121*
Collier, J. W., 61, *67*
Comes, R. D., 86, *93*, 137, 140, *147*
Crafts, A. S., 48, *66*, 137, *147*
Crane, J. C., 194, *196*
Cruzado, H. J., 133, 141, *148*, 161, *168*, 193, 195, *196*, *197*

Currier, H. B., 85, *94*
Dale, J. E., 185, *189*
Danielson, L. L., 4, *13*
Darwin, C., 10, *13*
Dawson, J. H., 61, *66*, 184, *188*
Day, B. E., 86, *94*, 137, 140, *147*
de Jong, F., 195, *196*
DeWet, J. M. J., 1, *13*
Dowler, C. C., 160, *168*
Dybing, C. D., 85, *94*
Eames, A. J., 56, 58, *67*
Eastin, E. F., 137, *147*
Ennis, W. B., 81, *95*
Evans, S. A., 104, *122*, 176, *189*, 258
Ferguson, F. F., 172, *189*, 212, *215*
Fogelman, R. W., 200, *206*
Fogg, J. M., 38, *45*, 149, *168*, 214, *215*
Foy, C. L., 85, *94*
Furtick, W. R., 5, 62, *67*
Gangstad, E. O., 212, *215*
Gentner, W. A., 90, *94*
Gilbert, F. A., 166, *168*
Gill, L. S., 182, 183, *188*
Gray, R. A., 136, *147*
Greenham, C. G., 183, *188*
Grogan, C. O., 137, *147*
Grummer, G., 5, *13*
Hacskaylo, J., 101, *121*
Hanson, C. H., 193, *197*
Hanway, D. G., 72, *77*
Harlan, H. V., 3, *13*
Harlan, J. R., 1, *13*
Harper, J. L., 31, *46*
Harwood, R. F., 83, *94*, 213, *215*
Havelka, U. D., 61, *67*
Hawkesworth, F. E., 182, *188*
Heeger, W. F., 162, *168*
Heinze, P. H., 194, *197*
Hiltibran, R. C., 172, *188*
Hilton, J. L., 87, 90, *94*

259

Hodgson, J. M., 84, *94*, 176, *189*
Hodgson, M. M., 171, *188*
Holloway, J. K., 208, 210, *215*
Holly, K., 84, *94*
Holm, L., 166, *168*
Horsfall, J. G., 205, *206*
Hruschka, H. W., 194, *197*
Huffaker, C. B., 207, 212, *215*
Isely, D., 179, *189*
Jackson, C. M., 111, *121*
Jansen, L. L., 87, 90, *94*, 98, *122*
Johanson, N. G., 51, *67*, 156, *168*
Jordan, L. S., 140, *147*
Juhren, G., 213, *216*
Juhren, M. C., 213, *216*
Kadambi, K., 183, *189*
Kennard, W. C., 161, *168*
Kerr, H. D., 35, *46*
King, L. J., 7, *13*, 183, 184, 185, *189*
Kingsley, J. M., 178, *189*
Kittock, D. L., 72, *77*
Knake, E. L., 61, *67*, 72, *77*
Koller, D., 33, 36, 42, *46*
Kulp, E. L., 5, *13*
Latshaw, W. L., 126, *147*
Lavy, T. L., 72, *77*
Lawrence, J. M., 89, 92, *94*
Lee, W. O., 164, 168, 184, *188*
Lefforge, J. H., 62, *66*
Leonard, O. A., 22, *27*, 53, *67*
Lilly, J. P., 181, *189*
Loomis, L. C., 181, *189*
Loomis, W. E., 59, *67*, 126, *147*
Loustalot, A. J., 56, *67*, 69, *77*, 131, 133, 141, *147*, *148*, 163, *168*
MacNeish, R. S., 8, *13*
Maletic, J. T., 117, *122*
Maltvick, E., 166, *168*
Marth, P. C., 193, 194, *197*
Mauldin, W. G., 23, *27*, 90, *94*, 131, *148*
Maxwell, R. C., 83, *94*, 213, *215*
Mitchell, J. W., 193, 194, *197*
Mootani, M. K., 61, *67*
Moreland, D. E., 87, *94*
Muzik, T. J., 23, *27*, 35, *46*, 49, 51, 56, *67*, 84, 89, *94*, *95*, 131, *147*, *148*, 156, *168*, 178, *189*, 195, 196, *196*, *197*
Norwood, B. L., 193, *197*
Palmer, R. O., 137, *147*
Patterson, R. E., 213, *215*
Peacock, J. F., 72, *77*
Phillips, W. M., 179, *189*
Pickering, E. R., 85, *94*
Pires, E. G., 101, *121*
Porterfield, W. A., 172, *189*, 212, *215*
Quick, C. R., 30, 33, *46*, 183, *189*
Radke, M. G., 172, *189*, 212, *215*

Raleigh, S. M., 213, *215*
Rasmussen, L. W., 43, *45*, 71, *77*
Ritchie, L. S., 172, *189*, 212, *215*
Robbins, W. W., 48, *66*, 71, *77*, 137, *147*
Robinson, D. W., 71, *77*
Robinson, E. L., 160, *168*, 185, *189*
Robocker, W. C., 35, *46*, 90, *94*
Roché, B. F., 49, 61, *67*, 84, *94*
Rydrych, D. J., 84, *94*
Sand, P. F., 160, *168*
Sargent, J. A., 85, *94*
Sax, K., 199, *206*
Schieferstein, R. H., 59, *67*
Seaman, D. E., 172, *189*, 212, *215*
Seeley, C. I., 84, *94*, 209, *215*
Seif, R., 72, *77*
Shaw, W. C., 4, *13*, 69, *77*, 87, *94*, 163, 168, 185, *189*
Shell, E. W., 172, *189*, 212, *216*
Shenberger, L. C., 62, *66*
Slade, P., 92, *94*, 143, *148*
Slife, F. W., 61, *67*, 72, *77*
Smith, E. V., 126, *147*
Stahler, L. M., 213, *216*
Staniforth, D. W., 61, *67*
Steinbauer, G. P., 32, *46*
Swan, D. G., 62, *67*
Swanson, C. P., 81, *95*
Thurston, J. M., 34, *46*
Timmons, F. L., 7, *13*, 86, *93*, 137, 140, *147*, 164, *168*, 171, 179, *188*, *189*
Torrey, J. G., 178, *189*
Ulrychová, M., 83, *95*, 213, *216*
Van Loon, H., 7, *13*
Van Overbeek, J., 6, *13*, 24, *27*, 89, 92, *95*, 194, 195, *197*
Velez, I., 6, *13*
Wain, R. L., 88, *95*
Walker, J. J., 101, *121*
Warren, G. F., 100, *121*
Watson, D. P., 58, *67*
Weaver, R. J., 81, *95*
Weber, C. P., 61, *67*
Weierich, A. J., 136, *147*
Welbank, P. J., 5, *14*
Went, F. W., 213, *216*
Whitehead, E. I., 213, *216*
Whitten, J., 199, *206*
Whitworth, J. W., 84, *94*, *95*, 178, *189*
Wiese, A. F., 61, *67*
Wilson, W. E., 181, *189*
Wojtaszek, T., 100, *121*
Woodford, E. K., 104, *122*, 176, *189*, 258
Yeo, R. R., 169, *189*
Zahnley, J. W., 126, *147*
Zohary, M., 2, *14*

SUBJECT INDEX

Abscission, 191–192
  defoliation, 191
  fruit thinning, 192
  preventing, 192
Absorption of herbicides (*see* Entry)
Achillea millefolium, 162
Acid equivalent, 114
Acid-soil indicators, 64
Acrolein:
  aquatic weeds, 171
  properties and uses, 255
Acrylaldehyde, 171, 255
Active ingredient (a.i.), 113–114
Adsorption of herbicides, 87
Aegilops cylindrica, 157
Aeginitia, 184
Aerial sprayers, 109–110
Age:
  and mutation in seeds, 37
  and response to herbicides, 79, 176,
    illus. 81, 82
  wheat and 2,4-D, 154–156, illus.
    154, 155
Agents of seed dispersal, 37 (*see also*
  Introduction of weeds)
Agropyron repens, 180–181
  control by chemicals, 180
  cultivation, 180
  inhibition by atrazine, 160
  inhibitors from, 5
Agropyron spicatum, 17
Agrostemna githago, 7
Aircraft, 109–110
Alfalfa:
  date of seeding, 163
  dwarfing, 193
  herbicides used in 163
Algae control, 170–171

Alhagi camelorum (*cont'd*):
  control by flooding, 71
  survival in manure, 35
Aliphatic acids (*see* Dalapon and TCA)
Allergies caused by weeds, 7
Allidochlor (*see* CDAA)
Allium, 3
Alternate hosts, 6
Amaranthus albus, 39
Amaranthus graecizans, 44
Amaranthus hybridus, 40, 61
Amaranthus retroflexus, 34
Ambrosia sp., 16
Amiben:
  characteristics, 139
  in tomatoes, 187
  properties and uses, 236
5-amino-4-chloro-2-phenyl-1-3(2H)-
    Pryidazinone
  (*see* Pyrazon)
3-amino-2,5-dichlorobenzoic acid (*see*
    Amiben)
3-amino-1,2,4-triazole (*see* Amitrole)
4-amino-3,5,6-trichloropicolinic acid
    (*see* Picloram)
Amino triazole (*see* Amitrole)
Amitrole:
  aquatic weeds, 172
  characteristics, 141–142
  chlorophyll formation, 142, illus. 142, 143
  horsetail rush, 181
  mode of action, 24
  plus ammonium thiocyanate (*see*
    Amitrole-T)
  properties and uses, 254
  quackgrass, 180
  thistle, 177
Amitrole-T, 142, 254

Ammonium sulphamate, 162, 254
Amsinckia intermedia:
  age and resistance, 80, illus. 81, 82
  competition, 62
AMS:
  for brush control, 162
  properties and uses, 254
Animals:
  for biological control, 208–212
  as seed dispersers, 42
Annual bluegrass (see *Poa annua*)
Annual dicotyledons, response to
    herbicides, 150, 162–163
Annual grasses, control by herbicides,
    152, 157, 163, 164
Annual monocotyledons, use of herbicides
    in, 150
Annual morning-glory, 40
Annual weeds:
  cultivation, 69
  definition, 28
  dicotyledons, 150, 162–163
  grasses, 152, 157, 163, 164
Aphids, influence of 2,4-D on
    reproduction, 213
Apion ulicis for gorse control, 211
Apoplast, 56, 85
Application methods, 96
Aquatic weeds, 169–172
  characteristics, 169
  control, 170–172, 212
  water loss, 6
Arceuthobium, 183
Aromatic oils, 171
Aromatic solvents, 255
Arsenic compounds, 125, 199, 203, 253, 256
Artemesia spp., 35, 162
Asexual propagation, 29
Asparagus, 150, 161
ATA (*see* Amitrole)
Atrazine:
  characteristics, 137–138
  for chemical fallowing, 138, 154
  in corn, 187, 213
  in home gardens, 187
  in maize, 187, 213
  properties and uses, 246
  for quackgrass control, 180
  seasonal effects, illus. 22
Atriplex rosea, 32
Auxin:
  effect on growth, 69
  relation to herbicidal action, 90
Avena sp.:
  mimicking barley, 3
  in peas and lentils, 163
  seed burial, 44

Avena sp. (*cont'd*):
  seed production, 30
  in small grains, 157
Bacteria (*see* Microorganisms)
Bamboo, response to herbicides, 152, 160
Bananas, 160
Band application, 96, 105
Barban:
  characteristics, 135
  properties and uses, 237
  wild oat control in grains, 157
  wild oat control in peas and lentils, 163
Barberry, as alternate host, 6, 213
Barley:
  mimicked by wild oats, 3
  weed control in, 152–158
Barnyard grass, 84
Basal bark application, 96, 174
Beans:
  weed competition, 61
  weed control in, 162–163
Bedding plants, 186
Beets, 163
Benefin, properties and uses, 252
Bensulide, properties and uses, 250
Biennials, 29
Bindweed (*see Convolvulus arvensis*)
Biological control:
  by animals, 208–212
  comparison with herbicides, 214
  by fungi, 212
  by insects, 208–212, illus. 209
  interaction with chemicals, 213
Biotypes, 83
Birdvine, *Loranthus* sp., 183
Black currant:
  as alternate host, 6
  herbicides used in, 167
Blowoff damage, 111
Blueberries, herbicides used in, 167
Blue bunch wheatgrass, 17
Blue mustard (*see Chorispora tenella*)
Boom:
  aircraft, 109
  dribble-bar, 106
  function, 101
  length, 104
  vibro-boom, 106
Borax, 127–128, properties and uses,
    256
Boron compounds, 127–128, 256
Bromacil, properties and uses, 247
5-bromo-3-*sec*-butyl-6-methyl-uracil,
    (*see* Bromacil)
Bromoxynil:
  properties and uses, 235
  in wheat, 157

Bromus tectorum:
  in bluegrass, 161
  on roadsides, 17
  in wheat, 152, 157
Brush control:
  chemically, 174–175
  mechanically, 174
  in pastures, 162
  along rivers, 213
Bull thistle, 29
Burning (*see* Fire)
Bush fruits, 167
Butyric acids:
  characteristics, 134
  properties and uses, 233
Cacodylic acid, properties and uses, 253
Cactoblastis cactorum, 210–211
Cactus moth, 210–211
Calcium cyanamide:
  characteristics, 128
  properties and uses, 255
Calculations for herbicide application:
  aircraft, 110
  ground sprayers, 113
Cambium, 56
  response to 2,4-D, 131
Camelthorn (*see Alhagi camelorum*)
Canada thistle (*see Cirsium arvense*)
Capsella bursa-pastoris:
  host for virus, 6
  impermeable seed coat, 34
Carbamates:
  characteristics, 134–136
  properties and uses, 237–239
Cardaria draba, control by flooding, 71
Carp, for aquatic weed control, 172, 212
Carpet weed, 40
Cattails, 16
CDAA:
  mode of action, 24
  properties and uses, 249
CDAA plus TCBC:
  characteristics, 137
  use in corn, 159
CDEC:
  characteristics, 135
  in cucurbits, 187
  properties and uses, 238
  in tomatoes, X-25, 187
Cellular response to herbicides, 89, 131
Cenchrus pauciflorus, as invading weed, 17
Centaurea repens, 71
Centrosema, as cover crop, 164
Cereals, weed control in, 152–159
Chaining for aquatic weeds, 170
Chemical fallowing, 138, 154

Chenopodium ambrosioides, 40
Chloramben (*see* Amiben)
Chlorate (*see* Sodium chlorate)
Chlorfenac (*see* Fenac), 185, 237
Chlorinated aliphatic acids:
  characteristics, 138
  properties and uses, 248
2-chloro-4,6-*bis* (isopropylamino)-1,3,5-
    triazine (*see* Propazine)
2-chloro-4,6-bis (ethylamino)-1,3,5-
    triazine (*see* Simazine)
4-chloro-2-butynyl N-(3-chlorophenyl)
    carbamate (*see* Barban)
2-chloroallyl diethyl-dithiocarbamate
    (*see* CDEC)
2-chloro-N, N-diallylacetamide (*see* CDAA)
2-chloro-4-ethylamino-6-isopropylamino-
    1,3,5-triazine (*see* Atraxine)
2-chloro-N-isopropylacetanilide (*see*
    Propachlor)
4-chloro-2-methyl-phenoxy-acetic acid
    (*see* MCPA)
Chlorophenoxy herbicides, 128–133,
    232–234
3-(*p*-chlorophenyl)-1,1 dimethylurea (*see*
    Monuron)
3-(*p*-chlorophenyl)-1,1-dimethylurea
    trichloroacetate (*see* Monuron TCA)
Chloropicrin, 145
Chloroxuron, properties and uses, 243
Chlorpropham (*see* CIPC)
Chlorthal (*see* DCPA)
Chorispora tenella
  competition, 62, illus. 62
  response to 2,4-D, 151
Christisonia, 184
Chrysolina hyperici, 209
Cinnabar moth, 211
CIPC:
  in annual dicotyledons, 163
  characteristics, 134
  for dodder control, 184
  in legumes, 163–164
  mode of action, 24
  properties and uses, 237
  in rice, 158
Cirsium arvense, 176–178, illus. 176
  biological control, 178, 211
  characteristics, 176
  competitive crops, 178
  control, 177
  dioecious flowers, 32
  distribution, 26
  pastures, 162
  roadside invader, 16
  small grains, 154
Cirsium vulgare, 29

Citrus, 166
Cleaning the sprayer (*see* Decontamination)
Climate:
    and biennial habit, 29
    and dormancy, 55
    and growth, 16
    and herbicide action, 25, illus. 23
    (*see also* Temperature)
Climax vegetation, illus. 4
Clover, 164
CMU (*see* Monuron)
Coast fiddleneck (*see* *Amsinckia*
    intermedia)
Coleoptile, 10
    as absorbing organ, 49
Compatibility of herbicides, 99–101
Competition, 5, 60, 74, 178, 179, illus. 61,
    62, 177
Conferences on weeds, 25
Conifers:
    response to herbicides, 153, 167
    weed control in, 62, illus. 79
Contact herbicides, 84, 96, 124
Contamination:
    seeds, 6, 41
    sprayers, 257–258
Convolvulus arvensis, 178–180
    characteristics, 178
    control, 71, 178–180
    in grains, 158
    obligate weed, 2
    root distribution, 54
Copper sulfate for aquatic weeds, 171
Corn:
    2,4-D effects, 159–160, illus. 160
    triazine and corn borer relationship, 213
    weed control in, 159–160, 187
Corn cockle, 7
Costs of weeds, 5, 69 (*see also* Losses)
Cotoran, 140
    properties and uses, 244
Cotton, weed control in, 163
Couchgrass (*see* *Agropyron repens*)
Crabgrass (*see* *Digitaria*)
Creeping thistle (*see* *Cirsium arvense*)
Crop rotation and weed population, 22
Cucurbits, weed control in, 187
Cultivation:
    for annual weeds, 69
    and dormancy, 33, 37
    depth, 70
    for *Cirsium arvense*, 177
    for *Convolvulus arvensis*, 179
    for perennial weeds, 69, 82, 83
    frequency and timing, 63–65, 69
    reasons for, 22, 68
    and weed seeds, 12

Cuscuta spp., 183
    control by fire, 72
Cuticle:
    diffusion through, 85
    formation, 48, illus. 48
    and waxes, 59, 85
Cyanamide:
    characteristics, 128
    properties and uses, 255
Cyperus rotundus, 30, illus. 31, 40
2,4-D, 129–133
    and aphid reproduction, 213
    combinations with other compounds,
        100–101, 154
    in crops, 154–162, 165, 187
    decortication, 193
    for brush control, 213
    fruit thinning, 192
    malformations, illus. 132
    mode of action, 24
    nitrate levels, 213
    photosynthesis, 92
    properties and uses, 232
    respiration, 131
    Striga control, 185
    translocation, 130
Dalapon:
    characteristics, 138
    for *Agropyron repens*, 180
    in annual dicotyledons, 163
    for aquatic grasses, 172
    in asparagus, 187
    for chemical fallowing, 154
    in legumes, 164
    mode of action, 24
    properties and uses, 248
Dandelion, 29, 80
Darnel, 2, 157
Darwin, Charles, 10
DATC (*see* Diallate)
Daucus carota:
    biennial nature, 29
    roadside weed, 16
2,4-DB:
    characteristics, 134
    in legumes, 164
    properties and uses, 233
DCPA:
    in bedding plants, 186
    properties and uses, 253
    vegetables, 187
DCU (*see* Dichloral urea)
Death of seeds, 37
Decomposition:
    2,4-D in soil, 133
    herbicides in soil, 87
Decontamination of sprayers, 119, 257, 258

Decortication, 193
2,4-DEP, properties and uses, 234
2,4-DES (see Sesone)
Desiccation, 192
Diallate:
 characteristics, 136
 in legumes, 164
 properties and uses, 238
 wild oat control in wheat, 157
3,5-dibromo-4-hydroxybenzonitrile
  (see Bromoxynil)
Dicamba:
 for bindweed control, 179
 characteristics, 139
 properties and uses, 236
 small grains, 157, 158
 in turf, 161
Dichlobenil:
 for Equisetum control, 181
 in garden annuals, 186
 properties and uses, 235
Dichloral urea, properties and uses, 240
S-2-3-dichloroallyl N,N-diisopropyl
  thiolcarbamate (see Diallate)
2,6-dichlorobenzonitrile (see Dichlobenil)
3,4-dichloro-2-methacrylamide:
 properties and uses, Appendix 14
3,6-dichloro-2-methoxybenzoic acid (see
  Dicamba)
2,4-dichlorophenoxyacetic acid (see 2,4-D)
4-(2,4-dichlorophenoxy)-butyric acid (see
  2,4-DB)
3-(3,4-dichlorophenyl)-1,1 dimethylurea
  (see Diuron)
3,4-dichloropropionanilide (see Propanil)
2,2-dichloropropionic acid (see Dalapon)
Dicryl, properties and uses, 249
Digitaria in lawns, 161
 host for striga, 185
 and mowing, 71
1,2-dihydropyridazine-3,6-dione (see
  Maleic hydrazide)
Dimethylarsinic acid, properties and uses,
I, I-dimethyl-4,4-bipyridylium dichloride
  (see Paraquat)
Dimethyl 2,3,5,6-tetrachloroterephthalate
  see DCPA)
N,N-di-(n-propyl)-2,6-dinitro-4-toluidine
  (see Trifluralin)
2,4-dinitro-6-sec butylphenol (see DNBP)
Dinitro (see DNBP)
Dinitrophenol (see DNBP)
Dinoseb (see DNBP)
Dioecious weeds, 32
Diphenamid:
 in garden annuals, 186
 properties and uses, 249

Dipropalin, properties and uses, 251
Diquat:
 characteristics, 142
 properties and uses, 251
Disodium 3,6-endoxohexahydrophthalate
  (see Endothal)
Disodium methane arsonate, 253
Dispersal of seeds (see Dissemination)
Dispersal unit:
 adaptations for spread, 42
 inhibitors in, 34-35
 squirting cucumber, 42
Dissemination of weeds, 37-44
 agents, 37-44
 animals, 37, 41-44
 east to west, 38
 major barriers, 40
 north to south, 40
 small areas, 41
 south to north, 40
 (see also Dispersal unit)
Disul-sodium (see Sesone)
Diuron:
 characteristics, 141
 in dicotyledons, 162-166
 mode of action, 24
 in monocotyledons, 157, 159
 properties and uses, 241
DNBP:
 amine salt of, 163
 characteristics, 140
 in citrus, 166
 in legumes, 164
 mode of action, 24
 and oil, 166
 properties and uses, 240
 salts of, 163
Dodder, 72
Dormancy, 33-37
 enforced, 37
 induced, 36
 innate, 34
 organs, 23, 33
 plants, 54
Dosage:
 importance of, 24, 199
 in toxicological research, 200
Downy brome (see Bromus tectorum)
Dredges, for aquatic weed control, 171
Dribble-bar, 106
Drift:
 and airplane spraying, 109
 and droplet size, 111-113, illus. 111
 and friction between neighbors, 21
 hazards from, 111
DSMA, properties and uses, 253
Dwarfing, 193

Dwarf-mistletoe, 183
Echinochloa crus-galli, 84
Ecological limitations, 17
Ecotypes:
　Cirsium arvense, 176, illus. 176
　Convolvulus arvensis, 178
　responses to herbicides, 12, 22, 83
Ectodesmata, 59
Elecampane, 39
Elongation:
　of roots, 49, 51
　of stems, 55
Embryo:
　root growth, 33
　rudimentary, 34
Emulsions, 97
Endothal:
　for aquatic weeds, 171
　characteristics, 143
　properties and uses, 252
Energy sources, 8
Entry of herbicides:
　into animals, 201
　into leaves, 84
　into roots, 50, 87
　and selectivity, illus. 80
Environment:
　adaption to, 34
　and growth activity, 22
　and herbicide action, 131
　and seed production, 31
　disturbed, 1
Epidermal hairs, 57
Epidermis, 55
Epilobium augustifolium, 34
Epinasty, 55, 131, illus. 132
EPTC:
　characteristics, 135
　in home gardens, 186
　properties and uses, 238
Equipment for applying chemicals, 101
Erbon, properties and uses, 234
Erodium cicutarium, 44
Erosion, 15, illus. 16, 127, 174
Establishment of weeds, 60
Esters:
　characteristics, 130
　damage from, 155
　volatility, 113, 130
1,1-ethylene-2,2-bipyridylium dibromide,
　(*see* Diquat)
Ethyl *N*, *N*-di-propylthiolcarbamate
　(*see* EPIC)
S-ethyl-hexahydro-l H-azepine-l-
　carbothioate (*see* Molinate)
European mistletoe (*see Viscum*)
Facultative weeds, 3

Fallowing (*see* Chemical fallowing)
Families of weeds, 38
Fenac:
　properties and uses, 237
　witchweed control, 185
Fenoprop (*see* Silvex)
Fenuron:
　characteristics, 140
　properties and uses, 241
FenuronTCA, properties and uses, 243
Ferns, 153
Filaree, 44
Fire, 72–73, illus. 73
　for aquatic weed control, 171
　for dodder control, 184
　in primitive agriculture, 72
　in relation to plant growth, 22
　nonselective, 72
　selective, 72
Fireweed, 34
Fish:
　asphyxiation from herbicide use, 169
　weed control, 172, 212
Flaming (*see* Fire)
Flavors caused by weeds, 5, 162
Flea beetle (*Haltica carduorum*), 178, 211
Flooding, 22
Flower types, 32
Foliage sprays, 84–86
Food and Drug Administration, 19
Forage and grazing plants as weeds, 39
Formulations, 97
Fumigants, 144–146
　carbon bisulphide, 144
　chloropicrin, 145
　metham, 136, 187, 239
　methyl bromide, 145
　SMDC, 136, 187, 239
Fungi as biological control, 212
Gardens, 185–187
Geranium spp., 44
Germination, 47–51
　and early growth, 47, illus. 50
　effect of 2,4-D on, 32, 156
　of weeds (*see* Dormancy)
Gibberellins, 10, 90
Gigantism, 2
Goatweed, 162, 209
Goatweed beetle, 209–210
Gooseberry, 167
Gorse, 162, 211
Granular herbicides, 97, 99
Grapes, 167
Grasses:
　in small grains, 157
　in turf, 161
Grazing animals, 212

Gromwell, 35
Growth and selective action, 22, 80
Growth inhibitors:
  in dispersal unit, 34
  in plants, 5
  in quackgrass, 180
  synthetic, 193–194
Growth stimulation, 194
Hairs and spray retention, 57
Halogeton glomeratus, 162
Harvester ants, 211–212
Health:
  effect of weeds on, 7
  and toxic chemicals, 199–202
Helicopter, 109
Henbane (*see Hyoscyamus niger*)
Herbaceous plants:
  annual plants, 150
  dictoyledons, 153, 162
  monocotyledons, 160
Hevea brasiliensis:
  increase in yield from chemicals, 195
  seed distribution, 44
3-(hexahydro-4,7-methanoindan-5-yl)-l,l-
  dimethylurea, (*see* Norea)
Hippomane mancinella, 7
History of weed control, 7–12
  chemicals, 10–12
  domestication of plants, 8
  energy sources, 8, illus. 9
  stages of weed control, 10, illus. 11
Hoary cress, 71
Horehound, 39
Hormones:
  history, 10
  relation to herbicide action, 90
Horsetail rush, 181
Human poisoning (*see* Health)
Humidity, 44
4-hydroxy-3,5-diiodobenzonitrile (*see*
  Ioxynil)
Hyoscyamus niger, 39
Hypericum perforatum, biological control,
  162, 209
IAA (*see* Indoleacetic acid)
Immature embryos (*see* Dormancy)
Indoleacetic acid (IAA):
  apical dominance, 71
  elongation, 91
  light, 10
Induced dormancy, 34–36
Inhibitor (*see* Growth inhibitors)
Injury:
  to livestock from weeds, 6
  by sandbur, 17
  and susceptibility to herbicides, 86
  and translocation of paraquat, 143

Inorganic herbicides, 125
Insects (*see* Biological control)
Interference of weeds with agriculture, 5
International trade in foodstuffs, 204–205
Introduction of weeds, 37–44, illus. 43
  across major barriers, 40
  agents, 37, illus. 44
  east to west, 38
  north to south, 40
  small areas, 41
  south to north, 40
  west to east, 39
Inula helenium, 39
Invasion of weeds, 42, (*see also*
  Introduction of weeds)
Invert emulsion, 97
Ioxynil:
  properties and uses, 235
  small grains, 157
IPC:
  in annual dicotyledons, 163
  in bluegrass, 161
  characteristics, 134
  for fruit thinning, 197
  in legumes, 164
  in properties and uses, 237
Ipomea as invader, 40
Irrigated crops, 172–173
  new areas, 41, 43
  water movement, illus. 173
Isopropyl *N*-(3-chlorophenyl)-carbamate
  (*see* CIPC)
Isopropyl *N*-phenylcarbamate (*see* IPC)
Jim Hill mustard, 151
Johnson grass, 40
Juncus maritimus, germination, 36
Klamath weed (see *Hypericum*)
Knapsack sprayer, 107
Lactic acid, seed killing, 33
Lawns, 161
Leaching of herbicides in soil, 87
Leaf:
  absorption, 58
  entry of herbicides, 84
  growth, 56
  malformation, 58
  structure, illus. 48, 57
Legumes, 162–163
Lespedeza, 163
Lettuce, 162
Life-span and storage conditions, 33
Light:
  and dormancy, 35
  and germination, 37
  and paraquat action, 143
  (*see also* Photodecomposition;
    Photosynthesis)

Linuron:
  in wheat, 154, 157
  properties and uses, 242
Lithospermum arvense, 35
Livestock poisoning, 6
Lolium temulentum:
  as obligate weed, 2
  in wheat, 157
Loranthus, 183
Losses due to weeds, 4–7, 60–62, 177
Machinery:
  and crop damage, 83
  and weed dissemination, 41
Maize (*see* Corn)
Maleic hydrazide:
  control of flowering, 195
  for fruit thinning, 192
  for inhibition, 193
  properties and uses, 248
Manchineel tree, 7
Manure:
  and damage from herbicides, 212
  and seed viability, 33, 41–42
  and seedling survival, 35
Marisa cornuarietus, control of aquatic
    weeds, 172
Marrubium vulgare, 39
Maturity (*see* age)
MCP (*see* MCPA)
MCPA:
  characteristics, 133
  properties and uses, 232
  in small grains, 157
MCPB, in legumes, 163–164
MCPP, properties and uses, 233
Mechanical control (*see* Physical control)
Mecoprop, properties and uses, 233
Medicago sativa, 39
Medicinal plants as weeds, 39
Melons, 187
Mesophyll, 57
Mesquite (*see Prosopis* sp.)
Metabolism, 92, 131
Metham (*see* SMDC)
Methods of weed control, illus. 9, 11
2-methoxy-4,6-*bis*(isopropyl-amino)-
    1,3,5-triazine (*see* Prometon)
Methyl bromide, 145
1-(2-methylcyclohexyl)-3-phenylurea (*see*
    Siduron)
6-methylmercapto-2,4-*bis*(isopropylamino)-
    s-triazine (*see* Prometryne)
Mexican tea, 40
MH (*see* Maleic hydrazide)
Microorganisms, decomposition of
    herbicides, 87, 234
Mint, 163

Misapplication of herbicides, 21, 110
Mistletoe, 42, 181–183
Mixing:
  and agitation, 104
  of herbicides, 99–101
Molinate, properties and uses, 239
Mollugo verticillata, as invader, 40
Monocotyledons, 152–162
  response to herbicides, 150, illus. 152
  straitjacket effect, 91
  structure, 56
Monosodium acid methane arsonate (*see*
    MSMA)
Monuron:
  characteristics, 141
  in annual dicotyledons, 163
  in asparagus, 187
  properties and uses, 241
MonuronTCA, properties and uses, 243
Morphological responses to herbicides, 89
Morphological factors in selectivity, 79,
    84–85
Movement of herbicides:
  in plants (*see* Translocation)
  in soil, 87
Mowing, 71, 171
MSMA, properties and uses, 253
Mulching, 73, 186
Mullein, 29, 57
Multiple effects of herbicides, 23
Mustard (*Brassica nigra*), 30, 34
Mutations in aged seeds, 37
NAA (naphthaleneacetic acid), in fruit
    thinning, 192
Naptalam (*see* NPA)
N-I-naphthyl phthalamic acid (*see* NPA)
Neburon:
  characteristics, 141
  properties and uses, 242
Nightshade, 7
Nonionic surfactants, 98
Norea, 140
  properties and uses, 244
Nozzles, 107–108
NPA:
  in asparagus, 187
  in cucurbits, 187
  properties and uses, 252
Nurse crops, 75
Nutsedge (*see Cyperus rotundus*)
Oats:
  tame, 154, 156
  wild, (*see Avena*)
Obligate weed, 2
Oils:
  around trees, 165
  as carriers, 97

Oils (*cont'd*):
  as herbicides, 97
  properties and uses, 255
Onion:
  as facultative weed, 3
  flaming for weed control, 72
Ontogeny and susceptibility, 149
Opuntia sp.:
  biological control, 210–211
  facultative weed, 3
  rangelands, 162
Orchards, 164–166
Ordam, in rice, 158
Ornamentals:
  as weeds, 38
  weed control in, 181
Orobanche, 184–185
Oryzopsis, 17, 33–37
Palms, 150, 160
Pantothenic acid, 90
Paper covers (*see* Mulching)
Paraquat:
  around treelike monocotyledons, 160
  characteristics, 142
  for desiccation, 192
  properties and uses, 251
Parasitic weeds, 181–185
  Arceuthobium, 183
  dodder, 183–184
  Loranthus, 183
  Orobanche, 184
  Phoradendron, 182
  Striga, 185
  Viscum, 182
Pastures and ranges, 161–162
PCA, properties and uses, 247
PCP:
  characteristics, 139–140
  desiccation, 192
  properties and uses, 240
  in rice, 158
Pebulate, properties and uses, 239
Pegohylemyia seneciella, 211
Pentachlorophenol (*see* PCP)
Pentanochlor, properties and uses, 250
Perennial weeds, 29
  control, 80
  cultivation, 69
  in dicotyledons, 162–167
  in grain crops, 158
  grasses, 161
  herbaceous weeds, 163
  monocotyledons, 150, 160
  woody species, 174–175
  (*see also* individual species)
Pericycle, response to 2,4-D, 51, 131, 132
Petroleum compounds (*see* Oils)

Petrolium derivatives, properties and
    uses, 255
Phalaris paradoxa, 2
Phenols:
  characteristics, 139
  properties and uses, 240
3-phenyl-1-1-dimethylurea (*see* Fenuron)
Phenyl mercuric acetate (*see* PMA)
Phenoxy herbicides (*see* Chlorophenoxy
    herbicides)
Phloem:
  damage from 2,4-D, 56, 132
  in roots, 51
  in stems, 55
  translocation in, 59
Phorandendron, 182
Photodecomposition:
  of herbicides, 87
  of substituted ureas, 140
  of triazines, 137
Photosynthesis:
  and paraquat action, 143
  and translocation of herbicides, 92
  reduction by 2,4-D, 131
Picloram:
  characteristics, 144
  for brush control, 162
  for *Cirsium arvense* control, 177
  for *Convolvulus arvense* control, 179
  in lawns and turf, 161
  properties and uses, 254
Pigweed (see *Amaranthus retroflexus*)
Pineapple:
  effect of maleic hybrazide, illus. 195
  flowering, 195
  response to herbicides, 150
Placement of herbicides, 87
Plantoga sp., 29
  flavor of milk, 162
  harvester ants, 211–212
Plantain (*see Plantago* sp.)
Plantation tree crops, 167
Plastic cover (*see* Mulching)
PMA, properties and uses, 253
Poa annua:
  in lawns and turf, 161
  in small grains, 157
Poisonous weeds, 7
Polygonum sp., dormancy in, 36
Pondweed, 169
Portulaca oleracea, 39
Potamogeton pectinatus, 169
Potassium cyanate, properties and uses, 256
Potatoes:
  color affected by herbicides, 194
  response to herbicides, 163
Poultry and seed viability, 42

Pressures, 108
Prevention of damage, 111
Prickly pear (*see Opuntia* spp.)
Primary root, 49
Primitive agriculture, 8, illus. 9, 11
    burning in, 72
    crop varieties, 63
Prometon, properties and uses, 245
Prometryne, properties and uses, 245
Propachlor, properties and uses, 250
Propagation, 29–30
Propanil:
    in rice, 158
    properties and uses, 249
Propazine, properties and uses, 246
Propham (*see* IPC)
Propionic acids:
    characteristics, 134
    properties and uses, 233
Prosopis sp., 35
Proteins:
    increased percentage following 2,4-D,
        92, 131
    shifts following herbicide application, 89
Pueraria, 164
Pump capacity, 104
Pumpkins, 187
Puncture vine, 42
Purslane, 39
Pyrazon, properties and uses, 247
Quackgrass (*see Agropyron repens*)
Quarantine to reduce weed seed, 42
Races:
    crops, 12, 83, 159
    resistant weeds, 12, 83
    weeds mimicking crops, 3
Ragweed, 16
Rainfall-dependent germination control,
    35
Rangelands, 161
Raphanus raphanistrum, 2
Raspberries, 167
Rate of seeding, 64
Registration of new chemicals, 19, 200
Regrowth:
    and age, 29, 176
    underground organs, 30
    woody plants, 175
Residues in plants and soils, 21, 203–206,
    illus. 204
Resistant plants, development of, 12, 21
Respiration, 131
Rhizome, 30, 33
Rhus sp. proliferation after fire, 34
Rice, 158
Roots, 48–55, illus. 48
    adventitious, 49

Roots (cont'd):
    damage from herbicides, 51, illus. 52,
        53, 54, 155
    distribution, 53
    early growth, 49, illus. 50
    hairs, 50
    malformations, 132
    primary tissues, 55
    reproduction from, 30, 176, 178
Rubber tree (*see Hevea brasiliensis*)
Rumex acetosella, 32
Rush (*see Juncus maritimus*)
Russian thistle, seed dissemination,
    illus. 44
Rye, 152
Sachs, Julius, 10
Safety precautions, 19
Sagebrush:
    2,4-D, 162
    rangelands, 35
Sago pondweed, 169
St. Johnswort, 162, 209–210
Salsola kali, seed dissemination, illus. 44
Saltbush, seed inhibition by light, 36
Salvinia auriculata, 57
Sandbur, 17
Screens, 43
Seed, 30–44
    dispersal, 37, illus. 43
    dormancy, 33–37
    production, 1, 30–32
    seedfly, 211
    structure, 33
    weevil, 211
Senecio jacobaea:
    age and susceptibility, 80
    biennial nature, 29
    biological control, 211
Senecio sp. seeds as poison, 7
Sesone:
    characteristics, 133
    in asparagus, 187
    in strawberries, 164
    properties and uses, 234
Setaria sp., 157
Sexual reproduction, 30
Shattercane, 3
Sheep sorrel, 32
Shepherd's purse, 6, 34
Shoot growth, illus. 48, 55, 56
Shrubs, weed control in, 167
Siduron, 140
    properties and uses, 244
Silvex:
    bindweed control, 179
    brush control, 162
    characteristics, 134

Silvex (cont'd):
  in turf, 161
  properties and uses, 233
Simazine:
  and virus damage, 213
  characteristics, 137
  in corn, 159
  in conifers, 62, illus. 79
  in maize, 159
  mode of action, 23
  properties and uses, 245
  on roadsides, 17
  quackgrass control, 181, 245
  in sorghum, 159
  in sweet corn, 187
  in treelike monocotyledons, 160
Sisymbrium officinale, 151
Small grains, 152–159
Smartweed, dormancy, 36
SMDC:
  characteristics, 136
  in gardens, 187
  properties and uses, 239
Snail, control of aquatic weeds, 172, 212
Sodium arsenite:
  as desiccant, 192
  characteristics, 125
  for aquatic weeds, 171
  for decortication, 193
  properties and uses, 256
Sodium chlorate:
  characteristics, 126
  desiccant, 192
  for decortication, 193
  erosion, illus. 127
  for general vegetation control, 173
  properties and uses, 256
  soil sterilant, 21, 158
  in wheat, 158
Sodium 2(2,4-dichlorophenoxy)ethyl
    sulphate (*see* Sesone)
Sodium tetraborate, (*see* Borax)
Soil-applied chemicals, 87–88
Soil fumigants (*see* Fumigants)
Soil sterilants, 173
  (*see also* specific compounds)
Solan, properties and uses, 250
Same as Pentanochlor
Solanum carolinense, control by flooding, 71
Solanum sp. berries, 7
Sorghum:
  invasion by, 40
  shattercane, 3
  weed competition in, 61
  weed control in, 159
Soybean:
  amiben in, 139

Soybean (*cont'd*):
  losses due to weeds, 61–62
Spider mite, 212
Spoilage due to weeds, 6
Spores, reproduction by, 32, 181
Spot treatment, 96
Spray drift, 111–113
Sprayers:
  aerial, 109–110
  band, 105
  decontamination, 257
  dribble-bar, 106
  ground, 102, illus. 102
  knapsack, 107, illus. 107
  nozzles, 107–108
  parts, 101
  pressures, 108–109
  requirements, 101
  tanks, 103, illus, 103
  vibro-boom, 106
Squashes, 187
Squirting cucumber, 42
Stages in weed control, 10
Stale seedbed, 65
Stem development, illus. 48, 55
Stipa sp., 17
Stolon, 30
Stomatal entry, 57
Storage conditions and seed survival, 33
Stork's bill, 44
Straitjacket effect, 91
Strawberries, 164
Striga sp., 159, 185
Stump treatment, 162, 175
Sugarcane, 150, 161
Sulfallate (*see* CDEC)
Sumac, 34
Sunfish for aquatic weed control, 172
Surfactants:
  characteristics, 98, illus. 99
  increasing toxic action, 57
Susceptibility:
  and age, 78–83, illus. 81, 82
  of cereals to 2,4-D, 155
  of crops and weeds, 78
  factors affecting, illus. 80
Swath width, 110
Sweet clover, 39
Symplast, 56, 85
Systemic action, 84–86
2,4,5-T:
  characteristics, 133
  for brush control, 161, 175
  for decortication, 193
  for fruit thinning, 192
  properties and uses, 233
Tanacetum vulgare, 16

Tanks, 103
Tansy ragwort (*see Senecio jacobaea*)
Tansy, 16
Taraxacum officinale, 29, 80
Taraxacum sp., planted in pastures, 162
Taxonomy and response to herbicides, 149
TBA:
    characteristics, 139
    as soil sterilant, 158
    properties and uses, 236
    witchweed control, 185
TCA:
    characteristics, 138
    in dicotyledons, 163
    in legumes, 164
    properties and uses, 248
    for quackgrass control, 180
Temperature:
    and 2,4-D action, 131
    and decomposition, 87
    and germination, 35–37
Terbacil, properties and uses, 247
Thlaspi arvense, 80
Tillage, 68–71
Tolerances:
    establishment, 19
    levels, 203–204
    toxicological studies, 200
Tomatoes, illus. 132, 187
Toxicity, 198–202
    acute, 200
    chronic, 202
    classes of pesticides, 203
    dermal, 201
    eye, 201
    oral, 200
    subacute, 201–202
    tolerance levels, 204
    trade, international, 204–205
2,4,5-TP (*see* Silvex)
Tractor-mounted sprayers, 102–106
Trailer-mounted sprayers, 102–103
Translocation:
    to active regions, 32
    of 2,4-D, 130
    of foliar-applied herbicides, 84–86
    and growth activity, 22
    lateral, 85
    patterns, 59, illus. 86
    of systemic herbicides, 88, 124
Trap crops, 185
Tree crops, 164–167
Triallate:
    properties and uses, 238
    wild oat control in wheat and barley,
        157

Triazines:
    characteristics, 137–138
    properties and uses, 245
Tribulus terrestris, 42
Trichloroacetic acid (*see* TCA)
S-2,3,3-trichloroallyl
        N-N-diisopropylthiolcarbamate
        (*see* Triallate)
2,3,6-trichlorobenzoic acid (*see* TBA)
2,3,6-trichlorophenylacetic acid (*see* fenac)
2,4,5-trichlorophenoxyacetic acid (*see*
        2,4,5-T)
2-(2,4,5-trichlorophenoxy)ethyl
        2,2-dichloropropionate (*see* Erbon)
2-(2,4,5-trichlorophenoxy)-propionic acid
        (*see* Silvex)
Trifluralin:
    in bedding plants, X-24, 186
    characteristics, 144
    in cotton, 163
    properties and uses, 251
    in tomatoes, 187
Trigonella arabica, germination controls, 36
Tumbling pigweed, 44
Turf, 161
Turf grasses, 75
Typha latifolia, 16
Tyrea jacobaea, 211
Ulex europeus:
    biological control, 211
    in rangeland, 162
Ureas, 5
Vapor drift, 110–111
Varieties:
    of crop susceptible to herbicides,
        12, 83
    (*see also* Races; Ecotypes; Biotypes)
Vegetables:
    introduced as weeds, 39
    weed control in, 187
Vegetative propagation, 29
Verbascum thapsis, 29, 57
Vernolate:
    in gardens, 186
    properties and uses, 239
Veromesser pergandei, 211
Vetch, 3, 39
Vibro-boom, 106
Vicia sp.:
    facultative weed, 1, 3
    introduced weed, 39
Vine fruits, 167
Virus:
    biological control, 212
    Capsella as alternate host, 6
    and simazine susceptibility, 83

Viscum, 182
Volatility:
   danger from, 110, 113
   and esters of 2,4-D, 130
   and herbicidal action, 88
Volume:
   rates, 104
   and retention of herbicide, 84
Water:
   and growth, 53, 64
   as herbicide carrier, 97
   loss from weeds, 6
   seed carrier, 41, 43
Water fern, 57
Waxes:
   leaves, 59, 85
   reduction by dalapon, 83
Weed Abstracts, 25
Weed Research, 25
Weed Science, 25
Weed Science Society of America, 25
Weed Society of America, 25

Wettability:
   of leaves, 84
   and surfactants, 98
Wheat:
   annual weeds in, 152–157
   chemical fallowing, 154
   dwarfing, 193
   perennial weeds in, 157
Wild carrot, 16, 29
Wild milograss, 17, 33
Wild oats (*see Avena*)
Wild onion, 2
Wild radish, 2
Wind as seed disseminator, 37, 41, 43
Winter annuals, 28
Witches'-broom, 183
Witchweed (*see Striga*)
Woody dicotyledons:
   control, 162
   response to herbicides, 164
Xylem, illus. 48, 59, 86
Yield losses due to weeds, 60

This book was set in Monophoto Times Roman by Holmes Typography, Inc., printed on permanent paper by The Maple Press Company, and bound by The Maple Press Company. The designer was Janet Bollow; the drawings were done by Mark Schroeder. The editors were James L. Smith, Alice S. Goehring, and Stuart A. Kenter. Charles A. Goehring supervised production.